one pots

100 EASY RECIPES
one pots

bay books

contents

chicken
and duck

chicken and coconut milk soup

150 g (5½ oz) dried rice vermicelli
1 lime
4 small red chillies, seeded and chopped
1 onion, chopped
2 garlic cloves, crushed
4 thin slices fresh ginger, finely chopped
2 lemongrass stems (white part only), chopped
1 tablespoon chopped coriander (cilantro)
   leaves
1 tablespoon peanut oil
750 ml (26 fl oz/3 cups) chicken stock
685 ml (23½ fl oz/2¾ cups) coconut milk
500 g (1 lb 2 oz) chicken tenderloins, cut
   into thin strips
4 spring onions (scallions), chopped
150 g (5½ oz) fried tofu puffs, sliced
90 g (3 oz/1 cup) bean sprouts
3 teaspoons soft brown sugar

serves 8

method Soak the vermicelli in boiling water for 5 minutes. Drain, cut into short lengths. Remove the lime zest with a vegetable peeler and cut it into long, thin strips.

Place the chilli, onion, garlic, ginger, lemongrass and coriander into a food processor and process in short bursts for 20 seconds, or until smooth.

Heat the oil in a large heavy-based saucepan over medium heat. Add the chilli mixture and cook, stirring frequently, for 3 minutes, or until fragrant. Add the stock, coconut milk and lime zest strips, and bring to the boil. Add the chicken and cook, stirring, for 4 minutes, or until tender.

Add the spring onion, tofu, bean sprouts and brown sugar, and season with salt. Stir over medium heat for 3 minutes, or until the spring onion is tender. Divide the noodles among eight bowls and pour the soup over the top. Garnish with chilli and coriander.

avgolemono with chicken

1 onion, halved
2 cloves
1 carrot, cut into chunks
1 bay leaf
500 g (1 lb 2 oz) boneless, skinless
chicken breasts
75 g (2½ oz/⅓ cup) short-grain rice
3 eggs, separated
60 ml (2 fl oz/¼ cup) lemon juice
2 tablespoons chopped flat-leaf
(Italian) parsley
4 thin lemon slices, to garnish

serves 4

method Stud the onion halves with the cloves and then place in a large saucepan with 1.5 litres (52 fl oz/6 cups) water. Add the carrot, bay leaf and chicken. Season with salt and freshly ground black pepper. Slowly bring to the boil, reduce the heat and simmer for 10 minutes, or until chicken is cooked.

Strain the stock into a clean saucepan, reserving the chicken and discarding the vegetables. Add the rice to the stock, bring to the boil, then reduce the heat and simmer for 15 minutes, or until tender. Tear the chicken into shreds.

Whisk the egg whites until stiff peaks form, then beat in the yolks. Slowly beat in the lemon juice. Gently stir in 150 ml (5 fl oz) of the hot (not boiling) soup and beat thoroughly. Add the egg mixture to the soup and stir gently over low heat until thickened slightly. It should still be quite thin. Do not let it boil or the eggs may scramble. Add the shredded chicken, and season to taste.

Set aside for 3–4 minutes to allow the flavours to develop, then sprinkle with the parsley. Garnish with lemon slices and serve.

mulligatawny

30 g (1 oz) butter
375 g (13 oz) chicken thigh cutlets, skin and
     fat removed
1 large onion, finely chopped
1 apple, peeled, cored and diced
1 tablespoon curry paste
2 tablespoons plain (all-purpose) flour
750 ml (26 fl oz/3 cups) chicken stock
50 g (2 oz/¼ cup) basmati rice
1 tablespoon chutney
1 tablespoon lemon juice
60 ml (2 fl oz/¼ cup) cream

serves 4

method Gently heat the butter in a large heavy-based saucepan. Cook the chicken on medium–high heat for 5 minutes, or until browned, then remove and set aside. Add the onion, apple and curry paste to the pan. Cook for 5 minutes, or until the onion is soft. Stir in the flour and cook for 2 minutes, then add half the stock. Continue stirring until the mixture boils and thickens.

Return the chicken to the pan with the remaining stock. Stir until boiling, then reduce the heat, cover and simmer for 1 hour. Add the rice for the last 15 minutes of cooking.

Remove the chicken from the pan. Remove the meat from the bones, shred and return to the pan. Add the chutney, lemon juice and cream, and season to taste.

roast duck and noodle broth

3 dried shiitake mushrooms
1 Chinese roast duck (1.5 kg/3 lb 5 oz)
500 ml (17 fl oz/2 cups) chicken stock
2 tablespoons light soy sauce
1 tablespoon Chinese rice wine
2 teaspoons sugar
400 g (14 oz) fresh flat rice noodles
2 tablespoons oil
3 spring onions (scallions), thinly sliced
1 teaspoon finely chopped fresh ginger
400 g (14 oz) bok choy (pak choy), leaves
separated
¼ teaspoon sesame oil

serves 4–6

method Soak the mushrooms in 250 ml (9 fl oz/1 cup) boiling water for 20 minutes. Drain, reserving the liquid and squeezing the excess liquid from the mushrooms. Discard the stems and thinly slice the caps.

Remove the skin and flesh from the duck. Discard the fat and carcass. Finely slice the duck meat and the skin (you need about 400 g/14 oz of duck meat).

Place the stock, soy sauce, rice wine, sugar and the reserved mushroom liquid in a saucepan over medium heat. Bring to a simmer and cook for 5 minutes.

Meanwhile, place the rice noodles in a heatproof bowl, cover with boiling water and soak briefly. Gently separate the noodles with your hands and drain well. Divide evenly among large soup bowls.

Heat the oil in a wok over high heat. Add the spring onion, ginger and mushroom, and cook for several seconds. Transfer to the broth with the bok choy and duck meat, and simmer for 1 minute, or until the duck has warmed through and the bok choy has wilted. Ladle the soup on the noodles and drizzle sesame oil on each serving. Serve immediately.

chicken marsala

60 ml (2 fl oz/¼ cup) olive oil
3 leeks (white part only), thinly sliced
1 teaspoon finely chopped rosemary
3 bay leaves, torn
1 kg (2 lb 4 oz) chicken pieces
seasoned plain (all-purpose) flour
1 large eggplant (aubergine), cut into cubes
2 zucchini (courgettes), roughly chopped
125 ml (4 fl oz/½ cup) Marsala (see Note)
300 ml (10½ fl oz) chicken stock
500 g (1 lb 2 oz/2 cups) tomato paste
   (concentrated purée)
200 g (7 oz) button mushrooms, halved

serves 4

method Heat the oil in a large heavy-based saucepan. Fry the leek, rosemary and bay leaves over low heat for 5 minutes, or until soft, stirring occasionally. Remove with a slotted spoon, leaving as much oil in the pan as possible.

Toss the chicken pieces in the seasoned flour. Add the chicken to the pan and brown well in batches over medium heat. Return all the chicken to the pan with the leek mixture.

Add the eggplant and zucchini, and cook, stirring, for 2–3 minutes, or until softened, turning the chicken over. Add the Marsala and stock, and cook for 15 minutes over medium–high heat.

Add the tomato paste and season well with salt and pepper. Bring to the boil, turning the chicken pieces in the sauce. Reduce the heat to a very gentle simmer, then cover and cook for 35 minutes. Add the mushrooms and cook, uncovered, for 5 minutes.

note *Marsala is a famous Italian fortified wine. It has a smoky, rich flavour and ranges from dry to sweet.*

100 EASY RECIPES ONE-POTS

chicken and cider stew with mash

1 kg (2 lb 4 oz) skinless, boneless chicken
thighs, cut into 2 cm (¾ inch) cubes
1½ tablespoons finely chopped thyme
1 tablespoon oil
90 g (3 oz) butter
3 French shallots (eschalots), thinly sliced
375 ml (13 fl oz/1½ cups) apple cider
1 kg (2 lb 4 oz) potatoes, cubed
2 large green apples, peeled, cored and sliced
into eighths
170 ml (5½ fl oz/⅔ cup) cream
thyme sprigs, to garnish

serves 4

method   Season the chicken thighs with 2 teaspoons of the thyme and salt and black pepper. Heat the oil and 20 g (¾ oz) of the butter in a large saucepan over medium–high heat. Cook the chicken in two batches for 2–3 minutes, or until evenly browned. Remove from the pan.

Add the shallots and the remaining thyme to the pan, and sauté for 2 minutes. Pour in the cider, then bring to the boil, scraping off any sediment that has stuck to the bottom of the pan. Return the chicken to the pan and cover. Reduce the heat to low–medium and cook for 35–40 minutes, or until the chicken is tender and the sauce has reduced (check every now and then to see if any water needs to be added to the sauce).

Meanwhile, cook the potato and apple in a saucepan of boiling water for 15–20 minutes, or until tender. Drain and return to the pan over low heat for 1 minute to allow any water to evaporate. Remove from the heat, and mash with a potato masher. With a wooden spoon, stir in 2 tablespoons of the cream and the remaining butter, then season to taste with salt and pepper.

Gently stir the remaining cream into the chicken stew and cook for a further 2–4 minutes, or until the sauce has thickened. Garnish with thyme sprigs and serve at once with the potato and apple mash and a crisp green salad.

chinese braised chicken

250 ml (9 fl oz/1 cup) soy sauce
1 cinnamon stick
90 g (3 oz/⅓ cup) sugar
80 ml (2½ fl oz/⅓ cup) balsamic vinegar
2.5 cm (1 inch) piece fresh ginger, thinly sliced
4 garlic cloves
¼ teaspoon dried chilli flakes
1.5 kg (3 lb 5 oz) chicken pieces (skin removed)
1 tablespoon sesame seeds, toasted

serves 4–6

method Combine 1 litre (35 fl oz/4 cups) water with the soy sauce, cinnamon stick, sugar, balsamic vinegar, ginger, garlic and chilli flakes in a saucepan. Bring to the boil, then reduce the heat and simmer for 5 minutes.

Add the chicken pieces and simmer, covered, for 50 minutes, or until cooked through. Serve the chicken on a bed of steamed vegetables, drizzled with the poaching liquid and sprinkled with toasted sesame seeds.

chicken and mushroom casserole

20 g (¾ oz) dried porcini mushrooms
1.5 kg (3 lb 5 oz) chicken pieces
30 g (1 oz/¼ cup) seasoned plain (all-purpose)
flour
2 tablespoons oil
1 large onion, chopped
2 garlic cloves, crushed
60 ml (2 fl oz/¼ cup) chicken stock
80 ml (2½ fl oz/⅓ cup) white wine
400 g (14 oz) tin whole peeled tomatoes
1 tablespoon balsamic vinegar
3 thyme sprigs
1 bay leaf
300 g (10½ oz) field mushrooms, thickly sliced
thyme leaves, extra, to garnish

serves 4

method Lightly toss the chicken in the seasoned flour to coat, and shake off any excess.

Heat the oil in a flameproof casserole dish, and cook the chicken over medium heat in batches until well browned all over. Set aside. Add the onion and garlic to the casserole dish, and cook for 3–5 minutes, or until the onion softens. Stir in the chicken stock.

Return the chicken to the dish with the porcini mushrooms (and any remaining liquid), wine, tomatoes, vinegar, thyme sprigs and bay leaf. Cover and bake for 30 minutes.

After 30 minutes, remove the lid and add the field mushrooms. Return to the oven and cook, uncovered, for 15–20 minutes, or until the sauce thickens slightly. Garnish with thyme leaves and serve with a salad.

thai duck and pineapple curry

1 tablespoon peanut oil
8 spring onions (scallions), sliced on the
    diagonal into 3 cm (1¼ inch) lengths
2 garlic cloves, crushed
2–4 tablespoons Thai red curry paste
750 g (1 lb 10 oz) Chinese roast duck, chopped
400 ml (14 fl oz) tin coconut milk
450 g (1 lb) tin pineapple pieces in syrup,
    drained
3 makrut (kaffir lime) leaves
1 large handful coriander (cilantro) leaves,
    chopped, plus extra leaves, to garnish
2 tablespoons chopped mint, plus extra leaves,
    to garnish

serves 4–6

method Heat a wok until very hot, add the peanut oil and swirl to coat the side. Add the spring onion, garlic and red curry paste, and stir-fry for 1 minute, or until fragrant.

Add the roast duck, coconut milk, pineapple pieces, makrut leaves, and half each of the coriander and mint. Bring to the boil, then reduce the heat and simmer for 10 minutes, or until the duck is heated through and the sauce has thickened slightly. Stir in the remaining fresh herbs. Garnish with extra coriander and mint leaves and serve with steamed jasmine rice.

vietnamese chicken curry

4 large chicken leg quarters (leg and thigh pieces)
1 tablespoon general-purpose Indian curry powder
1 teaspoon caster (superfine) sugar
80 ml (2½ fl oz/⅓ cup) oil
300 g (1 lb 2 oz) orange sweet potato, cut into 3 cm (1¼ inch) cubes
1 large onion, cut into thin wedges
4 garlic cloves, chopped
1 lemongrass stem (white part only), finely chopped
2 bay leaves
1 large carrot, cut into 1 cm (½ inch) pieces on the diagonal
400 ml (14 fl oz) tin coconut milk

serves 6

method Remove the skin and any excess fat from the chicken. Pat dry with paper towels and cut each piece into 3 even pieces, making 12 pieces. Place the curry powder, sugar, ½ teaspoon black pepper and 2 teaspoons salt in a bowl, and mix well. Rub the curry mixture into the chicken pieces. Place the chicken on a plate, cover with plastic wrap and put in the refrigerator overnight.

Heat the oil in a large saucepan. Add the sweet potato and cook over medium heat for 3 minutes, or until lightly golden. Remove with a slotted spoon.

Remove all but 2 tablespoons of the oil from the pan. Add the onion and cook, stirring, for 5 minutes. Then add the garlic, lemongrass and bay leaves, and cook for 2 minutes.

Add the chicken and cook, stirring, over medium heat for 5 minutes, or until the chicken is well coated in the mixture and starting to change colour. Add 250 ml (9 fl oz/1 cup) water and simmer, covered, for 20 minutes. Stir once or twice.

Stir in the carrot, sweet potato and coconut milk, and simmer on a low heat, uncovered, stirring occasionally, for 30 minutes, or until the chicken is cooked and tender. Be careful not to break up the sweet potato cubes. Serve with steamed rice or rice stick noodles.

chicken with feta and olives

2 tablespoons oil
8 chicken pieces (1.2 kg/2 lb 10 oz)
1 onion, chopped
25 g (1 oz) oregano, leaves picked
2 tablespoons tomato paste (concentrated
   purée)
2 x 400 g (14 oz) tins chopped tomatoes
150 g (5½ oz) black olives
150 g (5½ oz) feta, crumbled, to serve

serves 4

method   Heat half the oil in a saucepan and cook the chicken pieces, in batches, for 3–4 minutes, or until golden. Remove from the pan and set aside.

In the same saucepan, heat the remaining oil and cook the onion and half the oregano leaves for 3 minutes, or until the onion is softened. Add the tomato paste to the onion mixture and stir for 2 minutes, then add the tomato and the chicken pieces.

Simmer, covered, for 40–50 minutes, or until the chicken is cooked through. Add the olives and remaining oregano leaves. To serve, spoon into bowls and top with the crumbled feta.

balti chicken

1 kg (2 lb 4 oz) chicken thigh fillets
80 ml (2½ fl oz/⅓ cup) oil
1 large red onion, finely chopped
4–5 garlic cloves, finely chopped
1 tablespoon grated fresh ginger
2 teaspoons ground cumin
2 teaspoons ground coriander
1 teaspoon ground turmeric
½ teaspoon chilli powder
425 g (15 oz) tin chopped tomatoes
1 green capsicum (pepper), cut into 3 cm
(1¼ inch) cubes
1–2 small green chillies, seeded and finely
chopped
1 very large handful chopped coriander
(cilantro) leaves
2 spring onions (scallions), chopped to garnish

serves 6

method Remove any excess fat or sinew from the chicken thigh fillets and cut into 4–5 pieces.

Heat a large wok over high heat, add the oil and swirl to coat the side. Add the onion and stir-fry over medium heat for 5 minutes, or until softened but not browned. Add the garlic and ginger, and stir-fry for 3 minutes.

Add the spices, 1 teaspoon salt and 60 ml (2 fl oz/¼ cup) water. Increase heat to high and stir-fry for 2 minutes, or until mixture thickens.

Add the tomato and 250 ml (9 fl oz/1 cup) water and cook, stirring often, for a further 10 minutes, or until the mixture is thick and pulpy and the oil comes to the surface.

Add the chicken to the wok, reduce the heat and simmer, stirring often, for 15 minutes. Add the capsicum and chilli, and simmer for 25 minutes, or until the chicken is tender. Add a little water if the mixture is too thick. Stir in the coriander and garnish with the spring onion. Serve with rice.

madrid chicken

1 orange
1 tablespoon olive oil
4 chicken breasts (skin and excess fat removed)
2 chorizo sausages (about 200 g/7 oz), cut into 1 cm (½ inch) slices (see Note)
250 ml (9 fl oz/1 cup) chicken stock
250 g (9 oz/1 cup) bottled tomato pasta sauce
12 kalamata olives
kalamata olives, extra, to garnish
flat-leaf (Italian) parsley, to garnish

serves 4

method Using a vegetable peeler, carefully cut 4 thin strips of orange zest (about 1 x 4 cm/½ x 1½ inches). Remove the peel and pith from the orange, and segment the flesh.

Heat the oil in a saucepan and brown the chicken and chorizo slices, in batches if necessary. (Leave the meat side of the chicken browning for 5 minutes.) Add the stock, tomato sauce and orange zest. Bring to the boil, then reduce the heat and simmer, covered, for 25 minutes.

Remove the lid, turn the chicken over and continue to simmer, uncovered, for about 25 minutes, or until the chicken is tender and the sauce reduced. Season with salt and freshly ground black pepper, and stir through the olives and orange segments. Garnish with extra olives and flat-leaf parsley.

note *Chorizo sausages can be replaced with any spicy sausages.*

lemon and rosemary chicken stew

8 large chicken drumsticks
60 g (2 oz) butter
2 garlic cloves, crushed
2 teaspoons finely grated lemon zest
2 tablespoons chopped rosemary
1 tablespoon plain (all-purpose) flour
375 ml (13 fl oz/1½ cups) chicken stock
2 tablespoons lemon juice

serves 4

method Using a sharp knife, make two deep cuts in the thickest part of each chicken drumstick.

Melt the butter in a large frying pan. Add the drumsticks and cook over medium heat for 2 minutes on each side, or until brown. Add the garlic, lemon zest and rosemary.

Blend the flour, stock and lemon juice until smooth. Add to the pan and bring to the boil. Reduce the heat and simmer, covered, for 25 minutes, or until the drumsticks are tender, stirring occasionally. Season, and serve, ladling the sauce over the chicken. Delicious with green beans.

hint *To check whether chicken is cooked, insert a skewer into the thickest part. If the juice runs clear, the chicken is cooked.*

chicken kapitan

1 teaspoon small dried shrimp
80 ml (2½ fl oz/⅓ cup) oil
6–8 red chillies, seeded and finely chopped
4 garlic cloves, finely chopped
3 lemongrass stems (white part only),
    finely chopped
2 teaspoons ground turmeric
10 macadamia nuts
2 large onions, chopped
250 ml (9 fl oz/1 cup) coconut milk
1.5 kg (3 lb 5 oz) chicken, cut into 8 pieces
125 ml (4 fl oz/½ cup) coconut cream
2 tablespoons lime juice
lime wedges, to serve

serves 4–6

method Put the shrimp in a frying pan and dry-fry (no oil) over a low heat, shaking the pan regularly, for 3 minutes, or until the shrimp are dark orange and are giving off a strong aroma. Transfer to a mortar and pound with a pestle until finely ground. Alternatively, you may process in a food processor.

Place half of the oil, the chilli, garlic, lemongrass, turmeric and nuts in a food processor, and process in short bursts until very finely chopped, regularly scraping down the side of the bowl.

Heat the remaining oil in a wok or frying pan, add the onion and ¼ teaspoon salt, and cook, stirring regularly, over low heat for 8 minutes, or until golden.

Add the spice mixture and ground shrimp, and stir for 5 minutes. If the mixture begins to stick, add 2 tablespoons of the coconut milk. It is important to cook the mixture thoroughly to allow the flavours to develop.

Add the chicken to the wok and cook, stirring, for 5 minutes, or until beginning to brown. Stir in the remaining coconut milk and 250 ml (9 fl oz/1 cup) water, and bring to the boil. Reduce the heat and simmer for 50 minutes, or until the chicken is cooked and the sauce has thickened slightly. Add the coconut cream and bring the mixture back to the boil, stirring constantly. Add the lime juice and serve immediately with rice and lime wedges.

100 EASY RECIPES ONE-POTS

chilli chicken with tacos

1 tablespoon olive oil
1 onion, finely chopped
500 g (1 lb 2 oz) minced (ground) chicken
1–2 teaspoons mild chilli powder
440 g (15½ oz) tin chopped tomatoes
2 tablespoons tomato paste (concentrated purée)
1–2 teaspoons soft brown sugar
425 g (15 oz) tin red kidney beans, drained and rinsed
taco shells, or corn chips, to serve
sour cream, to serve

serves 4

method Heat the oil in a large saucepan. Add the chopped onion and cook over medium heat for 3 minutes, or until soft. Increase the heat to high and add the chicken. Cook until the chicken has browned, breaking up any lumps with a wooden spoon.

Add the chilli powder to the chicken and cook for 1 minute. Stir in the tomato, tomato paste and 125 ml (4 fl oz/½ cup) water.

Bring to the boil, then reduce the heat and simmer for 30 minutes. Stir through the sugar to taste and the kidney beans. Season. Serve along with warmed corn chips or in taco shells with the sour cream.

nonya chicken curry

curry paste

2 red onions, chopped
4 small red chillies, seeded and sliced
4 garlic cloves, sliced
2 lemongrass stems (white part only), sliced
3 cm x 2 cm (1¼ inch x ¾ inch) piece fresh
  galangal, sliced
8 makrut (kaffir lime) leaves, roughly chopped
1 teaspoon ground turmeric
½ teaspoon shrimp paste, roasted (see Note)

2 tablespoons oil
750 g (1 lb 10 oz) chicken thigh fillets, cut into
  bite-sized pieces
400 ml (14 fl oz) tin coconut milk
60 g (2 oz/¼ cup) tamarind purée
1 tablespoon fish sauce
3 makrut (kaffir lime) leaves, finely shredded,
  to garnish

serves 4

method To make the curry paste, place all the ingredients in a food processor or blender and process to a thick paste.

Heat a wok or large saucepan over high heat, add the oil and swirl to coat the side. Add the curry paste and cook, stirring occasionally, over low heat for 8–10 minutes, or until fragrant. Add the chicken and stir-fry with the paste for 2–3 minutes.

Add the coconut milk, tamarind purée and fish sauce to the wok, and simmer, stirring occasionally, for 15–20 minutes, or until the chicken is tender. Garnish with the makrut leaves. Serve with rice and steamed bok choy (pak choy).

note *To dry-roast the shrimp paste, wrap it in foil and place it under a hot grill (broiler) for 1 minute.*

chicken curry with apricots

18 dried apricots
1 tablespoon ghee or oil
2 x 1.5 kg (3 lb 5 oz) chickens, cut into pieces
3 onions, thinly sliced
1 teaspoon grated fresh ginger
3 garlic cloves, crushed
3 large green chillies, seeded and finely chopped
1 teaspoon cumin seeds
1 teaspoon chilli powder
½ teaspoon ground turmeric
4 cardamom pods, bruised
4 large tomatoes, peeled and cut into eighths (see Note)

serves 6–8

method Soak the dried apricots in 250 ml (9 fl oz/1 cup) hot water for 1 hour.

Melt the ghee in a large saucepan, add the chicken in batches and cook over high heat for 5–6 minutes, or until browned. Remove from the pan. Add the onion and cook, stirring often, for 10 minutes, or until the onion has softened and turned golden brown.

Add the ginger, garlic and chopped chilli, and cook, stirring, for 2 minutes. Stir in the cumin seeds, chilli powder and ground turmeric, and cook for a further 1 minute.

Return the chicken to the pan, add the cardamom, tomato and apricots, with any remaining liquid, and mix well. Simmer, covered, for 35 minutes, or until the chicken is tender.

Remove the chicken, cover and keep warm. Bring the liquid to the boil and boil rapidly, uncovered, for 5 minutes, or until it has thickened slightly. To serve, spoon the liquid over the chicken. Serve with steamed rice mixed with raisins, grated carrot and toasted flaked almonds.

note *To peel the tomatoes, score a cross in the base of each one, then cover with boiling water for 30 seconds. Drain, then cool under cold water. Peel the skin away from the cross.*

chicken with balsamic vinegar

2 tablespoons olive oil
8 chicken pieces
125 ml (4 fl oz/½ cup) chicken stock
125 ml (4 fl oz/½ cup) dry white wine
125 ml (4 fl oz/½ cup) balsamic vinegar
  (see Note)
40 g (1½ oz) chilled butter

serves 4

method Heat the oil in a large flameproof casserole dish over medium heat and cook the chicken, in batches, for 7–8 minutes, or until browned. Pour off any excess fat.

Add the stock, bring to the boil, then reduce the heat and simmer, covered, for 30 minutes, or until the chicken is cooked through.

Add the white wine and vinegar and increase the heat to high. Boil for 1 minute, or until the liquid has thickened. Remove from the heat, stir in the butter until melted, and season. Spoon the sauce over the chicken to serve, accompanied by roast potatoes and salad.

note *Use a good-quality balsamic vinegar, as the cheaper varieties can be too acidic.*

moroccan chicken

1 tablespoon Moroccan spice blend (see Note)
800 g (1 lb 12 oz) skinless, boneless chicken
thighs, halved
1 tablespoon oil
60 g (2 oz) butter
1 large onion, cut into wedges
1 cinnamon stick
2 garlic cloves, crushed
2 tablespoons lemon juice
250 ml (9 fl oz/1 cup) chicken stock
75 g (2½ oz/⅓ cup) pitted prunes, halved
280 g (10 oz/1½ cups) couscous
lemon wedges, to serve

serves 4

method Sprinkle half the spice blend over the chicken. Heat the oil and 20 g (³/₄ oz) of the butter in a large deep-sided frying pan over medium heat. Cook the chicken in batches for 5 minutes, or until evenly browned. Remove from the pan, then add the onion and cinnamon stick, and cook for 2–3 minutes before adding the garlic. Return the chicken to the pan and add the lemon juice and the remaining spice blend. Season to taste with salt and pepper, then cook, covered, for 5 minutes.

Add the stock and prunes to the pan, and bring to the boil. Reduce the heat to low–medium and cook, uncovered, for 15 minutes, or until the chicken is cooked and the liquid has reduced. Before serving, stir 20 g (³/₄ oz) of the butter into the sauce.

About 10 minutes before the chicken is ready, place the couscous in a heatproof bowl, add 375 ml (13 fl oz/1½ cups) boiling water and stand for 3–5 minutes. Stir in the remaining butter and fluff the couscous with a fork until the butter has melted and the grains have separated. Serve with the chicken and lemon wedges.

note *Depending on the quality and freshness of the Moroccan spice blend you buy, you may need to use a little more than specified in the recipe.*

duck and coconut curry

curry paste

1 red onion, chopped
2 garlic cloves
2 coriander (cilantro) roots, chopped
2 teaspoons chopped fresh ginger
1½ teaspoons coriander seeds, dry-roasted
   and ground
1 teaspoon cardamom seeds, dry-roasted
   and ground
1 teaspoon fenugreek seeds, dry-roasted
   and ground
1 teaspoon brown mustard seeds, dry-roasted
   and ground
10 black peppercorns, ground
2 teaspoons garam masala
¼ teaspoon ground turmeric
2 teaspoons tamarind purée

6–8 boneless, skinless duck breasts
1 red onion, sliced
125 ml (4 fl oz/½ cup) white vinegar
500 ml (17 fl oz/2 cups) coconut milk
2 tablespoons coriander (cilantro) leaves

serves 6

method To make the curry paste, place all the ingredients in a food processor and process to a thick paste. Put aside.

Trim any excess fat from the duck breasts, then place, skin side down, in a large saucepan and cook over medium heat for 10 minutes, or until the skin is brown and any remaining fat has melted. Turn the fillets over and cook for 5 minutes, or until tender. Remove and drain on paper towels.

Reserve 1 tablespoon duck fat, discarding the remaining fat. Add the onion and cook for 5 minutes, then add the curry paste and stir over low heat for 10 minutes, or until fragrant.

Return the duck to the pan and stir to coat with the paste. Stir in the vinegar, coconut milk, 1 teaspoon salt and 125 ml (4 fl oz/½ cup) water. Simmer, covered, for 45 minutes, or until the duck breasts are tender. Stir in the coriander just prior to serving. Serve with steamed rice and naan bread.

tomato chicken casserole

1.5 kg (3 lb 5 oz) chicken pieces
40 g (1½ oz) butter
1 tablespoon oil
1 large onion, chopped
2 garlic cloves, chopped
1 small green capsicum (pepper), chopped
130 g (3½ oz) mushrooms, thickly sliced
1 tablespoon plain (all purpose) flour
250 ml (9 fl oz/1 cup) white wine
1 tablespoon white wine vinegar
4 tomatoes, peeled, seeded and chopped
2 tablespoons tomato paste (concentrated purée)
90 g (3 oz/½ cup) small black olives
2 large handfuls flat-leaf (Italian) parsley, chopped

serves 4

method Preheat the oven to 180°C (350°F/Gas 4). Remove the excess fat from the chicken pieces and pat dry with paper towels. Heat 2 teaspoons of the butter and 2 teaspoons of the oil in a large flameproof casserole dish. Cook half the chicken over high heat until browned all over, then set aside. Heat another 2 teaspoons of the butter and the remaining oil, and cook the remaining chicken. Set aside.

Heat the remaining butter in the casserole dish and cook the onion and garlic for 2–3 minutes over medium–high heat. Add the capsicum and mushroom, and cook, stirring, for 3 minutes. Stir in the flour and cook for 1 minute. Add the wine, vinegar, tomato and tomato paste, and cook, stirring, for 2 minutes, or until slightly thickened.

Return the chicken to the casserole dish and make sure it is covered by the tomato and onion mixture. Place in the oven and cook, covered, for 1 hour, or until the chicken is tender. Stir in the olives and parsley. Season with salt and freshly cracked black pepper, and serve with pasta.

green chicken curry

500 ml (17 fl oz/2 cups) coconut cream (do not shake the tin—see Note)
90 g (3 oz/⅓ cup) Thai green curry paste
2 tablespoons grated palm sugar (jaggery) or soft brown sugar
2 tablespoons fish sauce
4 makrut (kaffir lime) leaves, finely shredded
1 kg (2 lb 4 oz) boneless, skinless chicken thigh or breasts, cut into thick strips
200 g (7 oz) bamboo shoots, trimmed and cut into thick strips
100 g (3½ oz) snake (yard-long) beans, trimmed and cut into 5 cm (2 inch) lengths
1 handful basil leaves

serves 4–6

method Place 125 ml (4 fl oz/½ cup) of the thick coconut cream from the top of the tin in a wok, and bring to the boil. Add the curry paste, then reduce the heat and simmer for 15 minutes, or until fragrant and the oil starts to separate from the cream. Add the palm sugar, fish sauce and makrut leaves to the pan.

Stir in the remaining coconut cream and the chicken, bamboo shoots and beans, and simmer for 15 minutes, or until the chicken is tender. Stir in the basil and serve with rice.

note *Do not shake the tin of coconut cream because good-quality coconut cream has a layer of very thick cream at the top that has separated from the rest of the cream. This has a higher fat content, which causes it to split or separate more readily than the rest of the coconut cream.*

chicken, artichoke and broad bean stew

155 g (5½ oz/1 cup) frozen broad (fava) beans
8 chicken thighs (skin removed, optional)
60 g (2 oz/½ cup) seasoned plain
(all-purpose) flour
2 tablespoons oil
1 large red onion, cut into small wedges
125 ml (4 fl oz/½ cup) dry white wine
310 ml (11 fl oz/1¼ cups) chicken stock
2 teaspoons finely chopped fresh rosemary
335 g (12 oz) marinated artichokes, well
drained and quartered
800 g (1 lb 12 oz) potatoes, cut into large
cubes
60 g (2 oz) butter

serves 4

method Remove the skins from the broad beans. Coat the chicken in the flour, shaking off the excess. Heat the oil in a saucepan or flameproof casserole dish, then brown the chicken in two batches on all sides over medium heat. Remove and drain on paper towels.

Add the onion to the pan and cook for 3–4 minutes, or until soft but not brown. Increase the heat to high, pour in the wine and boil for 2 minutes, or until reduced to a syrup. Stir in 250 ml (9 fl oz/1 cup) of the stock and bring just to the boil, then return the chicken to the pan with the rosemary. Reduce the heat to low and simmer, covered, for 45 minutes.

Add the artichokes to the pan, increase the heat to high and return to the boil. Reduce to a simmer and cook, uncovered, for 10–15 minutes. Add the beans and cook for a further 5 minutes.

Meanwhile, cook the potato in a saucepan of boiling water for 15–20 minutes, or until tender. Drain, then return to the pan. Add the butter and the remaining stock, and mash with a potato masher. Serve on the side of the stew.

beef and veal

vietnamese beef noodle soup

400 g (14 oz) rump steak, trimmed
1 litre (35 fl oz/4 cups) beef stock
½ onion
1 star anise
1 cinnamon stick
1 tablespoon fish sauce
pinch ground white pepper
200 g (7 oz) fresh thin round rice noodles
2 spring onions (scallions), thinly sliced
30 mint leaves
90 g (3 oz/1 cup) bean sprouts, trimmed
1 small white onion, thinly sliced
1 small red chilli, thinly sliced

serves 4

method Wrap the meat in plastic wrap and freeze for 30–40 minutes, or until partially frozen. Thinly slice the meat across the grain.

Place the stock in a large heavy-based saucepan with the onion half, star anise, cinnamon stick, fish sauce, white pepper and 500 ml (17 fl oz/2 cups) water, and bring to the boil over high heat. Reduce the heat to low– medium and simmer, covered, for 20 minutes. Discard the onion, star anise and cinnamon stick.

Meanwhile, cover the noodles with boiling water and gently separate. Drain and refresh with cold water. Divide the noodles and spring onion among the serving bowls. Top with equal amounts of beef, mint leaves, bean sprouts, onion slices and chilli. Ladle the simmering broth into the bowls, and serve.

note *It is important that the broth is kept hot as the heat will cook the slices of beef.*

hot beef borscht

500 g (1 lb 2 oz) stewing beef, cut into cubes
500 g (1 lb 2 oz) beetroot (beets)
1 onion, finely chopped
1 carrot, cut into short strips
1 parsnip, cut into short strips
75 g (2½ oz/1 cup) finely shredded cabbage
sour cream, to serve
snipped chives, to serve

serves 4–6

method Put the beef and 1 litre (35 fl oz/4 cups) water in a large heavy-based saucepan, and bring slowly to the boil. Reduce the heat, cover and simmer for 1 hour. Skim the surface of the stock to remove the fat as required.

Cut the stems from the beetroot, wash well and place in a large, heavy based saucepan with 1 litre (35 fl oz/4 cups) water. Bring to the boil, then reduce the heat and simmer for 40 minutes, or until the beetroot is tender. Drain, reserving 250 ml (9 fl oz /1 cup) of the liquid. Allow to cool, then peel and grate the beetroot.

Remove the meat from the stock and cool. Skim any remaining fat from the surface of the stock. Return the meat to the stock and add the onion, carrot, parsnip, beetroot and reserved beetroot liquid. Bring to the boil, reduce the heat, cover and simmer for 45 minutes.

Stir in the cabbage and simmer for a further 15 minutes. Season to taste. Serve with the sour cream and chives.

beef and peppercorn stew

1 kg (2 lb 4 oz) chuck steak, cut into 3 cm
   (1¼ inch) cubes
2 teaspoons cracked black peppercorns
40 g (1½ oz) butter
2 tablespoons oil
1 large onion, thinly sliced
2 garlic cloves, sliced
1½ tablespoons plain (all-purpose) flour
2 tablespoons brandy
750 ml (26 fl oz/3 cups) beef stock
1 tablespoon worcestershire sauce
2 teaspoons dijon mustard
500 g (1 lb 2 oz) baby new potatoes
60 ml (2 fl oz/¼ cup) cream
2 tablespoons chopped parsley

serves 4

method Toss the steak in the peppercorns. Heat half the butter and half the oil in a large heavy-based saucepan. Brown half the steak over high heat, then remove and set aside. Heat the remaining butter and oil, and brown the remaining steak. Remove from the pan and set aside.

Add the onion and garlic to the pan and cook, stirring, until the onion is golden. Add the flour and stir until browned. Remove from the heat.

Combine the brandy, beef stock, worcestershire sauce and mustard, and gradually stir into the onion mixture. Return to the heat, add the steak and any juices, then simmer, covered, for 1¼ hours.

Add the potatoes and simmer, uncovered, for a further 30 minutes, or until the meat and potatoes are tender. Stir in the cream and parsley, and season to taste with salt and freshly ground black pepper. This is delicious served with a green salad.

chilli con carne

185 g (6½ oz) dried black-eyed peas
1½ tablespoons oil
900 g (2 lb) trimmed chuck steak, cut into chunks
3 onions, thinly sliced
2 garlic cloves, chopped
2 teaspoons ground cumin
1 tablespoon paprika
½ teaspoon allspice powder
1–2 teaspoons chilli powder
650 g (1 lb 7 oz) tomatoes, peeled, seeded and finely chopped
1 tablespoon soft brown sugar
1 tablespoon red wine vinegar

serves 6

method Put the peas in a bowl, cover with plenty of water and leave to soak overnight. Drain well.

Heat 1 tablespoon of the oil in a large heavy-based saucepan and cook the meat in two batches over medium–high heat for 2 minutes, or until well browned. Remove from the pan.

Pour the rest of the oil into the saucepan and add the onion. Cook over medium heat for 5 minutes, or until translucent. Add the garlic and spices and cook, stirring, for 1 minute, or until aromatic. Add 500 ml (17 fl oz/2 cups) water and stir in.

Return the meat to the pan with the peas and tomato. Bring to the boil, then reduce the heat to low and simmer, partially covered, for 2 hours, or until the meat is tender and the chilli con carne is thick and dryish, stirring occasionally. Towards the end of the cooking time the mixture may start to catch, so add a little water if necessary. Stir through the sugar and vinegar, and season with salt to taste. This is delicious served with flour tortillas and grated cheddar cheese.

beef and lentil curry

3–4 small dried red chillies
60 ml (2 fl oz/¼ cup) oil
2 red onions, cut into thin wedges
4 garlic cloves, finely chopped
1 tablespoon grated fresh ginger
1 tablespoon garam masala
3 cardamom pods, lightly crushed
1 cinnamon stick
2 teaspoons ground turmeric
750 g (1 lb 10 oz) chuck steak, cut into cubes
400 g (14 oz) tin chopped tomatoes
95 g (3 oz/½ cup) brown or green lentils
125 g (4½ oz/½ cup) red lentils
200 g (7 oz) pumpkin (winter squash), diced
150 g (5½ oz) eggplant (aubergine), diced
125 g (4½ oz) baby English spinach
1 tablespoon tamarind purée
2 tablespoons grated palm sugar (jaggery) or soft brown sugar

serves 6

method Soak the chillies in boiling water for 10 minutes, then drain and finely chop.

Heat the oil in a large saucepan. Add the onion and cook, stirring, over medium heat for 5 minutes, or until soft. Add the garlic and ginger, and cook for a further 2 minutes.

Add the chilli, garam masala, cardamom pods, cinnamon, turmeric and ½ teaspoon black pepper. Cook, stirring, for 2 minutes, or until fragrant. Add beef and stir constantly for 3–4 minutes, or until meat is coated in spices.

Add the tomato, lentils, 1 teaspoon salt and 750 ml (26 fl oz/3 cups) water. Simmer, covered, for 1 hour until tender. Stir often to prevent burning. Add extra water, if needed.

Add the pumpkin and eggplant to pan, and cook, covered, for 20 minutes, or until tender. Stir in the spinach, tamarind and palm sugar, and cook for a further 10 minutes.

paprika veal with caraway noodles

60 ml (2 fl oz/¼ cup) oil
1 kg (2 lb 4 oz) veal shoulder, diced
1 large onion, thinly sliced
3 garlic cloves, finely chopped
60 g (2 oz/¼ cup) Hungarian paprika
½ teaspoon caraway seeds
2 x 400 g (14 oz) tins chopped tomatoes,
one drained
350 g (12 oz) fresh fettuccine
40 g (1½ oz) butter, softened

serves 4

method Heat half the oil in a large saucepan over medium–high heat, then brown the veal in batches for 3 minutes per batch. Remove the veal from the pan and set aside with any pan juices.

Add the remaining oil to the pan and sauté the onion and garlic over medium heat for 5 minutes, or until softened. Add the paprika and ¼ teaspoon of the caraway seeds, and stir for 30 seconds.

Add all the chopped tomatoes and their liquid plus 125 ml (4 fl oz/½ cup) water. Return the veal to the pan with any juices, increase the heat to high and bring to the boil. Reduce the heat to low, then cover and simmer for 1¼ hours, or until the meat is tender and the sauce has reduced and thickened.

About 15 minutes before the veal is ready, cook the pasta in a large saucepan of rapidly boiling salted water according to the packet instructions until al dente. Drain, then return to the pan. Stir in the butter and the remaining caraway seeds. Serve immediately with the paprika veal.

beef rendang

2 onions, roughly chopped
2 garlic cloves, crushed
400 ml (14 fl oz) tin coconut milk
2 teaspoons ground coriander seeds
½ teaspoon ground fennel seeds
2 teaspoons ground cumin seeds
¼ teaspoon ground cloves
1.5 kg (3 lb 5 oz) chuck steak, cut into 3 cm
   (1¼ inch) cubes
4–6 small fresh red chillies, chopped
1 tablespoon lemon juice
1 lemongrass stem (white part only), bruised,
   cut lengthways
2 teaspoons grated palm sugar (jaggery) or
   soft brown sugar
coriander (cilantro) sprigs, to garnish

serves 6

method   Place the coconut milk in a large saucepan and bring to the boil, then reduce the heat to medium and cook, stirring occasionally, for 15 minutes, or until the milk has reduced by half and the oil has separated. Do not allow the milk to brown.

Add the coriander seeds, fennel, cumin and cloves to the pan, and stir for 1 minute. Add the meat and cook for 2 minutes, or until it changes colour. Add the onion mixture, chilli, lemon juice, lemongrass and palm sugar. Cook, covered, over medium heat for 2 hours, or until the liquid has reduced and the mixture has thickened. Stir frequently to prevent it sticking to the bottom of the pan.

Uncover and continue cooking until the oil from the coconut milk begins to emerge again, letting the curry develop. Be careful that it does not burn. The curry is cooked when it is brown and dry. Serve with rice and coriander sprigs.

steak and kidney stew

1 kg (2 lb 4 oz) chuck steak, trimmed
8 lamb kidneys
60 ml (2 fl oz/¼ cup) oil
1 bacon slice, rind removed, cut into long, thin strips
40 g (1½ oz) butter
1 large onion, chopped
300 g (10½ oz) button mushrooms, halved
250 ml (9 fl oz/1 cup) Muscat
2–3 garlic cloves, crushed
¼ teaspoon ground allspice
½ teaspoon paprika
2 teaspoons coriander seeds, lightly crushed
1 tablespoon wholegrain mustard
250 ml (9 fl oz/1 cup) beef stock
2–3 tablespoons soft brown sugar
1–2 teaspoons thyme leaves
1–2 teaspoons rosemary chopped

serves 4–6

method Cut the steak into 2–3 cm (1 inch) cubes. Cut the kidneys in half, remove the core and any fat, then slice them in half again.

Heat 1 teaspoon of the oil in a large heavy-based saucepan. Add the bacon and cook over medium heat until just crisp. Remove and then set aside.

Heat 2 tablespoons of the oil and 30 g (1 oz) of the butter in the pan. Brown the steak cubes in batches, then set aside.

Add the onion to the pan and cook for 3 minutes, or until soft and golden. Add the mushrooms and cook, stirring, for 3 minutes, until starting to brown. Stir in half the Muscat and simmer for 3–4 minutes. Remove and set to the side.

Add the remaining oil and butter to the pan. Stir in the garlic, allspice, paprika and coriander seeds, and cook for 1 minute. Add the kidney and cook until just starting to brown. Stir in the mustard and remaining Muscat, and simmer for 2 minutes.

Stir in the bacon, steak, and onion and mushroom mixture. Stir in the stock, bring to the boil, then reduce the heat, cover and simmer for 1 hour. Add the sugar. Simmer, covered, for 40 minutes, then uncovered for 20 minutes, stirring in the herbs during the last 10 minutes.

red beef and eggplant curry

250 ml (9 fl oz) tin coconut cream (do not shake the tin)
2 tablespoons Thai red curry paste
500 g (1 lb 2 oz) round or topside steak, cut into strips (see Note)
2 tablespoons fish sauce
1 tablespoon grated palm sugar (jaggery) or soft brown sugar
5 makrut (kaffir lime) leaves, halved
500 ml (17 fl oz/2 cups) coconut milk
8 Thai eggplants (aubergines), halved
2 tablespoons finely shredded Thai basil leaves

serves 4

method Place the thick coconut cream from the top of the tin in a wok and bring to the boil. Boil for 10 minutes, or until the oil starts to separate. Add the curry paste and simmer, stirring to prevent it sticking to the bottom, for 5 minutes, or until fragrant.

Add the meat and cook, stirring, for 3–5 minutes, or until it changes colour. Add the fish sauce, palm sugar, makrut leaves, coconut milk and remaining coconut cream, and simmer for 1 hour, or until the meat is tender and the sauce has slightly thickened.

Add the eggplant and cook for 10 minutes, or until tender. If the sauce is too thick, add a little water. Stir in half the shredded basil. Garnish with the remaining basil leaves and serve with steamed rice.

note *Cut the meat into 5 x 5 x 2 cm (2 x 2 x ¾ inch) pieces, then cut across the grain at a 45° angle into 5 mm (¼ inch) thick slices.*

japanese-style sukiyaki

sauce

½–1 teaspoon dashi granules
80 ml (2½ fl oz/⅓ cup) soy sauce
2 tablespoons sake (dry rice wine)
2 tablespoons mirin (sweet rice wine)
1 tablespoon caster (superfine) sugar

300 g (10½ oz) shirataki noodles
50 g (2 oz) lard
5 large spring onions (scallions), cut into 1 cm
(½ inch) slices on the diagonal
16 fresh shiitake mushrooms, cut into smaller
pieces if large
800 g (1 lb 12 oz) rump steak, thinly sliced
across the grain
100 g (3½ oz) watercress, trimmed
4 eggs (optional)

serves 4

method To make the sauce, dissolve the dashi granules in 125 ml (4 fl oz/½ cup) water. Add the soy sauce, sake, mirin and sugar, and stir until combined.

Drain the noodles, then soak them in boiling water for 2 minutes. Rinse in cold water and drain well.

Melt the lard in a large frying pan over medium heat. Cook the spring onion, mushrooms and beef in batches, stirring, for 1–2 minutes each batch, or until just brown. Return the meat, spring onion and mushrooms to the pan, then add the sauce and watercress. Cook for 1 minute, or until heated through and the watercress has wilted—the sauce needs to just cover the ingredients but not drown them.

To serve, divide the noodles among four serving bowls and spoon the sauce evenly over the top. If desired, crack an egg into each bowl and break up through the sauce using chopsticks until it partially cooks.

chinese beef in soy

700 g (1 lb 9 oz) chuck steak, trimmed and cut
   into 2 cm (¾ inch) cubes
80 ml (2½ fl oz/⅓ cup) dark soy sauce
2 tablespoons honey
1 tablespoon wine vinegar
60 ml (2 fl oz/¼ cup) soya bean oil, or
   cooking oil
4 garlic cloves, chopped
8 spring onions (scallions), thinly sliced
1 tablespoon finely grated fresh ginger
2 star anise
½ teaspoon ground cloves
375 ml (13 fl oz/1½ cups) beef stock
125 ml (4 fl oz/½ cup) red wine
sliced spring onions (scallions), extra, to garnish

serves 4

method Place the meat in a non-metallic dish. Combine the soy sauce, honey and vinegar in a small bowl, then pour over the meat. Cover with plastic wrap and marinate for at least 2 hours, or preferably overnight. Drain, reserving the marinade, and pat the cubes dry.

Place 1 tablespoon of the oil in a saucepan and brown the meat in 3 batches, for 3–4 minutes per batch—add another tablespoon of oil, if necessary. Remove the meat. Add the remaining oil and fry the garlic, spring onion, ginger, star anise and cloves for 1–2 minutes, or until fragrant.

Return all the meat to the pan, and add the reserved marinade, stock and wine. Bring to the boil, then reduce the heat and simmer, covered, for 1¼ hours. Cook, uncovered, for a further 15 minutes, or until the sauce is syrupy and the meat is tender.

Garnish with the extra sliced spring onion and serve immediately with steamed rice.

100 EASY RECIPES ONE-POTS

corned beef

1 tablespoon oil
1.5 kg (3 lb 5 oz) piece corned silverside, trimmed
1 tablespoon white vinegar
1 tablespoon soft brown sugar
4 cloves
4 black peppercorns
2 bay leaves
1 garlic clove, crushed
1 large parsley sprig
4 carrots
4 potatoes
6 small onions

onion sauce

30 g (1 oz) butter
2 white onions, chopped
2 tablespoons plain (all-purpose) flour
330ml (11 fl oz/1⅓ cups) full-cream (whole) milk

horseradish cream

60 ml (2 fl oz/¼ cup) horseradish relish
1 tablespoon white vinegar
125 ml (4 fl oz/½ cup) cream

serves 6–8

method Heat the oil in a deep, heavy-based saucepan. Cook the meat over medium–high heat, turning until well browned all over. Remove the pan from the heat and add the vinegar, sugar, cloves, peppercorns, bay leaves, garlic and parsley sprig.

Pour over enough water to cover. Cover and return to the heat, reduce the heat and bring slowly to a simmering point. Then simmer for a further 30 minutes.

Cut the carrots and potatoes into large pieces and add to the pan with the onions. Simmer, covered, for 1 hour, or until tender. Remove the vegetables and keep warm. Reserve 125 ml (4 fl oz/½ cup) of the cooking liquid.

Meanwhile to make the onion sauce, heat the butter in a small saucepan. Cook the onion gently for 10 minutes, or until soft but not browned. Transfer the onion to a bowl. Add the flour to the pan and stir over low heat for 2 minutes, or until the flour is lightly golden. Gradually add the milk and the reserved cooking liquid, and stir until the sauce boils and thickens. Boil for 1 minute, then remove from the heat and stir in the onion. Season to taste.

To make the horseradish cream, combine all of the ingredients in a bowl until smooth.

Drain the meat from the pan, discarding the remaining liquid and spices. Slice the meat, and serve it with the vegetables, onion sauce and horseradish cream. Garnish with bay leaves if desired.

japanese beef hotpot

300 g (10½ oz) beef fillet, trimmed
1.5 litres (52 fl oz/6 cups) chicken stock
2 cm x 6 cm (¾ inch x 2½ inch) piece fresh
    ginger, thinly sliced
80 ml (2½ fl oz/⅓ cup) light soy sauce
2 tablespoons mirin
1 teaspoon sesame oil
200 g (7 oz) fresh udon noodles
150 g (5½ oz) English spinach, stems removed,
    thinly sliced
400 g (14 oz) cabbage, finely shredded
100 g (3½ oz) fresh shiitake mushrooms, stems
    removed and caps thinly sliced
200 g (7 oz) firm tofu, cut into 2 cm (¾ inch)
    cubes
80 ml (2½ fl oz/⅓ cup) ponzu sauce, or 60 ml
    (2 fl oz/¼ cup) soy sauce combined with
    1 tablespoon lemon juice

serves 4

method Wrap the beef fillet in plastic wrap and freeze for 40 minutes, or until it begins to harden. Remove and slice as thinly as possible across the grain.

Place the stock, ginger, soy sauce, mirin and sesame oil in a 2.5 litre (87 fl oz/10 cup) flameproof casserole dish or hotpot over medium heat, and simmer for 3 minutes. Separate the noodles gently with chopsticks, add to the stock and cook for 1–2 minutes. Add the spinach, cabbage, mushrooms and tofu, and simmer for 1 minute, or until the leaves have wilted.

Divide the noodles among four serving bowls using tongs, and top with the beef slices, vegetables and tofu. Ladle the hot stock on top and serve the ponzu sauce on the side.

note *Traditionally, raw beef slices are arranged on a plate with the tofu, mushrooms, vegetables and noodles. The stock and seasoning are heated on a portable gas flame at the table. Guests dip the meat and vegetables in the hot stock and eat as they go, dipping into the sauce. The noodles are added at the end and served with the broth.*

osso bucco

12 meaty pieces veal shank, osso bucco style
40 g (1½ oz/⅓ cup) seasoned plain
(all-purpose) flour
20 g (¾ oz) butter
80 ml (2½ fl oz/⅓ cup) olive oil
1 onion, diced
1 carrot, diced
1 celery stalk, diced
1 bay leaf
1 garlic clove, crushed
500 ml (17 fl oz/2 cups) veal or chicken stock
250ml (9 fl oz/1 cup) white wine
80 ml (2½ fl oz/⅓ cup) lemon juice

gremolata

4 tablespoons flat-leaf (Italian) parsley
2 garlic cloves, finely chopped
1 tablespoon grated lemon zest

serves 4–6

method Lightly dust the veal shanks in the seasoned flour. Put the butter and 60 ml (2 fl oz/¼ cup) of the oil in a large deep-sided frying pan over high heat and heat until sizzling. Add the veal and cook in batches for 5 minutes, or until brown all over. Remove from the pan.

Heat the remaining oil in the pan, add the onion, carrot, celery and bay leaf, and cook for 10 minutes, or until softened and starting to brown. Add the garlic, stock, wine and lemon juice, and stir to combine, scraping the bottom of the pan to remove any sediment. Return the veal to the pan, bring to the boil, then reduce the heat to low, cover and simmer for 1½–2 hours, or until the veal is very tender and falling off the bone and the sauce has reduced. Season to taste.

To make the gremolata, finely chop the parsley and mix together with the garlic and lemon zest. Sprinkle over just before serving. Serve with soft polenta.

madras beef curry

1 tablespoon oil or ghee
1 onion, chopped
55–90 g (2–3 oz/¼– ⅓ cup) Madras curry paste
1 kg (2 lb 4 oz) skirt or chuck steak, trimmed of
    fat and cut into 2.5 cm (1 inch) cubes
60 g (2 oz/¼ cup) tomato paste
    (concentrated purée)
250 ml (9 fl oz/1 cup) beef stock
coriander (cilantro) sprigs, to garnish

serves 4

method Heat the oil in a large frying pan, add the onion and cook over medium heat for about 10 minutes, or until browned. Add the curry paste and stir for 1 minute, or until fragrant. Then add the meat and cook, stirring, until coated with the curry paste.

Stir in the tomato paste and stock. Reduce the heat and simmer, covered, for 1¼ hours, Add more stock or water if necessary. Simmer uncovered for 15 minutes, or until the meat is tender. Garnish with coriander and serve with steamed rice.

spiced beef and potatoes

spice paste

2 onions, chopped
2 garlic cloves, chopped
2 teaspoons grated lemon zest
2 small red chillies, chopped
2 teaspoons ground coriander
2 teaspoons ground cumin
1 teaspoon ground turmeric
½ teaspoon ground cardamom
1 teaspoon garam masala

2 tablespoons oil
1 kg (2 lb 4 oz) lean chuck steak, cut into
3 cm (1¼ inch) cubes
185 ml (6 fl oz/¾ cup) coconut cream
1 tablespoon tamarind sauce
500 g (1 lb 2 oz) baby potatoes, halved

serves 4

method To make the spice paste, combine all the ingredients in a food processor, and process for 1 minute, or until very finely chopped.

Heat the oil in a heavy-based saucepan. Cook the meat quickly in small batches over medium–high heat until well browned. Drain meat on paper towels.

Add the spice paste to the pan and stir over medium heat for 2 minutes. Return the meat to the pan with the coconut cream, tamarind sauce and 125 ml (4 fl oz/½ cup) water, and bring to the boil. Reduce the heat to a simmer and cook, covered, for 30 minutes, stirring occasionally.

Add the potato and cook, covered, for 30 minutes. Remove the lid and cook for another 30 minutes, or until the meat is tender and almost all of the liquid has evaporated.

beef pot roast

300 g (10½ oz) baby brown onions
2 carrots
3 parsnips, peeled
40 g (1½ oz) butter
1–1.5 kg (2 lb 4 oz–3 lb 5 oz) eye of silverside,
    trimmed of fat (see Note)
60 ml (2 fl oz/¼ cup) dry red wine
1 large tomato, finely chopped
250 ml (9 fl oz/1 cup) beef stock
mild or hot English mustard, to serve

serves 6

method Put the onions in a heatproof bowl and cover with boiling water. Leave for 1 minute, then drain well. Allow them to cool, then peel off the skins.

Cut the carrots and parsnips in half lengthways, then into even-sized pieces. Heat half the butter in a large heavy-based saucepan that will tightly fit the meat (it will shrink during cooking), add the onions, carrot and parsnip, and cook, stirring, over medium–high heat until browned. Remove from the pan. Add the remaining butter to the pan and add the meat, browning well all over. Increase the heat to high and pour in the wine. Bring to the boil, then add the tomato and stock. Return to the boil, then reduce the heat to low, cover and simmer for 2 hours, turning once. Add the vegetables and simmer, covered, for 1 hour.

Remove the meat from the pan and put it on a board ready for carving. Cover with foil and leave it to stand while finishing the sauce.

Increase the heat to high and boil the pan juices with the vegetables for 10 minutes to reduce and thicken slightly. Skim off any excess fat, and taste before seasoning. Slice the meat and arrange on a serving platter or individual serving plates with the vegetables. Drizzle generously with the pan juices. Serve with mustard and pepper.

note *Eye of silverside is a tender, long-shaped cut of silverside that carves easily into serving-sized pieces. A regular piece of silverside or topside may be substituted.*

beef stroganoff

1 kg (2 lb 4 oz) piece rump steak, trimmed
40 g (1 ½ oz/⅓ cup) plain (all-purpose) flour
¼ teaspoon ground black pepper
60 ml (2 fl oz/¼ cup) olive oil
1 large onion, chopped
500 g (1 lb 2 oz) baby mushrooms
1 tablespoon sweet paprika
1 tablespoon tomato paste
2 teaspoons French mustard
125 ml (4 fl oz/½ cup) dry white wine
60 ml (2 fl oz/¼ cup) chicken stock
185 g (6½ oz/¾ cup) sour cream
1 tablespoon finely chopped flat-leaf (Italian)
parsley

serves 6

method Slice the meat across the grain into short, thin pieces. Combine the flour and pepper. Toss the meat in the seasoned flour, shaking off the excess.

Heat 2 tablespoons of the oil in a heavy-based saucepan. Cook the meat quickly in small batches over medium–high heat until well browned. Drain on paper towels.

Heat the remaining oil in the pan. Cook the onion over medium heat for 3 minutes, or until softened. Add the mushrooms and stir for 5 minutes.

Add the paprika, tomato paste, mustard, wine and stock to the pan, and bring to the boil. Reduce the heat and simmer for 5 minutes, uncovered, stirring occasionally. Return the meat to the pan along with the sour cream, and stir until combined and just heated through. Sprinkle with the chopped parsley just before serving.

thai beef and pumpkin curry

2 tablespoons oil
750 g (1 lb 10 oz) blade steak, thinly sliced
90 g (3 oz/⅓ cup) Massaman curry paste
2 garlic cloves, finely chopped
1 onion, sliced lengthways
6 curry leaves, torn
750 ml (26 fl oz/3 cups) coconut milk
450 g (1 lb) butternut pumpkin (squash),
    roughly diced
2 tablespoons chopped unsalted peanuts
1 tablespoon grated palm sugar (jaggery) or
    soft brown sugar
2 tablespoons tamarind purée
2 tablespoons fish sauce
curry leaves, extra, to garnish

serves 6

method Heat a wok or frying pan over high heat. Add the oil and swirl to coat the side. Add the meat in batches and cook for 5 minutes, or until browned. Remove the meat from the wok.

Add the curry paste, garlic, onion and curry leaves to the wok, and stir to coat. Return the meat to the wok and cook, stirring, over medium heat for 2 minutes.

Add the coconut milk to the wok, then reduce the heat to low and gently simmer for 45 minutes. Add the pumpkin and simmer for 25–30 minutes, or until the meat and the pumpkin are tender and the sauce has thickened.

Stir in the peanuts, palm sugar, tamarind purée and fish sauce, and simmer for 1 minute. Garnish with curry leaves and season with cracked black pepper. Serve with steamed rice.

creamy veal with mushrooms

750 g (1 lb 10 oz) veal steaks, cut into 1 cm
(½ inch) strips
30 g (1 oz/¼ cup) plain (all-purpose) flour
30 g (1 oz) butter
1 garlic clove, crushed
1 tablespoon dijon mustard
250 ml (9 fl oz/1 cup) cream
125 ml (4 fl oz/½ cup) white wine
1 tablespoon chopped fresh thyme
250 ml (9 fl oz/1 cup) chicken stock
375 g (13 oz) button mushrooms, halved

serves 4

method Toss the meat in the flour (inside a plastic bag prevents mess), shaking off the excess. Heat the butter and garlic in a large frying pan. Add the meat and cook quickly in small batches over medium heat until well browned. Drain thoroughly on paper towels.

Brown the mushrooms in the pan, then add the mustard, cream, wine, thyme and chicken stock. Bring to the boil, then reduce the heat and simmer, covered, for 10–15 minutes, stirring occasionally, until the sauce thickens.

Add the veal and cook for a further 3–5 minutes, or until the meat is tender and warmed through. Delicious served with pasta and steamed vegetables.

beef bourguignon

1 kg (2 lb 4 oz) stewing beef, cubed
30 g (1 oz/¼ cup) seasoned plain (all-purpose) flour
1 tablespoon oil
150 g (5½ oz) bacon slices, diced
8 bulb spring onions (scallions), greens trimmed to 2 cm (¾ inch)
200 g (7 oz) button mushrooms
500 ml (17 fl oz/2 cups) red wine
2 tablespoons tomato paste (concentrated purée)
500 ml (17 fl oz/2 cups) beef stock
1 bouquet garni (see Note)

serves 4

method Toss the beef in the seasoned flour until evenly coated, shaking off any excess. Heat the oil in a large saucepan over high heat. Cook the beef in three batches for about 3 minutes, or until well browned all over, adding a little extra oil as needed. Remove from the pan.

Add the bacon to the pan and cook for 2 minutes, or until browned. Remove with a slotted spoon and add to the beef. Add the spring onions and mushrooms, and cook for 5 minutes, or until the onions are browned. Remove.

Slowly pour the red wine into the pan, scraping up any sediment from the bottom with a wooden spoon. Stir in the tomato paste and stock. Add the bouquet garni and return the beef, bacon and any juices. Bring to the boil, then reduce the heat and simmer for 45 minutes. Return the spring onions and mushrooms to the pan. Cook for 1 hour, or until the meat is very tender and the sauce is glossy. Serve with steamed new potatoes or mash.

note *To make a bouquet garni, wrap the green part of a leek around a bay leaf, a sprig of thyme, a sprig of parsley and celery leaves, and tie with string. The combination of herbs can be varied according to taste.*

french-style beef pot roast

2 tablespoons oil
2 kg (4 lb 8 oz) rolled beef brisket, trimmed
750 ml (26 fl oz/3 cups) beef stock
250 ml (9 fl oz/1 cup) red wine
60 ml (2 fl oz/¼ cup) brandy
2 onions, quartered
3 garlic cloves, crushed
3 tomatoes, peeled, seeded and chopped
2 bay leaves
1 large handful chopped parsley
2 tablespoons thyme leaves
12 pitted black olives
6 small carrots, thickly sliced
2 tablespoons plain (all-purpose) flour

serves 6

method   Heat the oil in a deep heavy-based saucepan. Cook the meat over medium–high heat until browned all over, then remove from the heat.

Add the stock to the pan with the wine, brandy, onion, garlic, tomato, bay leaves, parsley and thyme. Cover and bring to simmering point over low heat. Simmer for 1½ hours.

Add the olives and carrot, and cook for 30 minutes. Remove the meat and leave it in a warm place, and covered with foil, for 10 minutes before slicing.

Combine the flour and 60 ml (2 fl oz/¼ cup) water to make a smooth paste. Add to the sauce, stir over medium heat until the sauce thickens, and cook for 3 minutes. Pour over the sliced meat to serve.

beef in beer with capers

1 kg (2 lb 4 oz) gravy beef
seasoned plain (all-purpose) flour
olive oil, for cooking
4 garlic cloves, finely chopped
500 ml (17 fl oz/2 cups) beef stock
375 ml (13 fl oz/1½ cups) beer
2 onions, chopped
3 bay leaves
55 g (2 oz/⅓ cup) stuffed or pitted green
    olives, sliced
6 anchovies
2 tablespoons capers, drained

serves 4–6

method Cut the beef into 4 cm (1½ inch) chunks. Lightly coat in the flour. Heat 60 ml (2 fl oz/ ¼ cup) of oil in a deep heavy-based saucepan, add the garlic, then brown the beef over a high heat.

Add the stock, beer, onion and bay leaves, season well and bring to the boil. Reduce the heat and gently simmer, covered, for 2½ hours, stirring about three times during cooking. Remove the lid and simmer for 30 minutes more. Stir, then mix in the olives.

Heat 2 teaspoons of oil in a small saucepan. Add the anchovies and capers, gently breaking up the anchovies. Cook over medium heat for 4 minutes, or until brown and crisp. To serve, place the meat on serving plates, drizzle with the sauce, sprinkle with anchovies and capers, and season with salt and freshly cracked black pepper.

note *The capers should be squeezed very dry before being added to the pan, or they will spit in the hot oil.*

massaman beef curry

1 tablespoon tamarind pulp
2 tablespoons oil
750 g (1 lb 10 oz) lean stewing beef, cubed
500 ml (17 fl oz/2 cups) coconut milk
4 cardamom pods, bruised
500 ml (17 fl oz/2 cups) coconut cream
2–3 tablespoons Massaman curry paste
8 baby onions, peeled (see Note)
8 baby potatoes, peeled and quartered
(see Note)
2 tablespoons fish sauce
2 tablespoons grated palm sugar (jaggery) or
soft brown sugar
80 g (3 oz/½ cup) unsalted peanuts, roasted
and ground
coriander (cilantro) leaves, to garnish

serves 4

method Place the tamarind pulp and ½ cup (125 ml/4 fl oz) boiling water in a bowl and set aside to cool. When cool, mash the pulp to dissolve in the water, then strain and reserve the liquid. Discard the pulp.

Heat the oil in a wok or a large saucepan and cook the beef in batches over high heat for 5 minutes, or until browned. Reduce the heat, add the coconut milk and cardamom, and simmer for 1 hour, or until the beef is tender. Remove the beef, strain and reserve the meat and also the cooking liquid separately.

Heat the coconut cream in the wok and stir in the curry paste. Cook for 5 minutes, or until the oil starts to separate from the cream.

Add the onions, potatoes, fish sauce, palm sugar, peanuts, beef mixture, reserved cooking liquid and tamarind water, and simmer for 25–30 minutes. Serve with coriander and rice.

note *Use small onions and potatoes, about 20–30 g (¾–1 oz) each.*

mexican beef stew

500 g (1 lb 2 oz) Roma tomatoes, halved
6 flour tortillas
1–2 red chillies, finely chopped
1 tablespoon olive oil
1 kg (2 lb 4 oz) stewing beef, cubed
½ teaspoon black pepper
2 onions, thinly sliced
375 ml (13 fl oz/1½ cups) beef stock
60 g (2 oz/¼ cup) tomato paste
   (concentrated purée)
375 g (13 oz) tin kidney beans, drained
1 teaspoon chilli powder
125 g (4½ oz/½ cup) sour cream
flat-leaf (Italian) parsley to garnish

serves 6

method Preheat the oven to 180°C (350°F/Gas 4). Grill (broil) the tomatoes, skin side up, under a hot grill (broiler) for 6–8 minutes, or until the skin is black and blistered. Place in a plastic bag and seal. Cool, remove the skin and roughly chop the flesh.

Bake two of the tortillas for 4 minutes, or until crisp. Break into pieces and put in a food processor with the tomato and chopped chilli. Process for 30 seconds, or until almost smooth.

Heat the oil in a large heavy-based saucepan. Brown the beef in batches, season with pepper, then remove. Add the onion to the pan and cook for 5 minutes. Return the meat to the pan. Stir in the processed mixture, stock and tomato paste, and bring to the boil. Reduce the heat, cover and simmer for 1¼ hours. Add the beans and chilli powder, and heat through.

Grill the remaining tortillas for 2–3 minutes on each side, then cool and cut into wedges. Serve the stew with the sour cream, and toasted tortilla wedges on the side.

hint *If this stew becomes too thick during cooking, thin it with a little extra stock.*

100 EASY RECIPES ONE-POTS

veal goulash

500 g (1 lb 2 oz) veal, cut into 2.5 cm
(1 inch) pieces
2 tablespoons plain (all-purpose) flour
2 tablespoons olive oil
2 onions, thinly sliced
2 garlic cloves, finely chopped
1 tablespoon sweet paprika
1 teaspoon ground cumin
440 g (15½ oz) tin chopped tomatoes
2 carrots, sliced
½ red capsicum (pepper), chopped
½ green capsicum (pepper), chopped
250 ml (9 fl oz/1 cup) beef stock
125 ml (4 fl oz/½ cup) red wine
125 g (4½ oz/½ cup) sour cream
chopped flat-leaf (Italian) parsley, to garnish

serves 4

method Put the veal and flour in a plastic bag and shake to coat the veal with the flour. Shake off any excess. Heat 1 tablespoon of the oil in a large, deep heavy-based saucepan over medium heat. Brown the meat well in batches, then remove the meat and set aside.

Add the remaining oil to the pan. Cook the onion, garlic, paprika and cumin for 5 minutes, stirring frequently. Return the meat and any juices to the pan with the tomato, carrot and capsicum. Cover and cook for 10 minutes.

Add the stock and wine, and season with salt and pepper. Stir well, then cover and simmer over very low heat for 1½ hours. Stir in half the sour cream, season with more salt and pepper if needed and serve garnished with parsley and the remaining sour cream if desired. Delicious served with buttered boiled small potatoes or noodles.

note *If you prefer your sauce to be a little thicker, cook, uncovered, for 5 minutes over high heat before adding the sour cream.*

thai beef and peanut curry

curry paste

8–10 large dried red chillies
6 red Asian shallots (eschalots), chopped
6 garlic cloves, chopped
1 teaspoon ground coriander
1 tablespoon ground cumin
1 teaspoon white pepper
2 lemongrass stems (white part only), sliced
1 tablespoon chopped fresh galangal
6 coriander (cilantro) roots
2 teaspoons shrimp paste
2 tablespoons roasted peanuts
peanut oil, if needed

1 tablespoon peanut oil
400 ml (14 fl oz) tin coconut cream (do not
   shake the tin)
1 kg (2 lb 4 oz) round or blade steak, thinly
   sliced
400 ml (14 fl oz) tin coconut milk
4 makrut (kaffir lime) leaves, whole
90 g (3 oz/⅓ cup) crunchy peanut butter
60 ml (2 fl oz/¼ cup) lime juice
2½ tablespoons fish sauce
30–45 g (1–1½ oz/¼–⅓ cup) grated palm
   sugar (jaggery) or soft brown sugar
Thai basil leaves, to garnish
chopped peanuts, extra, to garnish

serves 4–6

method To make the curry paste, soak the chillies in boiling water for 5 minutes, or until soft.
Remove the stem and seeds, then chop. Place all the curry paste ingredients in a food processor and
process to a smooth paste. Add a little peanut oil if it is too thick.

Place the oil and the thick cream from the top of the coconut cream (reserving the rest) in a large
saucepan over high heat. Add 6–8 tablespoons of the curry paste and cook, stirring, for 5 minutes, or
until fragrant. Cook for 5–10 minutes, or until the coconut cream splits and becomes oily.

Add the beef, the reserved coconut cream, the coconut milk, makrut leaves and peanut butter, and cook
for 8 minutes, or until the beef just starts to change colour. Reduce the heat and simmer for 1 hour, or
until the beef is tender.

Stir in the lime juice, fish sauce and palm sugar, and transfer to a serving dish. Garnish with the Thai
basil leaves, and extra peanuts, if desired, and serve immediately.

beef and red wine stew

30 g (1 oz) butter
2 tablespoons oil
1 kg (2 lb 4 oz) topside steak, trimmed and cut
into 3 cm (1¼ inch) cubes
100 g (3½ oz) bacon pieces, cut into 1.5 cm
(⅝ inch) cubes
18 baby onions
2 garlic cloves, crushed
30 g (1 oz/¼ cup) plain (all-purpose) flour
500 ml (17 fl oz/2 cups) red wine
750 ml (26 fl oz/3 cups) beef stock
300 g (10½ oz) small mushrooms, halved

serves 6

method   Heat the butter and oil in a heavy-based saucepan. Cook the meat quickly in small batches over medium–high heat until browned, then drain on paper towels.

Add the bacon, onions and garlic to the pan, and cook, stirring, for 2 minutes, or until browned. Add the flour and stir over low heat until lightly golden. Gradually pour in the wine and stock, and stir until smooth. Stir continuously over medium heat for 2 minutes, or until the mixture boils and thickens.

Return the meat to the pan and reduce the heat to a simmer. Cook, covered, for 1½ hours, or until the meat is tender, stirring occasionally. Add the mushrooms and cook for 15 minutes. Delicious served with mashed potato.

lamb

lamb hotpot

2 tablespoons olive oil
8 lamb shanks
2 onions, sliced
4 garlic cloves, finely chopped
3 bay leaves, torn in half
1–2 teaspoons hot paprika
2 teaspoons sweet paprika
1 tablespoon plain (all-purpose) flour
60 g (2 oz/¼ cup) tomato paste
  (concentrated purée)
1.5 litres (52 fl oz/6 cups) vegetable stock
4 potatoes, chopped
4 carrots, sliced
3 celery stalks, thickly sliced
3 tomatoes, seeded and chopped

serves 4

method To make the lamb stock, heat 1 tablespoon of the oil in a large heavy-based saucepan over medium heat. Brown the shanks well in two batches, then drain on paper towels.

Add the remaining oil to the pan and cook the onion, garlic and bay leaves over low heat for about 10 minutes, stirring regularly. Add the paprikas and flour and cook, stirring, for 2 minutes. Gradually add the combined tomato paste and vegetable stock. Bring to the boil, stirring continuously, and return the shanks to the pan. Reduce the heat to low and simmer, covered, for 1½ hours, stirring occasionally.

Remove and discard the bay leaves. Remove the shanks, allow to cool slightly and then cut the meat from the bone. Discard the bone. Cut the meat into pieces and refrigerate. Refrigerate for about 1 hour, or until fat forms on the surface and it can be spooned off.

Return the meat to the stock along with the potato, carrot and celery, turn the heat up to medium–high and bring to the boil. Reduce the heat and simmer for 15 minutes. Season with salt and pepper, and add the chopped tomato to serve.

mongolian lamb hotpot

250 g (9 oz) dried rice vermicelli
600 g (1 lb 5 oz) lamb backstraps, thinly sliced
across the grain
4 spring onions (scallions), sliced
1.5 litres (52 fl oz/6 cups) light chicken stock
3 cm x 6 cm (1¼ inch x 2½ inch) piece fresh
ginger, cut into 6 slices
2 tablespoons Chinese rice wine
300 g (10½ oz) silken firm tofu, cut into 1.5 cm
(⅝ inch) cubes
300 g (10½ oz) Chinese broccoli (gai larn), cut
into 4 cm (1½ inch) lengths
90 g (3 oz/2 cups) shredded Chinese
cabbage (wong bok)

sauce

80 ml (2½ fl oz/⅓ cup) light soy sauce
2 tablespoons Chinese sesame paste
1 tablespoon Chinese rice wine
1 teaspoon chilli and garlic paste

serves 6

method Place the vermicelli in a large heatproof bowl, cover with boiling water and soak for about 6 minutes. Drain well and divide among six serving bowls. Top with the lamb slices and spring onion.

To make the sauce, put the soy sauce, sesame paste, rice wine and the chilli and garlic paste in a small bowl and mix together.

Place the stock, ginger and rice wne in a 2.5 litre (87 fl oz/10 cup) flameproof hotpot or large saucepan. Cover and bring to the boil over high heat. Add the tofu, Chinese broccoli and Chinese cabbage and simmer, uncovered, for 1 minute, or until the cabbage has wilted. Divide the tofu, broccoli and cabbage among the serving bowls, then ladle on the hot stock. Drizzle a little of the sauce on top and serve the rest on the side.

lamb and bean casserole

300 g (10½ oz/1½ cups) borlotti (cranberry)
   beans or red kidney beans
1 kg (2 lb 4 oz) boned leg of lamb
1½ tablespoons olive oil
2 bacon slices, rind removed, chopped
1 large onion, chopped
2 garlic cloves, crushed
1 large carrot, chopped
500 ml (17 fl oz/2 cups) dry red wine
1 tablespoon tomato paste (concentrated
   purée)
375 ml (13 fl oz/1½ cups) beef stock
2 large rosemary sprigs
2 thyme sprigs
small thyme sprigs, extra, to garnish

serves 6

method Put the beans in a bowl and cover with plenty of water. Leave to soak overnight, then drain well.

Preheat the oven to 160°C (315°F/Gas 2–3). Trim any excess fat from the lamb and cut the lamb into 3 cm (1¼ inch) pieces.

Heat 1 tablespoon of the oil in a large flameproof casserole dish. Add half the meat and toss over medium–high heat for 2 minutes, or until browned. Remove from the dish and repeat with the remaining lamb. Remove from the dish.

Heat the remaining olive oil in the casserole dish and add the bacon and onion. Cook over medium heat for 3 minutes, or until the onion is translucent. Add the garlic and carrot, and cook for 1 minute, or until aromatic.

Return the meat and any juices to the casserole dish, increase the heat to high and add the wine. Bring to the boil and cook for 2 minutes. Add the beans, tomato paste, stock, rosemary sprigs and thyme sprigs, return to the boil, then cover, place in the oven and cook for 2 hours, or until the meat is tender. Stir occasionally during cooking. Skim off any excess fat, remove the sprigs of herbs. Season and garnish with extra thyme sprigs to serve.

lamb korma

2 kg (4 lb 8 oz) leg of lamb, boned
1 onion, chopped
2 teaspoons grated fresh ginger
3 garlic cloves
2 teaspoons ground coriander
2 teaspoons ground cumin
1 teaspoon cardamom seeds
large pinch cayenne pepper
2 tablespoons ghee or oil
1 onion, extra, sliced
2½ tablespoons tomato paste (concentrated purée)
125 g (4½ oz/½ cup) plain yoghurt
125 ml (4 fl oz/½ cup) coconut cream
55 g (2 oz/½ cup) ground almonds
toasted slivered almonds, to serve

serves 4–6

method Trim any excess fat or sinew from the lamb, cut it into 3 cm (1¼ inch) cubes and place in a large bowl.

Place the chopped onion, ginger, garlic, coriander, cumin, cardamom seeds, cayenne pepper and ½ teaspoon salt in a food processor. Process the ingredients until they form a smooth paste. Add the spice mixture to the cubed lamb and mix well to coat the lamb in the spices. Leave to marinate for 1 hour.

Heat the ghee in a large saucepan, add the sliced onion and cook, stirring, over low heat for about 7 minutes, or until the onion is soft. Add the lamb and spice mixture, and cook, stirring constantly, for 8–10 minutes, or until the lamb changes colour. Stir in the tomato paste, yoghurt, coconut cream and ground almonds.

Reduce the heat and simmer the curry, covered, stirring occasionally, for 50 minutes, or until the meat is tender. Add a little water if the mixture becomes too dry. Season the curry with salt and pepper, and garnish with the toasted slivered almonds. Serve with steamed rice.

lamb meatballs

1 kg (2 lb 4 oz) minced (ground) lamb
1 onion, finely chopped
2 garlic cloves, finely chopped
2 tablespoons finely chopped flat-leaf (Italian)
   parsley
2 tablespoons finely chopped coriander
   (cilantro) leaves
½ teaspoon cayenne pepper
½ teaspoon ground allspice
½ teaspoon ground ginger
½ teaspoon ground cardamom
1 teaspoon ground cumin
1 teaspoon paprika

sauce

2 tablespoons olive oil
1 onion, finely chopped
2 garlic cloves, finely chopped
2 teaspoons ground cumin
½ teaspoon ground cinnamon
1 teaspoon paprika
2 x 400 g (14 oz) tins chopped tomatoes
2 teaspoons harissa
1 bunch coriander (cilantro) leaves, chopped

serves 4

method Preheat the oven to 180°C (350°F/Gas 4). Lightly grease two baking trays. Place the lamb, onion, garlic, herbs and spices in a bowl, and mix together well and then season. Roll tablespoons of the mixture into balls and place on trays. Bake for 18–20 minutes, or until browned.

Meanwhile, to make the sauce, heat the oil in a large saucepan, add the onion and cook over medium heat for 5 minutes, or until soft. Add the garlic, cumin, cinnamon and paprika, and cook for 1 minute, or until fragrant.

Stir in the tomato and harissa, and bring to the boil. Reduce heat and simmer for 20 minutes, then add the meatballs and simmer for another 10 minutes, or until cooked. Stir in the coriander, and serve.

lamb's liver and bacon stew

1 lamb's liver, about 750 g (1 lb 10 oz)
(see Note)
30 g (1 oz/¼ cup) cornflour (cornstarch)
¼ teaspoon ground black pepper
6 bacon slices, cut into large pieces
2 tablespoons oil
2 onions, thinly sliced
1 beef stock (bouillon) cube, crumbled

serves 6

method Wash the liver and cut it into thin slices, discarding any veins or discoloured spots. Pat the liver dry with paper towels. Combine the cornflour and pepper. Toss the liver slices in the seasoned cornflour, shaking off the excess.

Cook the bacon in a heavy-based saucepan until crisp, then drain on paper towels. Heat the oil in the pan and cook the onion gently until golden, then remove from the pan.

Cook the liver quickly in small batches over medium heat until well browned, then drain on paper towels. Return the liver, bacon and onion to the pan. Dissolve the stock cube in 250 ml (9 fl oz/1 cup) boiling water, then gradually add to the pan. Stir over medium heat for 10 minutes, or until the liquid boils and thickens. Sprinkle with cracked black pepper and serve immediately.

note *Soaking the liver in milk for 30 minutes before cooking will result in a milder taste.*

lamb tagine

1.5 kg (3 lb 5 oz) leg or shoulder of lamb, cut
  into 2.5 cm (1 inch) pieces
3 garlic cloves, chopped
80 ml (2½ fl oz/⅓ cup) olive oil
2 teaspoons ground cumin
1 teaspoon ground ginger
1 teaspoon ground turmeric
1 teaspoon paprika
½ teaspoon ground cinnamon
2 onions, thinly sliced
600 ml (21 fl oz) beef stock
¼ preserved lemon, pulp discarded, zest rinsed
  and cut into thin strips
425 g (15 oz) tin chickpeas, drained
35 g (1 oz) cracked green olives (see Note)
1 large handful chopped coriander (cilantro)
  leaves, plus extra to garnish

serves 6–8

method Place the lamb pieces in a non-metallic bowl, add the garlic, 2 tablespoons of the oil and the ground cumin, ginger, turmeric, paprika, cinnamon, and ½ teaspoon ground black pepper and 1 teaspoon salt. Mix well to coat, then leave to marinate for 1 hour.

Heat the remaining oil in a large saucepan, add the lamb in batches and cook over high heat for 2–3 minutes, or until browned. Remove from the pan. Add the onion and cook for 2 minutes, then return the meat to the pan and add the beef stock. Reduce the heat and simmer, covered, for 1 hour.

Add the preserved lemon strips, drained chickpeas and olives, and cook, uncovered, for a further 30 minutes, or until the lamb is tender and the sauce has reduced and thickened. Stir in the coriander. Serve in bowls and garnish with extra coriander.

note *Cracked green olives are marinated in herbs and are available from specialty shops.*

lamb shanks in tomato sauce on polenta

2 tablespoons olive oil
1 large red onion, sliced
4 French-trimmed lamb shanks
(about 250 g/9 oz each) (see Note)
2 garlic cloves, crushed
400 g (14 oz) tin chopped tomatoes
125 ml (4 fl oz/½ cup) red wine
2 teaspoons chopped rosemary
150 g (5½ oz/1 cup) instant polenta
50 g (2 oz) butter
50 g (2 oz/½ cup) grated parmesan cheese
rosemary, extra, to garnish

serves 4

method Preheat the oven to 160°C (315°F/Gas 2–3). Heat the oil in a 4 litre (140 fl oz/16 cup) flameproof casserole dish over medium heat and sauté the onion for 3–4 minutes, or until softening and becoming transparent. Add the lamb shanks and cook for 2–3 minutes, or until lightly browned. Add the garlic, tomato and wine, then bring to the boil and cook for 3–4 minutes. Stir in the rosemary. Season with ¼ teaspoon each of salt and pepper.

Cover and bake for 2 hours. Remove the lid, return to the oven and simmer for a further 15 minutes, or until the lamb just starts to fall off the bone. Check periodically that the sauce is not too dry, adding water if needed.

About 20 minutes before serving, bring 1 litre (35 fl oz/4 cups) water to the boil in a saucepan. Add the polenta in a thin stream, whisking continuously, then reduce the heat to very low. Simmer for 8–10 minutes, or until thick and coming away from the side of pan. Stir in the butter and parmesan. To serve, spoon the polenta onto serving plates, top with the shanks and tomato sauce. Top with rosemary.

note *French-trimmed lamb shanks are lamb shanks with the meat scraped back to make a neat lamb 'drumstick'. If these are unavailable, you can use regular lamb shanks instead.*

lamb rogan josh

1 tablespoon ghee or oil
2 onions, chopped
125 g (4½ oz/½ cup) plain yoghurt
1 teaspoon chilli powder
1 tablespoon ground coriander
2 teaspoons ground cumin
1 teaspoon ground cardamom
½ teaspoon ground cloves
1 teaspoon ground turmeric
3 garlic cloves, crushed
1 tablespoon grated fresh ginger
400 g (14 oz) tin chopped tomatoes
1 kg (2 lb 4 oz) boned leg of lamb, cut into
   2.5 cm (1 inch) cubes
30 g (1 oz/¼ cup) slivered almonds
1 teaspoon garam masala
coriander (cilantro) leaves, to garnish

serves 4–6

method Heat the ghee in a large saucepan, add the onion and cook, stirring, for 5 minutes, or until soft. Stir in the yoghurt, chilli powder, coriander, cumin, cardamom, cloves, turmeric, garlic and ginger. Add the tomato and 1 teaspoon salt, and simmer for 5 minutes.

Add the lamb and stir until coated. Cover and cook over low heat, stirring occasionally, for 1–1½ hours, or until the lamb is tender. Uncover and simmer until the liquid thickens.

Meanwhile, toast the almonds in a dry frying pan over medium heat for 3–4 minutes, shaking the pan gently, until the nuts are golden brown. Remove from the pan at once to prevent them from burning.

Add the garam masala to the curry and mix through well. Sprinkle the slivered almonds and coriander leaves over the top. Serve with steamed rice and chapattis.

navarin of lamb

8 lamb noisettes (see Notes)
seasoned plain (all-purpose) flour
2 tablespoons oil
2 celery stalks, sliced thinly
12 baby carrots, peeled (see Notes)
12 new potatoes, halved
6 thyme sprigs
1 large handful flat-leaf (Italian) parsley,
chopped
2 onions, chopped
2 garlic cloves, crushed
40 g (1½ oz/⅓ cup) plain (all-purpose) flour
625 ml (21½ fl oz/2½ cups) chicken stock
250 ml (9 fl oz/1 cup) red wine
60 g (2 oz/¼ cup) tomato paste
(concentrated purée)
chopped flat-leaf (Italian) parsley, extra,
to garnish

serves 4

method   Toss the lamb in the seasoned flour, shaking off the excess. Preheat the oven to 180°C (350°F/Gas 4).

Heat the oil in a heavy-based saucepan. In batches, brown the lamb well on both sides over medium–high heat. Remove the lamb from the heat, drain well on paper towels, then transfer to a greased, 3 litre (105 fl oz/12 cup) casserole dish. Top with the celery, carrots, potatoes, thyme sprigs and parsley.

Cook the onion and garlic in the same saucepan, stirring over medium heat for 5–10 minutes, or until the onion is soft.

Add the flour and stir for 1 minute, or until the onion is coated. Add the stock, wine and tomato paste and stir until the sauce boils and thickens. Pour the sauce over the lamb and vegetables. Bake, covered, for 1¼ hours, or until the lamb is tender. Carefully remove the string from the lamb, and sprinkle with extra parsley to serve.

notes *A noisette is a round slice of meat, cut from a boned loin and tied with string to hold its shape. For this recipe you could also use a boned leg of lamb, cut into 3 cm (1¼ inch) cubes. If baby carrots are not available, use four sliced carrots instead.*

pork

pasta and bean soup

200 g (7 oz) dried borlotti (cranberry) beans (see Note)
60 ml (2 fl oz/¼ cup) olive oil
90 g (3 oz) piece pancetta, finely diced
1 onion, finely chopped
2 garlic cloves, crushed
1 celery stalk, thinly sliced
1 carrot, diced
1 bay leaf
1 rosemary sprig
1 flat-leaf (Italian) parsley sprig
400 g (14 oz) tin chopped tomatoes, drained
1.6 litres (56 fl oz) vegetable stock
2 tablespoons finely chopped flat-leaf (Italian) parsley
150 g (5½ oz) ditalini or other small dried pasta
extra virgin olive oil, to serve
grated parmesan cheese, to serve

serves 4

method Place the beans in a large bowl, cover with cold water and soak overnight. Drain and rinse.

Heat the oil in a large saucepan, add the pancetta, onion, garlic, celery and carrot, and cook over medium heat for 5 minutes, or until golden. Season. Add the bay leaf, rosemary, parsley sprig, tomato, stock and beans. Bring to the boil. Reduce heat and simmer for 1½ hours, or until tender. Add boiling water if needed.

Discard the bay leaf, rosemary and parsley sprigs. Scoop out 250 ml (9 fl oz/1 cup) of the mixture and purée in a food processor. Return to the pan, season, and add chopped parsley and pasta. Simmer for 6 minutes, or until al dente. Remove from heat and set aside for 10 minutes. Serve drizzled with olive oil, sprinkled with parmesan and pepper if desired.

note *If you prefer, you can use three 400 g (14 oz) tins drained borlotti beans. Simmer with the other vegetables for 30 minutes.*

eight-treasure noodle soup

10 g (¼ oz) dried shiitake mushrooms
375 g (13 oz) fresh thick hokkein (egg) noodles
1.2 litres (42 fl oz/5 cups) chicken stock
60 ml (2 fl oz/¼ cup) light soy sauce
2 teaspoons Chinese rice wine
200 g (7 oz) boneless, skinless chicken breasts,
cut into 1 cm (½ inch) strips on the diagonal
200 g (7 oz) Chinese barbecued pork (char siu),
cut into 5 mm (¼ inch) slices
¼ onion, finely chopped
1 carrot, cut into 1 cm (½ inch) sliced on the
diagonal
120 g (4 oz) snow peas (mangetout), cut in
half on the diagonal
4 bulb spring onions (scallions), thinly sliced

serves 4

method Soak the mushrooms in boiling water for 20 minutes, or until soft. Drain and squeeze out any excess liquid. Discard the stems and thinly slice the caps.

Bring a large saucepan of water to the boil and cook the noodles for 1 minute, or until cooked through. Drain, then rinse with cold water. Divide evenly among four deep warmed serving bowls.

Meanwhile, bring the chicken stock to the boil in a large saucepan over high heat. Reduce the heat to medium and stir in the soy sauce and rice wine. Simmer for 2 minutes. Add the chicken and pork and cook for 2 minutes, or until the chicken is cooked and the pork is heated through. Add the onion, carrot, snow peas, mushrooms and half the spring onion, and cook for 1 minute, or until the carrot is tender.

Divide the vegetables and meat among the serving bowls and ladle on the hot broth. Garnish with the remaining spring onion.

pork and coriander stew

1½ tablespoons coriander seeds
800 g (1 lb 12 oz) pork fillet, cut into 2 cm
(¾ inch) cubes
1 tablespoon plain (all-purpose) flour
60 ml (2 fl oz/¼ cup) olive oil
1 large onion, thinly sliced
375 ml (13 fl oz/1½ cups) red wine
250 ml (9 fl oz/1 cup) chicken stock
1 teaspoon sugar
fresh coriander (cilantro) sprigs, to garnish

serves 4–6

method Crush the coriander seeds in a mortar with a pestle. Combine the pork, seeds and ½ teaspoon cracked pepper. Cover and marinate overnight in the refrigerator.

Combine the flour and pork, and toss to coat. Heat 2 tablespoons of the oil in a saucepan and cook the pork in batches over high heat. Remove.

Heat the remaining oil, add the onion and cook over medium heat for 2–3 minutes, or until golden. Return the meat to the pan, add the wine, stock and sugar. Season. Bring to the boil, then reduce the heat and simmer, covered, for 1 hour.

Remove the meat. Return the pan to the heat and boil over high heat for 3–5 minutes, or until the liquid reduces and thickens. Pour over the meat and garnish with coriander. Serve with boiled potatoes.

ham, leek and potato ragu

50 g (2 oz) butter
2 tablespoons olive oil
250 g (9 oz) piece double-smoked ham, cut
into cubes (see Note)
3 garlic cloves, finely chopped
3 leeks (white part only), sliced
1.5 kg (3 lb 5 oz) potatoes, peeled and cut into
large chunks
500 ml (17 fl oz/2 cups) chicken stock
2 tablespoons brandy
125 ml (4 fl oz/½ cup) cream
1 tablespoon each of chopped oregano and
parsley

serves 4–6

method Heat the butter and oil in a large heavy-based saucepan. Cook the ham, garlic and leek over low heat for 10 minutes, stirring regularly. Add the potato and cook for 10 minutes, stirring regularly.

Slowly stir in the stock and brandy. Cover and gently simmer. Cook for another 15–20 minutes until the potato is tender but still chunky, and sauce has thickened. Add cream and herbs, and season. Simmer for another 5 minutes.

note *You can use any type of ham for this recipe. A double-smoked ham will give a good, hearty flavour.*

pork and eggplant hotpot

olive oil, for cooking
375 g (13 oz) slender eggplants (aubergines),
   cut into 3 cm (1¼ inch) slices
8 bulb spring onions (scallions)
400 g (14 oz) tin chopped tomatoes
2 garlic cloves, crushed
2 teaspoons ground cumin
500 g (1 lb 2 oz) pork fillet, cut into 3 cm
   (1¼ inch) thick slices
seasoned plain (all-purpose) flour
170 ml (5½ fl oz/⅔ cup) cider
1 rosemary sprig
2 tablespoons chopped toasted almonds

serves 4

method Heat 60 ml (2 fl oz/¼ cup) of oil in a large heavy-based frying pan. Brown the eggplant in batches over high heat, adding oil as needed. Remove and set aside.

Quarter the spring onions along their length. Add some oil to the pan and fry the spring onion over medium heat for 5 minutes. Add the tomato, garlic and cumin, and cook for 2 minutes. Remove from the pan and set aside.

Coat the pork in the seasoned flour, shaking off any excess. Brown in batches over medium–high heat until golden, adding oil as needed. Remove and set aside.

Add the cider to the pan and stir well, scraping down the side and base. Allow to boil for 1–2 minutes, then add 125 ml (4 fl oz/½ cup) water. Reduce the heat and stir in the spring onion and tomato mixture. Add the pork, season, and poke the rosemary sprig into the stew. Partially cover and simmer gently for 20 minutes.

Layer the eggplant on top, partially cover and cook for 25 minutes, or until the pork is tender. Just before serving, gently toss the almonds through.

caramel pork with shanghai noodles

500 g (1 lb 2 oz) Shanghai noodles
700 g (1 lb 9 oz) boneless pork belly
2 teaspoons peanut oil
150 g (5½ oz) caster (superfine) sugar
5 garlic cloves, crushed
5 slices fresh ginger, 5 mm (¼ inch) thick
2 lemongrass stems (white part only), bruised
1 teaspoon white pepper
500 ml (17 fl oz/2 cups) chicken stock
70 ml (3 fl oz) fish sauce
100 g (3½ oz) tinned bamboo shoots,
drained well
4 spring onions (scallions), cut into 3 cm
(1¼ inch) pieces
1 tablespoon lime juice
1 tablespoon chopped coriander (cilantro)
leaves (optional)
1 bunch bok choy (pak choy), (optional)

serves 4

method Cook the Shanghai noodles in a large saucepan of boiling water for 4–5 minutes, or until tender. Rinse, drain and cut the noodles into 10 cm (4 inch) lengths.

Preheat the oven to 180°C (350°F/Gas 4). Cut the pork belly across the grain into 1 cm (½ inch) thick slices, then cut each slice into 2 cm (¾ inch) pieces. Heat the oil in a 4 litre (140 fl oz/16 cup) flameproof casserole dish over medium–high heat. Cook the pork in two batches for 5 minutes, or until it starts to brown all over. Remove the pork and drain off the fat.

Add the sugar and 2 tablespoons water to the casserole dish, stirring until the sugar has dissolved and scraping up any sediment that may have stuck to the bottom. Increase heat to high and cook for 2–3 minutes without stirring until dark golden, being careful not to burn—you should just be able to smell the caramel.

Return the pork to the casserole dish, then stir in the garlic, ginger, lemongrass, white pepper, stock, 2 tablespoons of the fish sauce and 375 ml (12 fl oz/1½ cups) water. Place the dish in the oven and bake, covered, for 1 hour, then remove the lid and cook for a further 1 hour, or until the pork is very tender. Carefully remove the ginger and the lemongrass stems.

Add the noodles to the casserole dish with the bamboo shoots, spring onion, lime juice and remaining fish sauce, and stir to combine. Return the dish to the oven for a further 10 minutes to heat through. Stir in the coriander, if desired, and serve with steamed bok choy and steamed Asian greens, if desired.

pork ball curry with egg noodles

200 g (7 oz) minced (ground) pork
3 garlic cloves, chopped
2 lemongrass stems, white part only, finely
    chopped
2.5 cm (1 inch) piece ginger, grated
1 tablespoon oil
1–2 tablespoons green curry paste, to taste
375 ml (13 fl oz/1½ cups) coconut milk
2 tablespoons fish sauce
2 teaspoons soft brown sugar
1 medium handful chopped Thai basil leaves
200 g (7 oz) fresh egg noodles
sliced spring onions (scallions), coriander
    (cilantro) leaves and sliced chillies, to serve

serves 4

method Finely chop the minced pork with a cleaver or large knife. Combine the pork, garlic, lemongrass and ginger in a bowl and mix thoroughly. Form teaspoonfuls into small balls.

Heat the oil in a wok, add the curry paste and cook over low heat, stirring constantly, for 1 minute, or until fragrant. Add the coconut milk and 250 ml (9 fl oz/1 cup) water to the wok. Stir until boiling, then reduce the heat and simmer for 5 minutes. Add the pork balls and simmer for 5 minutes, or until cooked. Add the fish sauce, brown sugar and Thai basil.

Cook the noodles in boiling water for 4 minutes, or until tender, then drain. Toss with the pork balls and curry sauce and then serve immediately, as the noodles will soak up the sauce. Scatter spring onions, coriander and chillies over the top.

italian sausage and chickpea stew

2 large red capsicums (peppers)
1 tablespoon olive oil
2 large red onions, cut into thick wedges
2 garlic cloves, finely chopped
600 g (1 lb 5 oz) Italian-style thin pork sausages
300 g (10½ oz) chickpeas, drained
150 g (5½ oz) flat mushrooms, thickly sliced
125 ml (4 fl oz/½ cup) dry white wine
2 bay leaves
2 teaspoons chopped rosemary
400 g (14 oz) tin chopped tomatoes

serves 4

method Cut the capsicums into large pieces, removing the seeds and membrane. Place skin side up, under a hot grill (broiler) until the skin blackens and blisters. Allow to cool in a sealed plastic bag. Peel away the skin, and slice diagonally into thick strips.

Meanwhile, heat the oil in a large non-stick frying pan. Add the onion and garlic, and stir over medium heat for 6 minutes, or until the onion is soft and browned. Remove the onion from the pan and set aside. Add the sausages to the same pan. Cook over medium heat, turning occasionally, for 8 minutes, or until the sausages are browned. Remove the sausages from the pan, allow to cool and slice diagonally into 3 cm (1¼ inch) pieces.

Combine the capsicum slices, onion, sausage pieces, chickpeas and mushrooms in the frying pan, and cook over medium–high heat.

Add the wine, bay leaves and rosemary to the pan. Bring to the boil, then reduce the heat to low and simmer for 3 minutes. Stir in the tomato and simmer for 20 minutes, or until the sauce has thickened slightly. Remove the bay leaves and season to taste with sugar, salt and cracked black pepper. Delicious served with fettuccine, grilled ciabatta bread, mashed potato, soft polenta or parmesan cheese shavings.

braised pork with prunes

4 lean pork loin medallions, about 175 g
   (6 oz) each
500 ml (17 fl oz/2 cups) chicken stock
2 tablespoons oil
1 large onion, cut into wedges
2 garlic cloves, crushed
1 tablespoon thyme leaves
1 large tomato, peeled, seeded and finely
   chopped
125 ml (4 fl oz/½ cup) cream
16 pitted prunes

serves 4

method Shape the meat into rounds by tying a length of string around the medallions. Tie with a bow for easy removal. Bring the stock to the boil in a medium saucepan. Reduce the heat to a simmer and cook for 5 minutes, or until reduced to 185 ml (6 fl oz/3/4 cup).

Heat the oil over high heat in a heavy-based frying pan. Cook the meat for 2 minutes each side to seal, turning once. Drain on paper towels.

Add the onion and garlic to the frying pan, and stir for 2 minutes. Return the meat to the pan with the thyme, tomato and stock, then reduce the heat to low. Cover the pan and bring slowly to simmering point. Simmer for 10 minutes, or until the meat is tender, turning once. Add the cream and prunes, and simmer for a further 5 minutes. Remove the string and serve with greens.

pork and tamarind curry

80 ml (2½ fl oz/⅓ cup) oil
2 onions, thickly sliced
4 large garlic cloves, crushed
30 g (1 oz/¼ cup) Sri Lankan curry powder
1 tablespoon grated fresh ginger
10 dried curry leaves or 5 fresh curry leaves
2 teaspoons chilli powder
¼ teaspoon fenugreek seeds
1.25 kg (2 lb 12 oz) lean pork shoulder, cubed
1 lemongrass stem (white part only), finely chopped
2 tablespoons tamarind purée
4 cardamom pods, crushed
400 ml (14 fl oz) tin coconut cream

cucumber sambal

1–2 large cucumbers, halved, seeded and finely chopped
500 g (1 lb 2 oz/2 cups) plain yoghurt
2 tablespoons coriander (cilantro) leaves, finely chopped
1 tablespoon lemon juice
2 garlic cloves, crushed

serves 6

method Heat the oil in a heavy-based Dutch oven or deep, lidded frying pan. Add the onion, garlic, curry powder, ginger, curry leaves, chilli powder, fenugreek seeds and 1 teaspoon salt, and cook, stirring, over medium heat for 5 minutes.

Add the pork, lemongrass, tamarind purée, cardamom and 375 ml (13 fl oz/1½ cups) hot water, then reduce the heat and simmer, covered, for 1 hour.

Stir in the coconut cream and simmer on a low heat, uncovered, for 40–45 minutes, or until the sauce has reduced and become thick and creamy.

To make the cucumber sambal, place the cucumber in a bowl and stir in the yoghurt, coriander, lemon juice and garlic. Season to taste with salt and pepper.

Serve the curry with the cucumber sambal, steamed basmati rice and chapattis.

pork, beer and chickpea stew

2 teaspoons ground cumin
1 teaspoon ground coriander
½ teaspoon chilli powder
¼ teaspoon ground cinnamon
400 g (14 oz) lean diced pork, trimmed
1 tablespoon plain (all-purpose) flour
1 tablespoon olive oil
1 large onion, finely chopped
3 garlic cloves, finely chopped
2 large carrots, finely chopped
2 celery stalks, thinly sliced
125 ml (4 fl oz/½ cup) chicken stock
125 ml (4 fl oz/½ cup) beer
2 ripe tomatoes, chopped
310 g (11 oz) tin chickpeas, rinsed
2 tablespoons chopped parsley

serves 4

method Cook the spices in a dry frying pan over low heat, shaking the pan, for 1 minute, or until aromatic.

Combine the pork with the spices and flour in a plastic bag and toss well. Remove the pork and shake off the excess flour. Heat the oil in a large heavy-based saucepan over high heat and cook the pork, tossing regularly, for 8 minutes, or until lightly browned.

Add the onion, garlic, carrot, celery and half the stock to the pan and toss well. Cover and cook for 10 minutes. Add the remaining stock, beer and tomato and season to taste. Bring to the boil, reduce the heat, cover with a tight-fitting lid, then simmer over low heat for 1 hour. Gently shake the pan occasionally, but do not remove the lid during cooking. Stir in the chickpeas and parsley. Simmer, uncovered, for 5 minutes and serve.

pork sausage and white bean stew

350 g (12 oz) dried white haricot beans
150 g (5½ oz) tocino, speck or pancetta,
unsliced
½ leek (white part only), thinly sliced
2 garlic cloves
1 bay leaf
1 small red chilli, halved and seeded
1 small onion
2 cloves
1 rosemary sprig
3 thyme sprigs
1 parsley sprig
60 ml (2 fl oz/¼ cup) olive oil
8 pork sausages
½ onion, finely chopped
1 green capsicum (pepper), finely chopped
½ teaspoon paprika
125 g (4½ oz/½ cup) tomato paste
(concentrated purée)
1 teaspoon cider vinegar

serves 4

method Soak the beans overnight in cold water. Drain and rinse the beans under cold water. Put them in a large saucepan with the tocino, leek, garlic, bay leaf and chilli. Stud the onion with the cloves and add to the saucepan. Tie the rosemary, thyme and parsley together, and add to the saucepan. Pour in 750 ml (26 fl oz/3 cups) cold water and bring to the boil. Add 1 tablespoon of the oil, reduce the heat and simmer, covered, for about 1 hour, or until the beans are tender. When necessary, add a little more boiling water to keep the beans covered.

Prick each sausage five or six times and twist tightly in opposite directions in the middle to give two short fat sausages joined in the middle. Put in a single layer in a large frying pan and add enough cold water to reach halfway up their sides. Bring to the boil and simmer, turning two or three times, until all the water has evaporated and the sausages brown lightly in the little fat that is left in the pan. Remove from the pan and cut the short sausages apart. Add the remaining oil, the chopped onion and capsicum to the pan, and fry over medium heat for 5–6 minutes. Stir in the paprika, cook for 30 seconds, then add the tomato paste. Season to taste. Cook, stirring, for 1 minute.

Remove the tocino, herb sprigs and any loose large pieces of onion from the bean mixture. Leave in any loose leaves from the herbs and any small pieces of onion. Add the sausages and sauce to the pan, and stir the vinegar through. Bring to the boil. Adjust the seasoning and serve.

seafood

prawn laksa

1 kg (2 lb 4 oz) raw prawns (shrimp)
80 ml (2½ fl oz/⅓ cup) oil
2–6 small red chillies, seeded
1 onion, roughly chopped
3 garlic cloves, halved
2 cm x 2 cm (¾ inch x ¾ inch) piece fresh
    ginger or galangal, chopped
3 lemongrass stems (white part only), chopped
1 teaspoon ground turmeric
1 tablespoon ground coriander
2 teaspoons shrimp paste
625 ml (21½ fl oz/2½ cups) coconut cream
2 teaspoons grated palm sugar (jaggery) or
    soft brown sugar
4 makrut (kaffir lime) leaves, crushed
1–2 tablespoons fish sauce
200 g (7 oz) packet fish balls
190 g (7 oz) fried tofu puffs
250 g (9 oz) dried rice vermicelli
125 g (4½ oz) bean sprouts, trimmed
1 large handful mint leaves, to serve
coriander (cilantro) leaves, to serve

serves 4

method Heat 2 tablespoons of the oil in a wok or large saucepan and add the prawn shells, tails and heads. Stir over medium heat for 10 minutes, or until orange, then add 1 litre (35 fl oz/4 cups) water. Bring to the boil, then reduce the heat and simmer for 15 minutes. Strain the stock through a fine sieve and reserve the liquid. Discard the shells and clean the pan.

Finely chop the chillies (use two for mild flavour, increase for hot), and process with the onion, garlic, ginger, lemongrass, turmeric, coriander and 60 ml (2 fl oz/¼ cup) of the prawn stock in a food processor.

Heat the remaining oil in the pan, add the chilli mixture and shrimp paste, and stir over medium heat for 3 minutes, or until fragrant. Pour in the remaining stock and simmer for 10 minutes. Add the coconut cream, palm sugar, makrut leaves and fish sauce, and simmer for 5 minutes. Add the prawns and simmer for 2 minutes, or until firm and light pink. Add the fish balls and fried tofu puffs, and simmer gently until just heated through.

Soak the rice vermicelli in a bowl of boiling water for 2 minutes, then drain and divide among serving bowls. Top with the bean sprouts and ladle the soup over the top. Garnish with the mint and coriander.

100 EASY RECIPES ONE-POTS

clam chowder

30 g (1 oz) butter
2 bacon slices, finely chopped
1 large onion, finely chopped
4 potatoes, cut into small cubes
500 ml (17 fl oz/2 cups) fish stock
1 bay leaf
125 ml (4 fl oz/½ cup) full-cream (whole) milk
4 x 105 g (3½ oz) tins baby clams (vongole),
drained and chopped
2 tablespoons finely chopped parsley
250 ml (9 fl oz/1 cup) cream
parsley, extra, to garnish

serves 4

method Heat the butter in a large saucepan. Cook the bacon and onion for 2–3 minutes, or until softened. Stir in the potato. Cook for a further 2–3 minutes, then gradually pour the stock into the pan. Add the bay leaf.

Bring the mixture to the boil, then reduce the heat and simmer, covered, for 20 minutes, or until the potato is cooked. Simmer for 10 minutes, or until the soup is reduced and slightly thickened. Discard the bay leaf.

Add the milk, clams, parsley and cream. Stir to gently reheat, but do not allow the soup to boil. Season with salt and freshly ground black pepper. Sprinkle with parsley to serve.

vietnamese fish and noodle soup

1 teaspoon shrimp paste
150 g (5½ oz) mung bean vermicelli
2 tablespoons peanut oil
6 garlic cloves, finely chopped
1 small onion, thinly sliced
2 long red chillies, chopped
2 lemongrass stems (white part only), thinly
   sliced
1.25 litres (44 fl oz/5 cups) chicken stock
60 ml (2 fl oz/¼ cup) fish sauce
1 tablespoon rice vinegar
4 ripe tomatoes, peeled, seeded and chopped
500 g (1 lb 2 oz) firm white fish fillets (snapper
   or blue-eyed cod), cut into 3 cm (1¼ inch)
   pieces
1 large handful mint, torn
1 very large handful coriander (cilantro) leaves
90 g (3 oz/1 cup) bean sprouts, trimmed
1 tablespoon mint, extra
1 tablespoon coriander (cilantro) leaves, extra
2 long red chillies, extra, sliced
lemon wedges, to serve

serves 4

method Wrap the shrimp paste in foil and place under a hot grill (broiler) for 1 minute. Set aside.

Soak the vermicelli in boiling water for 3–4 minutes. Rinse under cold water, drain and then cut into 15 cm (6 inch) lengths.

Heat the oil in a heavy-based saucepan over medium heat. Add the garlic and cook for 1 minute, or until golden. Add the onion, chilli, lemongrass and paste, and cook, stirring, for a further minute. Add the stock, fish sauce, vinegar and tomato. Bring to the boil, then reduce the heat to medium and simmer for 10 minutes. Add the fish and simmer gently for 3 minutes, or until cooked. Stir in the mint and coriander.

Divide noodles and sprouts among bowls and ladle the soup on top. Top with extra mint, coriander and chilli. Serve with lemon wedges.

crab curry

4 raw large blue swimmer or mud crabs
1 tablespoon oil
1 large onion, finely chopped
2 garlic cloves, crushed
1 lemongrass stem (white part only), finely chopped
1 teaspoon sambal oelek (South-East Asian chilli paste)
1 teaspoon ground cumin
1 teaspoon ground turmeric
1 teaspoon ground coriander
270 ml (9½ fl oz) coconut cream
500 ml (17 fl oz/2 cups) chicken stock
1 large handful basil leaves

serves 6

method Pull back the apron and remove the top shell from the crabs. Remove the intestines and grey feathery gills. Cut each crab into four pieces. Use a cracker to crack the claws open; this will make it easier to eat later and will also allow the flavours to get into the crabmeat.

Heat the oil in a large saucepan or wok. Add the onion, garlic, lemongrass and sambal oelek, and cook for 2–3 minutes, or until softened. Add the cumin, turmeric, coriander and ½ teaspoon salt, and cook for a further 2 minutes, or until fragrant.

Stir in the coconut cream and stock. Bring to the boil, then reduce the heat, add the crab pieces and cook, stirring occasionally, for 10 minutes, or until the liquid has reduced and thickened slightly and the crabs are cooked. Scatter the basil leaves over the crab and serve with rice.

moroccan seafood with coriander

2 tablespoons olive oil
2 red onions, roughly chopped
1 red capsicum (pepper), chopped
4 garlic cloves, crushed
2 teaspoons ground cumin
1 teaspoon ground coriander
2 teaspoons sweet paprika
½ teaspoon dried chilli flakes
250 ml (9 fl oz/1 cup) chicken or fish stock
425 g (15 oz) tin chopped tomatoes
80 ml (2½ fl oz/⅓ cup) orange juice
1 tablespoon sugar
40 g (1½ oz/⅓ cup) raisins
375 g (13 oz) baby new potatoes
500 g (1 lb 2 oz) baby octopus, cleaned
12 raw king prawns (shrimp), peeled and
    deveined, leaving the tails intact
1 kg (2 lb 4 oz) thick white fish fillets, cut into
    chunks

coriander purée

2 very large handfuls coriander (cilantro) leaves
2 tablespoons ground almonds
80 ml (2½ fl oz/⅓ cup) extra virgin olive oil
½ teaspoon ground cumin
1 teaspoon honey

serves 6

method Heat the olive oil in a large saucepan and then cook the onion over medium heat for about 5 minutes, or until soft. Add the capsicum and garlic, and cook for another minute. Add the cumin, coriander, paprika and chilli flakes, and cook until fragrant.

Pour in the stock, tomato, orange juice, sugar and raisins, and bring to the boil. Add the potatoes, reduce the heat to low and gently simmer for 20–30 minutes, or until the potatoes are just tender. Season to taste.

Use a small sharp knife to remove the octopus heads; slit the heads open and remove the gut. Grasp the body firmly and push the beak out with your index finger; remove and discard. Add the octopus, prawns and fish to the pan and cook, covered, for 10 minutes, or until the fish flakes when tested with a fork.

To make the coriander purée, place the coriander leaves and ground almonds in a food processor. With the motor running, drizzle in the oil and process until smooth, then add the cumin, honey and salt to taste. Process until well combined.

To serve, dish the stew onto serving plates and drizzle a spoonful of purée on top. Serve with couscous and a green leaf salad.

seafood and fennel stew

2 tablespoons olive oil
1 large fennel bulb, thinly sliced
2 leeks (white part only), thinly sliced
2 garlic cloves, crushed
½ teaspoon paprika
2 tablespoons Pernod or Ricard
200 ml (7 fl oz) dry white wine
18 mussels, scrubbed and hairy beards removed
¼ teaspoon saffron threads
¼ teaspoon thyme leaves
6 baby octopus
16 raw prawns (shrimp), peeled and deveined, leaving the tails intact
500 g (1 lb 2 oz) swordfish steaks, cut into large chunks
400 g (14 oz) baby new potatoes
fennel greens, to garnish

serves 6

method Heat the oil in a large saucepan over medium heat. Add the fennel, leek and garlic. Stir in the paprika, season lightly and cook for 8 minutes, or until softened. Add the Pernod and wine, and stir for 1 minute, or until reduced by one-third.

Add the mussels, firstly discarding any open or cracked ones. Cover and cook for 1 minute, or until opened, discarding any that do not open. Remove from the pan to cool; remove from the shells and set aside.

Add the saffron and thyme to the pan, and cook for 1–2 minutes, stirring. Adjust the seasoning and transfer to a large, flameproof casserole dish.

Use a small sharp knife to remove the octopus heads. Grasp the bodies and push the beaks out with your index finger; remove and discard. Slit the heads and remove the gut. Mix the octopus, prawns, fish and potatoes into the stew. Cover and cook gently for 10 minutes, or until tender. Add the mussels, cover and heat through. Garnish with fennel greens and serve.

stuffed squid stew

100 ml (3½ fl oz) olive oil
1 large onion, finely chopped
2 garlic cloves, crushed
80 g (3 oz/1 cup) fresh breadcrumbs
1 egg, lightly beaten
60 g (2 oz) kefalotyri cheese, grated
60 g (2 oz) haloumi cheese, grated
4 large or 8 small squid (1 kg/2 lb 4 oz), cleaned
  (see Note)
1 small onion, finely chopped, extra
2 garlic cloves, crushed, extra
500 g (1 lb 2 oz) firm ripe tomatoes, peeled
  and diced
150 ml (5 fl oz) red wine
1 tablespoon chopped oregano
1 tablespoon chopped flat-leaf (Italian) parsley

serves 4

method Heat 2 tablespoons of the oil in a frying pan, add the onion and cook over medium heat for 3 minutes. Remove. Combine with the garlic, breadcrumbs, egg and cheeses. Season.

Pat the squid tubes dry with paper towels and, using a teaspoon, fill them three-quarters full with the stuffing. Do not pack them too tightly or the stuffing mixture will swell and burst out during cooking. Secure the ends with wooden toothpicks.

Heat the remaining oil in a large frying pan, add the squid and cook for 1–2 minutes on all sides. Remove. Add the extra onion and cook over medium heat for 3 minutes, or until soft, then add the extra garlic and cook for a further 1 minute. Stir in the tomato and wine, and simmer for 10 minutes, or until thick and pulpy, then stir in the oregano and parsley. Return the squid to the pan and cook, covered, for 20–25 minutes, or until tender. Serve warm with the tomato sauce or cool with a salad.

note *Ask the fishmonger to clean the squid. Or, discard the tentacles and cartilage. Rinse the tubes under running water and pull off the skin.*

spicy prawns

1 kg (2 lb 4 oz) raw prawns (shrimp), peeled
and deveined, leaving the tails intact
(reserve shells and heads)
1 teaspoon ground turmeric
60 ml (2 fl oz/¼ cup) oil
2 onions, finely chopped
4–6 garlic cloves, finely chopped
1–2 small green chillies, seeded and chopped
2 teaspoons ground cumin
2 teaspoons ground coriander
1 teaspoon paprika
90 g (3 oz/⅓ cup) plain yoghurt
80 ml (2½ fl oz/⅓ cup) thick (double/heavy)
cream
2 large handfuls coriander (cilantro) leaves,
chopped

serves 4–6

method Bring 1 litre (35 fl oz/4 cups) water to the boil in a large saucepan. Add the reserved prawn shells and heads, reduce the heat and simmer for 25–30 minutes. Skim any scum that forms on the surface during cooking with a skimmer or slotted spoon. Drain, discard the shells and heads, and return the liquid to the pan. You will need 750 ml (26 fl oz/3 cups) liquid. Make up with water, if necessary. Add the turmeric and peeled prawns, and cook for 1 minute, or until the prawns just turn pink. Remove the prawns and set the stock aside.

Heat the oil in a large saucepan. Cook the onion on low–medium heat, stirring, for 8 minutes, or until light golden brown. Take care not to burn the onion. Add the garlic and chilli, cook for 2 minutes, then add the cumin, coriander and paprika, and cook, stirring, for 2–3 minutes, or until it becomes fragrant.

Gradually add the reserved prawn stock, bring to the boil and cook, stirring occasionally, for 35 minutes, or until the mixture has reduced by half and thickened.

Remove from the heat and stir in the yoghurt. Add the prawns and stir over low heat for 2–3 minutes, or until the prawns are warmed through, but do now allow the mixture to boil. Stir in the cream and coriander leaves. Cover and leave to stand for 15 minutes to allow the flavours to infuse. Reheat gently and serve with rice.

note *You can also remove the prawn tails, if you prefer.*

SEAFOOD

whole fish casserole

1.25 kg (2 lb 12 oz) whole red bream or
red snapper, cleaned
1 lemon
1 lemon, sliced, extra
60 ml (2 fl oz/¼ cup) olive oil
800 g (1 lb 12 oz) potatoes, thinly sliced
3 garlic cloves, thinly sliced
1 large handful finely chopped parsley
1 small red onion, thinly sliced
1 small dried chilli, seeded and finely chopped
1 red capsicum (pepper), cut into thin rings
1 green capsicum (pepper), cut into thin rings
2 bay leaves
3–4 thyme sprigs
60 ml (2 fl oz/¼ cup) dry sherry

serves 4–6

method Cut off and discard the fins from the fish and place it in a large non-metallic dish. Cut 2 thin slices from one end of the whole lemon and reserve. Squeeze the juice from the rest of the lemon inside the fish. Add 2 tablespoons of the oil. Refrigerate, covered, for 2 hours.

Preheat the oven to 190°C (375°F/Gas 5) and lightly oil a shallow earthenware baking dish large enough to hold the whole fish. Spread half the potato on the base and scatter the garlic, parsley, onion, chilli and capsicum on top. Season with salt and pepper. Cover with the rest of the potato. Pour in 80 ml (2½ fl oz/⅓ cup) water and sprinkle the remaining oil over the top. Cover the dish with foil and bake for 1 hour.

Increase the oven temperature to 220°C (425°F/Gas 7). Season the fish inside and out with salt and pepper, and place the bay leaves and thyme inside the cavity. Make three or four diagonal slashes on each side. Cut the reserved lemon slices in half and fit these into the slashes on one side of the fish, to resemble fins. Nestle the fish into the potatoes with extra lemon slices on top. Bake, uncovered, for 30 minutes, or until the fish is cooked through and the potato is golden and crusty.

Pour the dry sherry over the fish and return to the oven for 3 minutes. Serve straight from the dish.

coconut seafood and tofu curry

2 tablespoons soya bean oil, or cooking oil
500 g (1 lb 2 oz) firm white fish (ling, perch), cut into 2 cm (¾ inch) cubes
250 g (9 oz) raw prawns (shrimp), peeled and deveined, leaving the tails intact
2 x 400 ml (14 fl oz) tins coconut milk
1 tablespoon Thai red curry paste
4 fresh or 8 dried makrut (kaffir lime) leaves
2 tablespoons fish sauce
2 tablespoons finely chopped lemongrass (white part only)
2 garlic cloves, crushed
1 tablespoon finely chopped fresh galangal
1 tablespoon shaved palm sugar (jaggery) or soft brown sugar
300 g (10½ oz) silken firm tofu, cut into 1.5 cm (⅝ inch) cubes
125 g (4½ oz/½ cup) bamboo shoots, trimmed and cut into matchsticks
1 large red chilli, thinly sliced
2 teaspoons lime juice
spring onions (scallions), chopped, to garnish
coriander (cilantro) leaves, to garnish

serves 4

method Heat the oil in a large frying pan or wok over medium heat. Sear fish and prawns for 1 minute on each side. Remove the seafood from the pan.

Place 60 ml (2 fl oz/¼ cup) of the coconut milk and the curry paste in the frying pan, and cook over medium heat for 2 minutes, or until fragrant and the oil separates. Add the remaining coconut milk, makrut leaves, fish sauce, lemongrass, garlic, galangal, palm sugar and 1 teaspoon salt. Cook over low heat for 15 minutes.

Add the tofu, bamboo shoots and chilli. Simmer for a further 3–5 minutes. Return to medium heat, add the seafood and lime juice, and cook for a further 3 minutes, or until the seafood is just cooked. Serve with steamed rice and garnish with the spring onion and coriander.

chu chee seafood

2 x 270 ml (9½ fl oz) tins coconut cream
(do not shake the tins)
55 g (2 oz/¼ cup) chu chee curry paste
500 g (1 lb 2 oz) scallops, roe removed
500 g (1 lb 2 oz) raw king prawns, peeled and
deveined, leaving the tails intact
2–3 tablespoons fish sauce
2–3 tablespoons grated palm sugar (jaggery)
or soft brown sugar
8 makrut (kaffir lime) leaves, finely shredded
2 red chillies, thinly sliced
2 large handfuls Thai basil leaves

serves 4

method   Place 250 ml (9 fl oz/1 cup) of the thick coconut cream from the top of the tins in a wok. Heat until just boiling, then stir in the curry paste, reduce the heat and simmer for 10 minutes, or until fragrant and the oil just begins to separate.

Stir in the remaining coconut cream, the scallops and prawns, and cook for 5 minutes, or until tender. Add the fish sauce, palm sugar, makrut leaves and chilli, and cook for 1 minute. Stir in half of the basil and garnish with the remaining leaves before serving.

100 EASY RECIPES ONE-POTS

french-style octopus

1 kg (2 lb/4 oz) baby octopus
60 ml (2 fl oz/¼ cup) olive oil
1 large brown onion, chopped
2 garlic cloves
500 g (1 lb 2 oz) ripe tomatoes, peeled, seeded
and chopped
350 ml (11 fl oz/1⅓ cups) dry white wine
¼ teaspoon saffron threads
2 thyme sprigs
2 tablespoons roughly chopped flat-leaf
(Italian) parsley

serves 6

method To clean the octopus, use a small sharp knife and cut each head from the tentacles. Remove the eyes by cutting a round of flesh from the base of each head. To clean the heads, carefully slit them open and remove the gut, avoiding the ink sac. Rinse thoroughly. Cut the heads in half. Push out the beaks from the centre of the tentacles from the cut side. Cut the tentacles into sets of four or two, depending on the size of the octopus. Rinse under running water.

Blanch all the octopus in boiling water for 2 minutes, then drain and allow to cool slightly. Pat dry with paper towels.

Heat the olive oil in a heavy-based frying pan and cook the onion for 7–8 minutes over medium heat until lightly golden. Add the octopus and garlic to the pan, and cook for another 2–3 minutes. Add the tomato, wine, saffron and thyme. Add just enough water to cover the octopus.

Simmer, covered, for 1 hour. Uncover and cook for another 15 minutes, or until the octopus is tender and the sauce has thickened a little. The cooking time will vary depending upon the size of the octopus. Season to taste. Serve hot or at room temperature, sprinkled with parsley.

creamy garlic seafood stew

12 scallops, with roe
500 g (1 lb 2 oz) skinless firm white fish fillets
   (see Note)
6 raw Moreton Bay bugs/flat-head lobster
   or crabs
500 g (1 lb 2 oz) raw prawns (shrimp), peeled
   and deveined, leaving the tails intact
50 g (2 oz) butter
1 onion, finely chopped
5–6 large garlic cloves, finely chopped
125 ml (4 fl oz/½ cup) white wine
500 ml (17 fl oz/2 cups) cream
1½ tablespoons dijon mustard
2 teaspoons lemon juice
2 tablespoons chopped flat-leaf (Italian)
   parsley
lemon wedges, to serve

serves 6

method Slice or pull off any membrane or hard muscle from the scallops. Cut the fish into 2 cm (3/4 inch) cubes. Cut the heads off the bugs, then use kitchen scissors to cut down around the sides of the tail so you can flap open the shell. Remove the flesh in one piece, then slice each piece in half. Refrigerate all the seafood, covered, until ready to use.

Melt the butter in a frying pan and cook the onion and garlic over medium heat for 2 minutes, or until the onion is softened (be careful not to burn the garlic— it may become a little bitter).

Add the wine to the pan and cook for 4 minutes, or until reduced by half. Stir in the cream, mustard and lemon juice, and simmer for 5–6 minutes, or until reduced to almost half.

Add the prawns to the pan and cook for 1 minute, then add the bug meat and cook for another minute, or until white. Add the fish and cook for 2 minutes, or until cooked through (the flesh will flake easily when tested with a fork). Finally, add the scallops and cook for 1 minute. If any of the seafood is still not cooked, cook for another minute or so, but be careful not to overcook as this will result in tough flesh. Remove the frying pan from the heat and toss the parsley through. Season to taste. Serve with lemon wedges and bread, if desired.

note *Try using perch, ling, bream, tuna or blue-eye.*

balinese seafood curry

curry paste

2 tomatoes, peeled, seeded and roughly chopped
5 small red chillies, seeded and chopped
5 garlic cloves, chopped
2 lemongrass stems (white part only), sliced
1 tablespoon coriander seeds, dry-roasted and ground
1 teaspoon shrimp powder, dry-roasted (see Note)
1 tablespoon ground almonds
¼ teaspoon ground nutmeg
1 teaspoon ground turmeric
60 g (2 oz/¼ cup) tamarind purée

1 tablespoon lime juice
250 g (9 oz) swordfish, cut into 3 cm (1¼ inch) cubes
60 ml (2 fl oz/¼ cup) oil
2 red onions, chopped
2 small red chillies, seeded and sliced
400 g (14 oz) raw prawns (shrimp), peeled and deveined, leaving the tails intact
250 g (9 oz) squid tubes, cut into 1 cm (½ inch) rings
125 ml (4 fl oz/½ cup) fish stock
Thai basil leaves, shredded, to garnish

serves 6

method To make the curry paste, place all the ingredients in a blender or food processor, and blend to a thick paste.

Place the lime juice in a bowl and season with salt and freshly ground black pepper. Add the swordfish, toss to coat well and leave to marinate for 20 minutes.

Heat the oil in a saucepan or wok, add the onion, sliced red chilli and curry paste, and cook, stirring occasionally, over low heat for 10 minutes, or until fragrant.

Add the swordfish and prawns, and stir to coat in the curry paste mixture. Cook for 3 minutes, or until the prawns just turn pink, then add the squid and cook for 1 minute.

Add the stock and bring to the boil, then reduce the heat and simmer for 2 minutes, or until the seafood is cooked and tender. Season to taste with salt and freshly ground black pepper. Garnish with the shredded Thai basil leaves and serve.

note If you cannot purchase shrimp powder, place some dried baby shrimp in a mortar and pestle and grind to a fine powder. Alternatively, you can place them in the small bowl of a food processor and process to a fine powder.

jungle curry prawns

curry paste

10–12 dried red chillies
4 red Asian shallots (eschalots), chopped
4 garlic cloves, sliced
1 lemongrass stem (white part only), sliced
1 tablespoon finely chopped fresh galangal
2 small coriander (cilantro) roots, chopped
1 tablespoon finely chopped fresh ginger
1 tablespoon shrimp paste, dry-roasted
60 ml (2 fl oz/¼ cup) oil

1 tablespoon oil
1 garlic clove, crushed
40 g (1½ oz/¼ cup) ground candlenuts
1 tablespoon fish sauce
300 ml (10½ fl oz) fish stock
1 tablespoon whisky
600 g (1 lb 5 oz) raw prawns (shrimp), peeled
   and deveined, leaving the tails intact
1 small carrot, slivered
200 g (7 oz) snake (yard-long) beans, trimmed
   and cut into 2 cm (¾ inch) lengths
50 g (2 oz) bamboo shoots
3 makrut (kaffir lime) leaves, crushed
basil leaves, to garnish

serves 6

method To make the curry paste, soak the chillies in 250 ml (9 fl oz/1 cup) boiling water for about 10 minutes, then drain and place in a food processor with the remaining curry paste ingredients. Season with salt and white pepper, and process to a smooth paste.

Heat a wok over medium heat, add the oil and stir to coat the side. Add 3 tablespoons of the curry paste and the garlic, and cook, stirring constantly, for 5 minutes, or until fragrant. Stir in the candlenuts, fish sauce, stock, whisky, prawns, vegetables and makrut leaves, and bring to the boil. Reduce the heat and simmer for 5 minutes, or until cooked through. Garnish with the basil and serve with steamed rice.

goan fish curry

60 ml (2 fl oz/¼ cup) oil
1 large onion, finely chopped
4–5 garlic cloves, chopped
2 teaspoons grated fresh ginger
4–6 small dried red chillies
1 tablespoon coriander seeds
2 teaspoons cumin seeds
1 teaspoon ground turmeric
¼ teaspoon chilli powder
30 g (1 oz/⅓ cup) desiccated coconut
270 ml (9½ fl oz) coconut milk
2 tomatoes, peeled and chopped
2 tablespoons tamarind purée
1 tablespoon white vinegar
6 curry leaves
1 kg (2 lb 4 oz) boneless, skinless firm fish fillets,
such as flake or ling, cut into 8 cm
(3 inch) pieces
coriander (cilantro) leaves, to garnish

serves 6

method Heat the oil in a large saucepan. Add the onion and cook, stirring, over low heat for 10 minutes, or until softened. Add the garlic and ginger, and cook for a further 2 minutes.

Place the chillies, coriander seeds, cumin seeds, turmeric, chilli powder and coconut in a frying pan, and dry-fry (no oil), stirring constantly, over medium heat for 2 minutes, or until aromatic. Place in a food processor and finely grind.

Add the spice mixture, coconut milk, tomato, tamarind purée, vinegar and curry leaves to the onion mixture. Stir to mix thoroughly, add 250 ml (9 fl oz/1 cup) water and simmer for 10 minutes, or until mixture has softened and just thickened. Stir frequently to prevent sticking.

Add the fish and cook, covered, over low heat for 10 minutes, or until cooked through. Stir gently once or twice during cooking and add water if needed. Garnish with coriander and serve with rice and pappadums.

vegetarian

chickpea and herb dumpling soup

1 tablespoon oil
1 onion, chopped
2 garlic cloves, crushed
2 teaspoons ground cumin
1 teaspoon ground coriander
¼ teaspoon chilli powder
2 x 300 g (10½ oz) tins chickpeas, drained
875 ml (30 fl oz/3½ cups) vegetable stock
2 x 400 g (14 oz) tins chopped tomatoes
1 tablespoon chopped coriander (cilantro)
   leaves

dumplings

125 g (4½ oz/1 cup) self-raising flour
25 g (1 oz) butter, chopped
2 tablespoons grated parmesan cheese
2 tablespoons mixed chopped herbs (chives,
   flat-leaf (Italian) parsley and coriander
   (cilantro) leaves)
60 ml (2 fl oz/¼ cup) full-cream (whole) milk
crusty bread, to serve

serves 4

method Heat the oil in a large saucepan and cook the onion over medium heat for 2–3 minutes, or until soft. Add the garlic, cumin, ground coriander and chilli, and cook for 1 minute, or until fragrant. Add the chickpeas, stock and tomato. Bring to the boil, then reduce the heat and simmer, covered, for 10 minutes. Stir in the coriander leaves.

To make the dumplings, sift the flour into a bowl and add the chopped butter. Rub the butter into the flour with your fingertips until it resembles fine breadcrumbs. Stir in the parmesan and mixed fresh herbs. Make a well in the centre, add the milk and mix with a flat-bladed knife until just combined. Bring the dough together into a rough ball, divide into eight portions and roll into balls.

Add the dumplings to the soup, cover and simmer for 20 minutes, or until a skewer comes out clean when inserted into the centre of the dumplings. Serve with cracked black pepper and crusty bread.

spiced lentil soup

1 eggplant (aubergine)
60 ml (2 fl oz/¼ cup) olive oil
1 onion, finely chopped
2 teaspoons brown mustard seeds
2 teaspoons ground cumin
1 teaspoon garam masala
¼ teaspoon cayenne pepper (optional)
2 large carrots, cut into cubes
1 celery stalk, diced
400 g (14 oz) tin chopped tomatoes
100 g (3½ oz/1 cup) puy or small blue-green
lentils
1 litre (35 fl oz/4 cups) vegetable stock
2 large handfuls coriander (cilantro) leaves,
roughly chopped
125 g (4½ oz/½ cup) plain yoghurt

serves 4

method Cut the eggplant into cubes, place in a colander, sprinkle with salt and leave for 20 minutes. Rinse well and pat the eggplant dry with paper towels.

Heat the oil in a large saucepan over medium heat. Add the onion and cook for 5 minutes, or until softened. Add the eggplant, stir to coat in oil and cook for 3 minutes, or until softened.

Add the spices and the cayenne pepper (if using) and cook, stirring, for 1 minute, or until fragrant and the mustard seeds begin to pop. Add the carrot and celery and cook for 1 minute. Stir in the tomato, lentils and stock and bring to the boil. Reduce the heat and simmer for 40 minutes, or until the lentils are tender and the liquid is reduced to a thick stew-like soup. Season to taste with salt and freshly ground black pepper.

Stir the coriander into the soup just before serving. Ladle the soup into four warmed bowls and serve with a dollop of the yoghurt on top.

chunky vegetable soup

100 g (3½ oz/½ cup) dried red kidney beans or
 borlotti (cranberry) beans (see Note)
1 tablespoon olive oil
1 leek, halved lengthways, chopped
1 small onion, diced
2 carrots, chopped
2 celery stalks, chopped
1 large zucchini (courgette), chopped
1 tablespoon tomato paste (concentrated
 purée)
1 litre (35 fl oz/4 cups) vegetable stock
400 g (14 oz) pumpkin (winter squash), cut into
 2 cm (¾ inch) cubes
2 potatoes, cut into 2 cm (¾ inch) cubes
crusty wholemeal bread, to serve

serves 6

method Put the beans in a large bowl, cover with cold water and soak overnight. Rinse, then transfer to a saucepan, cover with cold water and cook on medium–high for 45 minutes, or until just tender. Drain and set aside.

Meanwhile, heat the oil in a large saucepan. Add the leek and onion, and cook over medium heat for 2–3 minutes without browning, or until they start to soften. Add the carrot, celery and zucchini, and cook for 3–4 minutes. Add the tomato paste and stir for a further 1 minute. Pour in the stock and 1.25 litres (44 fl oz/5 cups) water, and bring to the boil. Reduce the heat to low and simmer for 20 minutes.

Add the pumpkin, potato and beans, and simmer on low–medium heat for a further 20 minutes, or until the vegetables are tender and the beans are cooked. Season to taste. Serve immediately with crusty bread.

note *To save time, use a 400 g (14 oz) tin of red kidney beans instead of dried beans. Rinse well and leave out Step 1.*

100 EASY RECIPES ONE-POTS

mexican bean chowder

155 g (5½ oz/¾ cup) dried red kidney beans
165 g (6 oz/¾ cup) dried Mexican black
beans (see Note)
1 tablespoon oil
1 onion, chopped
2 garlic cloves, crushed
½–1 teaspoon chilli powder
1 tablespoon ground cumin
2 teaspoons ground coriander
2 x 400 g (14 oz) tins chopped tomatoes
750 ml (26 fl oz/3 cups) vegetable stock
1 red capsicum (pepper), chopped
1 green capsicum (pepper), chopped
440 g (15½ oz) tin corn kernels
2 tablespoons tomato paste (concentrated
purée)
grated cheddar cheese, to serve
sour cream, to serve

serves 6

method Soak the kidney beans and black beans in separate bowls in plenty of cold water overnight. Drain. Place in a large saucepan, cover with water and bring to the boil. Reduce the heat and simmer for 45 minutes, or until tender. Drain.

Heat the oil in a large saucepan, add the onion and cook over medium heat until soft. Add the garlic, chilli powder, cumin and coriander, and cook for 1 minute. Stir in the tomato, stock, capsicum, corn and tomato paste. Cook, covered, for 25–30 minutes. Add the beans during the last 10 minutes of cooking. Stir occasionally. Serve topped with the grated cheddar and a spoonful of sour cream.

note *Mexican black beans are also known as black turtle beans.*

VEGETARIAN

barley soup with golden parsnips

200 g (7 oz) pearl barley
1 tablespoon oil
2 onions, chopped
2 garlic cloves, finely chopped
2 carrots, chopped
2 potatoes, chopped
2 celery stalks, chopped
2 bay leaves, torn in half
2 litres (70 fl oz/8 cups) vegetable stock
125 ml (4 fl oz/½ cup) full-cream (whole) milk
40 g (1½ oz) butter
3 parsnips, cubed
1 teaspoon soft brown sugar
chopped flat-leaf (Italian) parsley, to serve

serves 6

method Soak the barley in water overnight. Drain. Place in a saucepan with 2 litres (70 fl oz/8 cups) water. Bring to the boil, then reduce the heat and simmer, partially covered, for 1¼ hours, or until tender. Drain the barley.

Heat the oil in a large saucepan, add the onion, garlic, carrot, potato and celery, and cook for 3 minutes. Stir well and cook, covered, for 15 minutes over low heat, stirring occasionally.

Add the barley, bay leaves, stock, milk, 2 teaspoons of salt and 1 teaspoon of pepper. Bring to the boil, then reduce the heat and simmer the soup, partially covered, for around 35 minutes. If the soup is too thick, add about 250 ml (9 fl oz/1 cup) cold water, a little at a time, until it reaches your preferred consistency.

While the soup is simmering, melt the butter in a frying pan, add the parsnip and toss in the butter. Sprinkle with the sugar and cook until golden brown and tender. Serve the parsnip on top of the soup and sprinkle with the parsley and, if desired, season with cracked black pepper.

creamy potato casserole

750 g (1 lb 10 oz) all-purpose potatoes (see Note)
1 onion
125 g (4½ oz/1 cup) grated cheddar cheese
375 ml (13 fl oz/1½ cups) cream
2 teaspoons vegetable stock powder

serves 4–6

method Preheat the oven to 180°C (350°F/Gas 4). Peel the potatoes and ~~thinly~~ *very* slice them. Peel the onion and slice it into rings.

Arrange a layer of overlapping potato slices in the base of a large casserole dish. Top the potato slices with a layer of the onion rings. Divide the grated cheese in half and set aside one half to use as a topping. Sprinkle a little of the remaining grated cheese over the onion rings. Continue layering in this order until all the potato and the onion have been used, finishing with a little of the grated cheese.

Pour the cream into a small jug, add the vegetable stock powder and whisk gently until the mixture is thoroughly combined. Carefully pour the cream mixture over the layered potato and onion slices, and sprinkle the top with the reserved grated cheese. Bake the casserole, uncovered, for 40 minutes, or until the potato is tender, the cheese has melted and the top is golden brown.

2 Hours (at least!)

note *Waxy or all-purpose potatoes are best to use in this recipe because they hold their shape better when slow-cooked. If you have a mandolin, use it to cut the potatoes into very thin slices. If not, make sure you use a very sharp knife.*

vegetable tagine

2 tablespoons oil
2 onions, chopped
1 teaspoon ground ginger
2 teaspoons ground paprika
2 teaspoons ground cumin
1 cinnamon stick
pinch saffron threads
1.5 kg (3 lb 5 oz) vegetables, peeled and cut
 into large chunks, such as carrot, eggplant
 (aubergine), orange sweet potato, parsnip,
 potato, pumpkin (winter squash)
½ preserved lemon, rinsed, pith and flesh
 removed, thinly sliced
400 g (14 oz) tin chopped tomatoes
250 ml (9 fl oz/1 cup) vegetable stock
100 g (3½ oz) dried pears, halved
50 g (2 oz) pitted prunes
2 zucchini (courgettes), cut into large chunks
300 g (10½ oz) couscous
1 tablespoon olive oil
2 tablespoons chopped flat-leaf (Italian)
 parsley
50 g (2 oz/⅓ cup) blanched almonds

serves 4–6

method Preheat the oven to 180°C (350°F/Gas 4). Heat the oil in a large flameproof dish, add the onion and cook over medium heat for 5 minutes. Add the spices and cook for 3 minutes.

Add the chopped mixed vegetables and cook, stirring, until coated and the vegetables soften. Add the lemon, tomato, stock, pears and prunes. Cover with a lid, transfer to the oven and cook for 30 minutes. Add the zucchini and cook for 15–20 minutes, or until the vegetables are tender.

Cover the couscous with the olive oil and 500 ml (17 fl oz/2 cups) boiling water, and stand until all the water absorbs. Fluff with a fork.

Remove the cinnamon stick from the vegetables, then stir in the parsley. Serve on a large platter with the couscous on the bottom and the vegetables on top. Sprinkle with almonds.

100 EASY RECIPES ONE-POTS

bean and capsicum stew

200 g (7 oz/1 cup) dried haricot beans (see Note)
2 tablespoons olive oil
2 large garlic cloves, crushed
1 red onion, halved and cut into thin wedges
1 red capsicum (pepper), cut into 1.5 cm (⁵⁄₈ inch) squares
1 green capsicum (pepper), cut into 1.5 cm (⁵⁄₈ inch) squares
2 x 400 g (14 oz) tins chopped tomatoes
2 tablespoons tomato paste (concentrated purée)
500 ml (17 fl oz/2 cups) vegetable stock
2 tablespoons chopped basil
125 g (4½ oz/⅔ cup) Kalamata olives, pitted
1–2 teaspoons soft brown sugar
basil leaves, to garnish

serves 4–6

method Put the beans in a large bowl, cover with cold water and soak overnight. Rinse well, then transfer to a saucepan, cover with cold water and cook for 45 minutes, or until just tender. Drain.

Heat the oil in a large saucepan. Cook the garlic and onion wedges over medium heat for 2–3 minutes, or until the onion is soft. Add the red and green capsicum, and cook for a further 5 minutes.

Stir in the tomato, tomato paste, stock and beans. Simmer, covered, for 40 minutes, or until the beans are cooked through. Stir in the basil, olives and sugar. Season with salt and pepper, garnish with basil leaves. Serve piping hot with crusty bread.

note *200 g (1 cup) of dried haricot beans yields about 2½ cups cooked beans. You can use 2½ cups tinned haricot or borlotti (cranberry) beans if you prefer.*

green tofu curry

curry paste

10 small green chillies
50 g (2 oz) red Asian shallots (eschalots)
2 garlic cloves
4 large handfuls finely chopped coriander
    (cilantro) stems and roots
1 lemongrass stem (white part only), chopped
2 tablespoons grated fresh galangal
1 tablespoon ground coriander
1 teaspoon ground cumin
1 teaspoon black peppercorns
½ teaspoon ground turmeric
1 tablespoon lime juice

2 tablespoons oil
1 onion, sliced
400 ml (14 fl oz) tin coconut cream
4–5 makrut (kaffir lime) leaves, torn
500 g (1 lb 2 oz) firm tofu, cut into 2 cm
    (¾ inch) cubes
1 tablespoon lime juice
1 tablespoon shredded Thai basil

serves 6

method To make the curry paste, place all the ingredients in a food processor and process until it is smooth.

Heat the oil in a frying pan, add the onion and cook for 5 minutes, or until soft. Add 4 tablespoons curry paste (or more for a stronger flavour) and cook, stirring, for 2 minutes. Stir in the coconut cream and 250 ml (9 fl oz/1 cup) water, and season with salt. Bring to the boil and add the makrut leaves and tofu. Reduce the heat and simmer for 8 minutes, stirring often. Stir in the lime juice and shredded Thai basil, and serve.

hint *The recipe for the curry paste makes 1 cup, but you will only need ⅓ cup. Freeze the remaining paste in two portions to use at a later date.*

yellow vegetable curry

60 ml (2 fl oz/¼ cup) oil
1 onion, finely chopped
2 tablespoons Thai yellow curry paste
250 g (9 oz) potato, diced
200 g (7 oz) zucchini (courgettes), diced
150 g (5½ oz) red capsicum (pepper), diced
100 g (3½ oz) green beans, trimmed
50 g (2 oz) bamboo shoots, trimmed
and sliced
250 ml (9 fl oz/1 cup) vegetable stock
400 ml (14 fl oz) tin coconut cream
Thai basil leaves, to garnish

serves 6

method   Heat the oil in a large saucepan, add the onion and cook over medium heat for about 5 minutes, or until softened. Add the curry paste and cook, stirring, for 2 minutes, or until fragrant.

Add all the vegetables and cook, stirring, over high heat for 2 minutes. Pour in the stock, reduce the heat to medium and cook, covered, for 15–20 minutes, or until the vegetables are tender. Cook, uncovered, over high heat for 5–10 minutes, or until the sauce has reduced slightly.

Stir in the coconut cream, and season with salt. Bring to the boil, stirring frequently, then reduce the heat and simmer for 5 minutes. Garnish with the Thai basil leaves.

spicy vegetable stew with dhal

dhal

165 g (6 oz/¾ cup) yellow split peas
5 cm (2 inch) piece fresh ginger, grated
2–3 garlic cloves, crushed
1 red chilli, seeded and chopped

2 tablespoons oil
1 teaspoon yellow mustard seeds
1 teaspoon cumin seeds
1 teaspoon ground cumin
½ teaspoon garam masala
1 red onion, cut into thin wedges
3 tomatoes, peeled, seeded and chopped
3 slender eggplants (aubergines), cut into 2 cm
    (¾ inch) slices
2 carrots, cut into 2 cm (¾ inch) slices
¼ cauliflower, cut into florets
375 ml (13 fl oz/1½ cups) vegetable stock
2 small zucchini (courgettes), cut into 3 cm
    (1¼ inch) slices
80 g (3 oz/½ cup) frozen peas
1 large handful coriander (cilantro) leaves,
    plus extra, to garnish.

serves 4–6

method Put the split peas in a bowl, cover with water and soak for 2 hours. Drain. To make the dhal put the split peas in a large saucepan with the ginger, garlic, chilli and 750 ml (26 fl oz/3 cups) water. Bring to the boil, reduce the heat and simmer for 45 minutes, or until soft.

Heat the oil in a large saucepan. Cook the spices over medium heat for 30 seconds, or until fragrant. Add the onion and cook for a further 2 minutes, or until the onion is soft. Stir in the tomato, eggplant, carrot and cauliflower.

Add the dhal mixture and stock, mix together well and simmer, covered, for 45 minutes, or until the vegetables are tender. Stir occasionally. Add the zucchini and peas during the last 10 minutes of cooking. Stir in the coriander leaves, then garnish and serve.

indonesian vegetable and coconut curry

curry paste

5 candlenuts or macadamia nuts
75 g (2½ oz) red Asian shallots (eschalots)
2 garlic cloves
2 teaspoons sambal oelek (South-East Asian chilli paste)
¼ teaspoon ground turmeric
1 teaspoon grated fresh galangal
1 tablespoon peanut butter

2 tablespoons oil
1 onion, sliced
400 ml (14 fl oz) tin coconut cream
200 g (7 oz) carrots, cut into matchsticks
200 g (7 oz) snake (yard-long) beans, trimmed, cut into 7 cm (2¾ inch) lengths
300 g (10½ oz) Chinese cabbage, roughly shredded
100 g (3½ oz) fresh shiitake mushrooms
¼ teaspoon sugar

serves 6

method To make the curry paste, place the candlenuts, shallots, garlic, sambal oelek, turmeric, galangal and peanut butter in a food processor, and process to a smooth paste.

Heat the oil in a large saucepan over low heat. Cook the curry paste, stirring, for 5 minutes, or until fragrant. Add the onion and cook for 5 minutes. Stir in 60 ml (2 fl oz/¼ cup) coconut cream and cook, stirring constantly, for 2 minutes, or until thickened. Add the carrot and beans, and cook over high heat for 3 minutes. Stir in the cabbage, mushrooms and 250 ml (9 fl oz/1 cup) water. Cook over high heat for 8–10 minutes, or until the vegetables are nearly cooked.

Stir in the remaining coconut cream and the sugar, and season with salt. Bring to the boil, stirring constantly, then reduce the heat and simmer for 8–10 minutes, to allow the flavours to develop.

potato curry

curry paste

4 cardamom pods
1 teaspoon grated fresh ginger
2 garlic cloves
6 small red chillies
1 teaspoon cumin seeds
40 g (1½ oz/¼ cup) raw cashew nut pieces
1 tablespoon white poppy seeds (khus)
   (see Note)
1 cinnamon stick
6 cloves

1 kg (2 lb 4 oz) potatoes, cubed
2 onions, roughly chopped
2 tablespoons oil
½ teaspoon ground turmeric
1 teaspoon besan (chickpea flour)
250 g (9 oz/1 cup) plain yoghurt
coriander (cilantro) leaves, to garnish

serves 6

method To make the curry paste, lightly crush the cardamom pods with the flat side of a heavy knife. Remove the seeds, discarding the pods. Place the seeds and the remaining curry paste ingredients in a food processor, and process to a smooth paste.

Bring a large saucepan of lightly salted water to the boil. Add the potato and cook for 5–6 minutes, or until just tender. Drain.

Place the onion in a food processor and process in short bursts until it is finely ground but not puréed. Heat the oil in a large saucepan, add the ground onion and cook over low heat for 5 minutes. Add the curry paste and cook, stirring, for a further 5 minutes, or until fragrant. Stir in the potato, turmeric, salt to taste and 250 ml (9 fl oz/1 cup) water.

Reduce the heat and simmer, tightly covered, for 10 minutes, or until the potato is cooked but not breaking up and the sauce has thickened slightly.

Combine the besan with the yoghurt, add to the potato mixture and cook, stirring, over low heat for 5 minutes, or until thickened again. Garnish with the coriander leaves.

note *White poppy seeds (khus) should not be mistaken for black and do not yield opium. They are off-white, odourless and flavourless until roasted when they have a slight sesame aroma and flavour. If they are not available, replace the poppy seeds with sesame seeds.*

ratatouille

100 ml (3½ fl oz) olive oil
500 g (1 lb 2 oz) eggplants (aubergines), cut
into 2 cm (¾ inch) cubes
375 g (13 oz) zucchini (courgettes), cut into
2 cm (¾ inch) slices
1 green capsicum (pepper), seeded, cut into
2 cm (¾ inch) cubes
1 red onion, cut into 2 cm (¾ inch) wedges
3 garlic cloves, finely chopped
¼ teaspoon cayenne pepper
2 teaspoons chopped thyme
2 bay leaves
6 vine-ripened tomatoes, peeled and roughly
chopped
1 tablespoon red wine vinegar
1 teaspoon caster (superfine) sugar
4 tablespoons shredded basil

serves 4–6

method Heat 2 tablespoons of the oil in a large saucepan and cook the eggplant over medium heat for 4–5 minutes, or until soft but not browned. Remove all the eggplant from the pan.

Add another 2 tablespoons oil to the pan and cook the zucchini slices for 3–4 minutes, or until softened. Remove the zucchini from the pan. Add the capsicum to the pan, cook for 2 minutes, then remove

Heat the remaining oil in the pan, add the onion wedges and cook for 2–3 minutes, or until softened. Add the garlic, cayenne pepper, thyme and bay leaves, and cook, stirring, for 1 minute. Return the cooked eggplant, zucchini and capsicum to the pan, and add the tomato, vinegar and sugar. Simmer for 20 minutes, stirring occasionally. Stir in the basil and season with salt and black pepper. You can serve ratatouille hot or cold.

note *Ratatouille takes quite a long time to prepare and so is traditionally made in large quantities. It is then eaten over several days as an hors d'oeuvre, side dish or main meal.*

chu chee tofu

curry paste

10 small red chillies
50 g (2 oz) red Asian shallots (eschalots),
　peeled
1 tablespoon finely chopped coriander
　(cilantro) stem and root
1 lemongrass stem (white part only), chopped
2 tablespoons grated fresh galangal
2 garlic cloves
1 tablespoon ground coriander
1 teaspoon ground cumin
1 teaspoon black peppercorns
½ teaspoon ground turmeric
1 tablespoon lime juice

1 tablespoon oil
1 onion, finely chopped
500 ml (17 fl oz/2 cups) coconut milk
200 g (7 oz) fried tofu puffs, halved on the
　diagonal
coriander (cilantro) sprigs, to garnish

serves 6

method To make the curry paste, place all the ingredients in a food processor or spice grinder and process until smooth.

Heat the oil in a large saucepan, add the onion and cook over medium heat for 4–5 minutes, or until it starts to brown. Add 3 tablespoons of the curry paste and cook, stirring, for 2 minutes.

Stir in the coconut milk and 125 ml (4 fl oz/½ cup) water, and season with salt. Bring slowly to the boil, stirring constantly. Add the tofu puffs, then reduce the heat and simmer, stirring frequently, for 5 minutes, or until the sauce thickens slightly. Garnish with the coriander sprigs.

vegetarian chilli

130 g (4½ oz/¾ cup) burghul (bulgur)
2 tablespoons olive oil
1 large onion, finely chopped
2 garlic cloves, crushed
1 teaspoon chilli powder
2 teaspoons ground cumin
1 teaspoon cayenne pepper
½ teaspoon ground cinnamon
2 x 400 g (14 oz) tins chopped tomatoes
750 ml (26 fl oz/3 cups) vegetable stock
440 g (15½ oz) tin red kidney beans, drained
and rinsed
2 x 300 g (10½ oz) tins chickpeas, drained
and rinsed
310 g (11 oz) tin corn kernels, drained
2 tablespoons tomato paste (concentrated
purée)
corn chips and sour cream, to serve

serves 6–8

method Soak the burghul in 250 ml (9 fl oz/1 cup) hot water for 10 minutes. Heat the oil in a large heavy-based saucepan and cook the onion for 10 minutes, stirring often, until soft and golden.

Add the garlic, chilli, cumin, cayenne and cinnamon, and cook, stirring, for 1 minute.

Add the tomato, stock and burghul. Bring to the boil and simmer for 10 minutes. Stir in the beans, chickpeas, corn and tomato paste, and simmer for 20 minutes, stirring often. Serve with corn chips and sour cream.

cheese and pea curry

paneer

2 litres (70 fl oz/8 cups) full-cream (whole) milk
80 ml (2½ fl oz/⅓ cup) lemon juice

curry paste

2 large onions, chopped
3 garlic cloves
1 teaspoon grated fresh ginger
1 teaspoon cumin seeds
3 dried red chillies
1 teaspoon cardamom seeds
4 cloves
1 teaspoon fennel seeds
2 pieces cassia bark

oil, for deep-frying
500 g (1 lb 2 oz) frozen peas
2 tablespoons oil
400 g (14 oz) tomato paste (concentrated purée)
1 tablespoon garam masala
1 teaspoon ground coriander
¼ teaspoon ground turmeric
1 tablespoon cream
coriander (cilantro) leaves, to garnish

serves 6

method To make the paneer, place the milk in a large saucepan, bring to the boil, stir in the lemon juice and turn off the heat. Stir the mixture for 1–2 seconds as it curdles. Place in a colander and leave for 30 minutes for the whey to drain off. Place the paneer curds on a clean, flat surface, cover with a plate, weigh down and leave for at least 4 hours.

To make the curry paste, place all the ingredients in a spice grinder or food processor, and grind to a smooth paste.

Cut the solid paneer into 2 cm (¾ inch) cubes. Fill a deep heavy-based saucepan one-third full of oil and heat to 180°C (350°F), or until a cube of bread browns in 15 seconds. Cook the paneer in batches for 2–3 minutes, or until golden. Drain on paper towels.

Cook the peas in a saucepan of boiling water for 3 minutes, or until tender. Drain.

Heat the oil in a large saucepan, add the curry paste and cook over medium heat for 4 minutes, or until fragrant. Add the tomato paste, spices, cream and 125 ml (4 fl oz/½ cup) water. Season with salt, and simmer over medium heat for 5 minutes. Add the paneer and peas, and cook for 3 minutes. Garnish with coriander leaves, and serve hot.

autumn vegetable stew

185 g (6 oz) frozen broad (fava) beans, thawed (see Notes)
150 g (5½ oz) baby onions (see Notes)
50 g (1¾ oz) butter
2 teaspoons olive oil
400 g (14 oz) small parsnips
150 g (5½ oz) Jerusalem artichokes
2 tablespoons plain (all-purpose) flour
580 ml (20¼ fl oz/3 cups) vegetable stock
300 ml (10½ fl oz) cream
2 teaspoons grated lemon zest
1 teaspoon grated orange zest
400 g (14 oz) baby carrots, trimmed
500 g (1 lb 2 oz) baby turnips, trimmed

serves 4–6

method Peel and discard the tough outer skin of the broad beans. Carefully peel the onions, leaving the flat root end attached, then cut a cross through the root end of each onion.

Heat the butter and oil in a large heavy-based saucepan until foamy. Add the onions and cook for 7 minutes over low–medium heat, turning often to colour evenly.

While the onions are browning, peel the parsnips and artichokes, and cut them into bite-sized pieces. Add to the saucepan and toss well. Scatter the flour over the onion, parsnip and artichokes, toss to coat and cook for 2 minutes.

Stir in the chicken stock, cream, lemon zest and orange zest. Bring to the boil, stirring, then reduce the heat and simmer for 7 minutes, or until the vegetables are half-cooked.

Add the carrots and turnips, and toss well. Cover the pan and cook for 4–5 minutes, or until the vegetables are just tender. Season well with salt and freshly ground black pepper, stir in the peeled broad beans to heat through, and serve.

notes *Fresh broad beans can be used. Add them with the carrots and turnips. Baby vegetables have a sweet, delicate flavour. If unavailable, choose the smallest vegetables and cook them for a few minutes longer.*

Published in 2010 by Bay Books,
an imprint of Murdoch Books Pty Limited

Murdoch Books Australia
Pier 8/9
23 Hickson Road
Millers Point NSW 2000
Phone: +61 (0) 2 8220 2000
Fax: +61 (0) 2 8220 2558
www.murdochbooks.com.au

Murdoch Books UK Limited
Erico House, 6th Floor
93–99 Upper Richmond Road
Putney, London SW15 2TG
Phone: +44 (0) 20 8785 5995
Fax: +44 (0) 20 8785 5985
www.murdochbooks.co.uk

Chief Executive: Juliet Rogers

Publisher: Lynn Lewis
Senior Designer: Heather Menzies
Photographer: Natasha Milne
Stylist: Kate Brown
Editor: Zoë Harpham
Editorial Coordinator: Liz Malcolm
Designer: Transformer
Production: Alexandra Gonzalez

ISBN: 978-1-74266-159-9

Printed by C & C Offset Printing Co. Ltd, China.

IMPORTANT: Those who might be at risk from the effects of salmonella poisoning (the elderly, pregnant women, young children and those suffering from immune deficiency diseases) should consult their doctor with any concerns about eating raw eggs.

OVEN GUIDE: You may find cooking times vary depending on the oven you are using. For fan-forced ovens, as a general rule, set the oven temperature to 20°C (35°F) lower than indicated in the recipe.

100 tried-and-tested recipes for the busy cook.

❖

Practical ideas that are bursting with flavour.

❖

Simple solutions to your everyday cooking needs.

bay books

ISBN 978-1742661599

9 781742 661599

American Red Cross
Lifeguarding
Instructor's Manual

Mosby
Lifeline

St. Louis Baltimore Berlin Boston Carlsbad Chicago London Madrid
Naples New York Philadelphia Sydney Tokyo Toronto

Mosby Lifeline
Dedicated to Publishing Excellence

American Red Cross certificates may be issued upon successful completion of a training program, which uses this textbook as an integral part of the course. By itself, the text material does not constitute comprehensive Red Cross training. In order to issue ARC certificates, your instructor must be authorized by the American Red Cross, and must follow prescribed policies and procedures. Make certain that you have attended a course authorized by the Red Cross. Ask your instructor about receiving American Red Cross certification, or contact your local chapter for more information.

Mosby Lifeline
Mosby-Year Book, Inc.
11830 Westline Industrial Drive
St. Louis, MO 63146

95 96 97 98 99   9 8 7 6 5 4 3 2 1

Acknowledgments

This manual was developed and produced through the combined effort of the American Red Cross and the Mosby-Year Book Publishing Company. Without the commitment to excellence of both paid and volunteer staff, this manual could not have been created.

The Health and Safety Program Development team at American Red Cross national headquarters responsible for designing and writing this book included: Lawrence D. Newell, Ed.D., NREMT-P, Manager; Rhonda Starr, Senior Associate; Martha F. Beshers, Bruce Carney, M.A.Ed., Michael Espino, and Paul Stearns, Associates; Mary F. Baudo, Michael Giles, Jr., and Patricia Appleford Terrell, Analysts; and Jane E. Moore, Desktop Publisher. Administrative support was provided by Elizabeth Taylor and Vicki Mills.

The following American Red Cross national headquarters Health and Safety paid and volunteer staff provided guidance and review: Ray Cranston, Program Development Volunteer Chairman; Karen D. White, Associate, Operations; and Cathy Brennan, Marketing Specialist. The Mosby-Year Book Editorial and Production team included: Claire Merrick, Executive Editor; John Probst and Ross Goldberg, Assistant Editors; Carol Sullivan Weis, Project Manager; Shannon Canty, Senior Production Editor; Kay Kramer, Director of Art & Design; Sheilah Barrett, Designer; Jerry Wood, Director of Manufacturing; Theresa Fuchs, Manufacturing Manager; and Patricia Stinecipher, Special Product Manager.

Special thanks go to Tom Lochhaas, ABD, Development Editor; Carol Fuchs, M.A., M.P.W., Joseph Matthews, Daniel Cima, Jeannette Ortiz Osorio, Mark Wieland, and Nick Caloyianis, Photographers; and to

Susan T. Dempf, Ph.D., Assistant Professor of Physical Education, Canisus College, Buffalo, New York, for her assistance as an external writer and reviewer.

We would also like to thank the University of Southern Mississippi M.C. Johnson Natatorium, Hattiesburg, Mississippi, and Pat Harrison, Waterway District, Flint Creek, Wiggins, Mississippi for providing locations for photographs in this manual.

Guidance, writing, and review were also provided by members of the American Red Cross Lifeguard Advisory Group:

Michael C. Giles, Sr., Advisory Group Chair, Aquatics Director and Risk Manager, Recreation Sports, The University of Southern Mississippi, Hattiesburg, Mississippi

Charles Bittenbring, Division Manager, Fairfax County Park Authority, Fairfax, Virginia

Robert L. Burhans, R.S., Chief Sanitarian, Bureau of Community, Sanitation and Food Protection, New York State Department of Health, Albany, New York

Molly A. Casey, M.S., Director, Safety Services, American Red Cross, Metropolitan Atlanta Chapter, Atlanta, Georgia

Gerald DeMers, Ph.D., Associate Professor and Director, Aquatic Program, Physical Education and Kinesiology Department, California Polytechnic State University, San Luis Obispo, California

Jerry J. Huey, Field Representative, Health and Safety Services, American Red Cross, Southeastern Michigan Chapter, Bloomfield Hills, Michigan

Charles Kunsman, M.S.Ed., Aquatic Manager, Ocasek Natatorium, University of Akron, Akron, Ohio

James P. Morgan, Director of Parks and Recreation, City of Lincoln, Lincoln, Nebraska

Frank Pia, Former Chief Lifeguard, Orchard Beach, Former Supervising Chief Lifeguard, Bronx, New York

Judith Sperling, Manager and Aquatics Director, Department of Cultural and Recreational Affairs, University of California at Los Angeles, Los Angeles, California

Margaret Sweeney-Fedders, Assistant Director of Safety, American Red Cross, Dayton Area Chapter, Dayton, Ohio

Kim Tyson, Aquatic Safety Lecturer, Department of Kinesiology, University of Texas, Austin, Texas

Thomas C. Werts, Recreation Specialist, Walt Disney World, Co., Orlando, Florida

External review was provided by the following chapter individuals:

Alexandra Barter, Mobile Bay Area Chapter, Mobile, Alabama

Kathy Bisson, Greater Manchester Chapter, Manchester, New Hampshire

Brian Chase, Pulaski County Chapter, Little Rock, Arkansas

Terri Elder, Midway Kansas Chapter, Wichita, Kansas

Betty Griffin, National Capital Chapter, Washington, D.C.

Harry Ladewig, Mile High Chapter, Denver, Colorado

Mary Smith, Cowlitz County Chapter, Longview, Washington

Pat Stejskal, Mid-America Chapter, Chicago, Illinois

Table of Contents

section a: administration

his manual is a resource for lifeguarding instructors authorized by the American Red Cross to teach the following American Red Cross courses:

- Lifeguard Training
- Community Water Safety
- CPR for the Professional Rescuer
- Lifeguarding Instructor Aide
- Challenge and Review courses for Lifeguard Training and CPR for the Professional Rescuer

Selected lifeguarding instructors may be eligible to teach the Safety Training for Swim Coaches course. For more information, contact your local American Red Cross unit.

With the successful completion of additional instructor training or orientations, lifeguarding instructors are qualified to teach the following American Red Cross programs:

- With an instructor course:
  - Waterfront Lifeguarding module
  - Waterpark Lifeguarding module
  - Head Lifeguard

Note: See Appendix E, Course Fact Sheets, for a list of prerequisites and requirements to become an instructor for the above courses and modules. For more information, contact your local American Red Cross unit.

- With an instructor orientation:
  - Community CPR
  - Adult CPR
  - Infant and Child CPR
  - Community First Aid and Safety
  - Standard First Aid

For more information on these orientations, contact your local American Red Cross unit.

This manual provides information and teaching suggestions to help you plan and conduct these courses safely and effectively, while maintaining Red Cross standards. You must be familiar with the material in American Red Cross *Lifeguarding Today* (Stock No. 654110), American Red Cross *CPR for the Professional Rescuer* (Stock No. 652048), American Red Cross *Community Water Safety* (Stock No. 654122), American Red Cross *Lifeguarding Today* video (Stock No. 654114), American Red Cross *CPR for the Professional Rescuer* video (Stock No. 652051), *Community First Aid* video (Stock No. 652035), and this instructor's manual before you can teach any of these courses. This manual also contains suggestions for teaching people who have special needs, such as people with disabilities. Instructors eligible to teach the Waterfront Lifeguarding module, the Waterpark Lifeguarding module, the Head Lifeguard course, and the Safety Training for Swim Coaches course must also become familiar with the appropriate materials for that module or course. These include—

- Chapter 13—*Lifeguarding Today,* "Waterfront Facilities."
- Chapter 14—*Lifeguarding Today,* "Waterpark Facilities."
- *American Red Cross Head Lifeguard.*
- *American Red Cross Safety Training for Swim Coaches* and *American Red Cross Safety Training for Swim Coaches Instructor's Manual.*

Purpose of the Program

The primary purpose of the American Red Cross Lifeguarding program is to provide lifeguard candidates and lifeguards with the skills and knowledge necessary to keep the patrons of aquatic facilities safe in and around the water.

Purpose and Format of the Lifeguarding Instructor's Manual

The purpose of this manual is to provide lifeguarding instructors with the information they need to teach Lifeguard Training, Community Water Safety, CPR for the Professional Rescuer, Lifeguarding Instructor Aide, and the review and challenge courses. It also provides information for Waterpark Lifeguarding, Waterfront Lifeguarding, and Head Lifeguard instructors to teach the Waterfront Lifeguarding module, the Waterpark Lifeguarding module, and the Head Lifeguard course. This manual also provides the necessary tools to evaluate the performance of course participants.

This instructor's manual has the following sections:

Section A, Administration, introduces the program, tells how to set up and teach courses, describes course organization, gives administrative information about program operation, discusses class safety, and describes course completion procedures.

Section B, Teaching Tools, contains course administration procedures, course outlines, and lesson plans for the following courses and modules:

- Lifeguard Training
- Waterfront Lifeguarding
- Waterpark Lifeguarding
- Head Lifeguard
- Community Water Safety
- Lifeguarding Instructor Aide

Section C, Appendixes, contains useful material, including skills check-off forms, written examinations and answer keys, and other materials. They are referred to where appropriate in this instructor's manual.

Instructor's Responsibilities

Your responsibilities as an American Red Cross Lifeguarding instructor are to —

- Represent the American Red Cross in a positive manner.
- Be familiar with course materials and know how to use them effectively.
- Plan, coordinate, and manage the course in conjunction with the local Red Cross unit.
- Create a nonthreatening environment that encourages participants to meet course objectives.
- Remain alert to your cultural and ethnic stereotypes and be creative and flexible in presenting material in a culturally sensitive and effective manner.
- Adapt your teaching approaches to the experience, ability, and culture of participants so that they can meet the course objectives.
- Provide for the health and safety of participants, including making sure that all teaching and practice areas are free of hazards and that materials and equipment are safe.
- Organize the class environment to enhance individual and group performance and to minimize distractions.
- Be prepared to answer participants' questions, or know where to find the answers.
- Cover all material required in a course.
- Be able to demonstrate the skills

required for completion of the Lifeguarding Instructor course.

- Use corrective feedback to evaluate participants' progress and correct problems.
- Supervise and give guidance to any Lifeguarding instructor aides assisting with a course.
- Administer and score the final examination.
- Ensure that participants meet course completion requirements.
- Submit completed course records and reports to the Red Cross within the time required by the local Red Cross unit.
- Issue course completion certificates.
- Be familiar with the Red Cross publications and brochures available at the local Red Cross unit.
- Identify potential instructor or instructor aide candidates and refer them to the appropriate Red Cross course.
- Promote other Red Cross courses and volunteer opportunities to course participants. Other Red Cross courses are listed on the inside back cover of *Lifeguarding Today*.
- Meet the obligations in the *Instructor Agreement* (Form 6574) and, if applicable, the *Authorized Provider Agreement* (Form 6575). See Appendixes B and C for a sample of these forms.

Note: Appendix A, Administrative Terms and Procedures, defines many of the terms and procedures you need to know as a Red Cross instructor.

2 organizing and conducting classes

his chapter explains how to organize and conduct courses and modules in the American Red Cross Lifeguarding program. Chapter 4 discusses program planning for lifeguarding instructors who are also program administrators.

Planning

Start planning several months before the first session of the course or module you intend to teach. Meet with your local Red Cross unit to discuss your proposed program. The unit will want to know the dates, times, and locations of the course(s). The unit will also assist you with—
- Your authorization to teach.
- Local policies and procedures and national guidelines.
- The *Instructor Agreement* (Form 6574) and, if applicable, the *Authorized Provider Agreement* (Form 6575). See Appendixes B and C for a sample of these forms.

Note: The purpose of the Instructor Agreement is to clarify the instructor's roles and responsibilities and the responsibilities of the local Red Cross unit. Every authorized American Red Cross instructor will be asked by his or her local unit to sign the Instructor Agreement.

Contact your local Red Cross unit for any other information you need before your first lesson and any time thereafter that you have questions.

Course Participants

Most of the participants will be preparing for a job that requires a lifeguarding or water safety background. Participants may include lifeguard candidates, camp counselors, water safety instructors, swim coaches, public safety personnel, adult youth leaders, and the general public. The participants may represent a broad range of backgrounds. They may differ in levels of education and experience. They may be taking courses in the lifeguarding program to fulfill employment requirements, to complete requirements for a major area of study or certification, or for personal satisfaction. There are prerequisites for enrollment in several of the lifeguarding courses. See the Administrative Notes section of each course outline or the course fact sheets in Appendix E for a list of individual course prerequisites.

Health Requirements for Course Participants

The American Red Cross has a responsibility to safeguard the health and safety of participants enrolled in any Red Cross course. The materials and procedures for teaching these courses have been written to reflect this concern.

As an American Red Cross instructor, one of your responsibilities is to protect participants from health risks. The procedures outlined in this manual are designed to—
- Limit the risk of transmission of communicable diseases.

have to be 15

- Limit the risk of one participant injuring another when practicing on a partner.
- Limit the risk that the strenuous activity involved in practice could cause injury or sudden illness.

When possible, prospective participants should be provided information about health requirements and safety before enrolling in the course. Ask participants to talk to you before any practice if they doubt they can participate in the practice activity.

People with certain health conditions may wish not to take part in the practice sessions. These conditions include a history of heart attack or other heart conditions, respiratory problems, or other physical limitations. Suggest that these participants check with their personal physician before participating in practice sessions involving physical activity. The American Red Cross advocates that, whenever possible, participants' activity levels should be adjusted as necessary to facilitate learning and help participants meet course objectives.

Tell people who take the course but cannot demonstrate the skills taught in the practice sessions that they cannot be given an American Red Cross course completion certificate. However, encourage them to participate to whatever extent possible. They can read the participant's manual, watch skill practice, and otherwise participate in class activities.

Course Lengths

The length of each course is provided in the Administrative Notes section of each course outline and in Appendix E, Course Fact Sheets. Keep in mind that these course lengths are minimum times and are based on 10 participants in a course. There may be some factors that may influence the length of a course. These are described later in the section "Lesson Planning/Modifying" of this chapter.

Instructor—Participant Ratio

The American Red Cross recommends that there be at least one instructor for every 10 participants in a course. With more than 10 participants, you should have a co-instructor or aide. Close supervision is needed to make practice effective and keep the class safe. You can help your participants reach their goals more easily if you keep the class size small. At least six participants per class are required for a course. For a class of fewer than six, prior written approval is needed from the health and safety administrator of the local Red Cross unit.

If you have participants with disabilities, you might want to have a smaller class or obtain additional help. Chapter 3 of this manual explains ways to meet the needs of these participants.

Lifeguarding Instructor Aides

Guidelines for training lifeguarding instructor aides are in Chapter 12. Instructor aides can help make large classes more successful, since participants get more individual attention. The more trained instructor aides you use, the more individual attention can be given and the faster your participants will progress. Instructor aides are not a substitute for a co-instructor.

Facilities
Classroom Environment

The sessions of all courses and modules covered in this instructor's manual require classroom space suitable for discussion, video viewing, first aid and CPR skills practice, and taking final written exams.

The classroom should provide a safe, comfortable, and appropriate learning environment. The room should be well-lighted and well-ventilated and comfortable in temperature. The classroom should have enough space for skill practice sessions, with a separate area for video viewing, lectures, discussions, and examinations, if possible. If the practice area is not carpeted, provide some knee protection (folded blankets or mats) for participants or allow them to bring their own padding materials. Urge participants to dress comfortably for practicing skills. The room should be convenient to restrooms and exits.

Usually, participants' chairs can be arranged in rows facing the front of the classroom. However, you also should consider the advantages of different seating arrangements or of rearranging seating during the class. Semicircular or circular arrangements may make participants feel more at ease at certain times. For example, participants may see each other more clearly while introducing themselves if they are in a circle or semicircle.

When participants are taking the final written examination, it may be better to have chairs arranged to allow everyone as much space as possible. This will help to reduce distractions. When participants are practicing, they may need to push their chairs against the wall to gain more floor space. Whatever seating arrangements you select, make sure that all participants can adequately see the monitor or screen when you use audiovisual materials and the area in which you present skill demonstrations.

To prevent injury, do not ask participants to move heavy equipment and furniture. If you need their help to move lighter items, be sure that two or more participants move these items and use proper lifting techniques — lifting with the legs and keeping the back straight.

Swimming Area

The swimming area requirements for each course are listed in the administrative notes section of each course outline. If you are unsure whether your swimming area is appropriate, contact your local Red Cross unit for advice before offering courses.

Lesson Planning/Modifying

The lesson plans in the *Lifeguarding Instructor's Manual* should be closely followed as much as possible, but facility demands as well as participant needs may require you to modify existing sessions.

A significant factor not accounted for in the lesson plans for each course is the time required to move participants from one place to another. For example, in progressing through a single skill sequence, there may be a different location for discussion, demonstration, land practice, shallow water practice, and deep water practice. Movement into and out of the water and along a deck or waterfront may significantly add to the time requirements for the course. Class movement must be considered when planning each session and may require modifications to a lesson plan. Also the lesson plans do not take into account relief breaks and breaks for lunch (if applicable). You have to consider this when planning each session.

Other factors that may influence lesson planning include—
- Classroom availability.
- Pool availability.
- Equipment availability.
- Number of participants.

- Skill level of participants.
- Weather (if outdoors).

Course Materials and Equipment

Participant's Manuals

The basic resource for Lifeguarding Program participants and instructors are the participant's manuals for the courses. These participant's manuals include:

Course	Participant's Manual(s)
Lifeguard Training	*Lifeguarding Today* *CPR for the Professional Rescuer*
Waterfront Lifeguarding	*Lifeguarding Today*, Chapter 13.
Waterpark Lifeguarding	*Lifeguarding Today*, Chapter 14.
Head Lifeguard	*Head Lifeguard*
Community Water Safety	*Community Water Safety*

These manuals have been designed to facilitate the learning and understanding of the material presented in the lessons. They include the following features:

Lifeguarding Today	*CPR for the Professional Rescuer*
- Objectives	- Objectives
- Key Terms	- Key Terms
- Sidebars	- Main Ideas
- Skill Summaries	- Sidebars
- Study Questions	- Figures and Tables
- Appendixes	- Review Questions
- Glossary	- Skill Sheets
	- Appendixes
	- Glossary

Head Lifeguard	*Community Water Safety*
- Objectives	- Self-Analysis Questions
- Key Terms	- Glossary
- Sidebars	
- Study Questions	
- Appendixes	
- Glossary	

The following is a brief description of each of these features:

- **Objectives**
  At the beginning of each chapter is a list of objectives that participants should be able to meet after reading the chapter and participating in appropriate class activities.

- **Key Terms**
  At the beginning of each chapter is a list of key terms the participant needs to know to understand the chapter. Some key terms are listed in more than one chapter when they are essential to the material in each. In the chapter, key terms are printed in bold italic type the first time they appear or are discussed.

- **Main Ideas**
  Following the key terms is a section giving the main ideas in that chapter (*CPR for the Professional Rescuer* only). Each major concept is expressed in one or two sentences.

- **Sidebars**
  Short articles within the chapters give additional information to enhance the main text. They appear on a contrasting background. Included is a variety of material ranging from historical information to further applications of the information in the chapter.

Figures and Tables

Extensive photographs and illustrations reinforce chapter concepts and information and show how to do the rescue, CPR, and first aid skills. Tables are included in many chapters. They provide additional information and summarize important concepts.

Study and Review Questions

At the end of each chapter is a group of study or review questions designed to help participants evaluate their retention and understanding of the information in the chapter.

Skill Sheets and Summaries

Illustrated skill sheets or skill summaries at the end of some chapters give step-by-step direction for performing certain skills shown in video segments and described in those chapters. Participants use the skill sheets or skill summaries when they practice skills taught in that class session.

Self-Analysis Questions

Located at the end of the *Community Water Safety* participant's manual, these questions are designed to help participants evaluate their retention and understanding of the information in the manual.

Appendixes

Appendixes at the end of most of the participant's manuals provide additional information on topics that participants will find useful.

Glossary

The glossary includes definitions of all the key terms and of other words in the participant's manuals that may be unfamiliar. All glossary terms appear in the participant's manuals in bold type the first time they are used or explained.

Instructor's Manual

Lesson Plans

Several items in the lesson plans can help you conduct the courses of the Lifeguarding program. These include:

Primary Points

The primary points summarize the critical material—the material that is most important for the participants to understand. They also represent the information participants need to meet the objectives and pass the final written exam(s).

Notes to the instructor are in the lesson plans in italicized print. These notes provide specific information, expected participant responses, or clarification on certain points in the lesson plans. In addition, boxed teaching and safety tips are in the lesson plans. The teaching tips are suggestions to help you enhance your lessons, and the safety tips identify areas where it is particularly important to provide additional measures to ensure the safety of the participants.

Activities

Activities are presented in the lesson plans to enhance the participants' understanding of the course material. Some of these activities include discussion, group activities, and skill practice.

Skill practice comprises the majority of class activities. Using the videos to provide skill demonstrations alleviates the need for long lectures and discussions.

Skill Practice

In skill practice sessions, participants practice the skill either on one another or on manikins. Practice on a "real" victim is important to give participants experience in handling a real person. Skills that require mouth-to-mouth contact, however, such as rescue breathing, CPR, and chest or abdominal thrusts are practiced only on manikins.

Written Examinations

Written examinations for the Lifeguard Training, CPR for the Professional Rescuer, Waterfront Lifeguarding, Waterpark Lifeguarding, and Head Lifeguard courses and modules are included in Appendix S of this manual. Two exams for each course or module are provided, so that one or the other may be used for a make-up exam. Give either exam A or exam B. Participants must pass the exam with a minimum score of 80 percent as part of the requirements for receiving an American Red Cross course completion certificate. The questions have been selected to test the participants' ability to meet the course objectives. Other questions may not be substituted.

Audiovisuals

The American Red Cross *Lifeguarding Today* video has been specifically designed to be used with the American Red Cross Lifeguard Training course, Waterfront Lifeguarding module, and Waterpark Lifeguarding module. The Lifeguard Training course also utilizes the *CPR for the Professional Rescuer* video and the *Community First Aid* video. Since these videos are an integral part of course instruction in the Lifeguarding program, they are required to conduct these courses.

Several recommended videos for the Community Water Safety course are available as supplements to the course. Your local Red Cross unit should be able to provide these for you:

■ *American Red Cross Home Pool Safety: It Only Takes a Minute* (Stock No. 329474)
■ *American Red Cross Water: The Deceptive Power* (Stock No. 329475)

Manikins

Adult, child, and infant manikins are required equipment for the Lifeguard Training course. A participant-to-manikin ratio of 2–to–1 or 3–to–1 is recommended. All manikins should be well maintained and working properly.

Some manikins need to be cleaned during use, as described later and in Appendix H. Some of the newer manikins have disposable plastic bags that protrude from the mouth and cover the manikin's face. Others have individual manikin faces that are applied at the time of practice and removed after an individual has practiced a skill. Manikins should be models that can be properly decontaminated after class according to the recommendations in Appendix H. To minimize the possibility of disease transmission, these recommendations should be followed strictly.

All manikins should be inspected frequently for cracks or rips in the face, which make it difficult or impossible to clean the manikin properly. Do not use any manikin that has cracks or rips in the face.

Manikin Decontamination Supplies

For manikins that need to be cleaned during use, you will need a decontaminating solution and a large number of gauze pads. The recommended solution is 1/4 cup of liquid chlorine bleach per gallon of tap water. This solution should be made before each class and discarded after use. Do not use scented bleach. The perfume in these bleaches may impart a taste to the plastics.

Since some people find bleach objectionable, 70 percent alcohol (isopropanol or ethanol) is suggested as an alternative. Although alcohol can kill many bacteria and viruses, there are some that it will not kill. However, if the manikin's face is scrubbed vigorously with

70 percent alcohol and a clean gauze pad, it is highly unlikely that any infectious disease will be transmitted. For more information on selecting one of these decontaminating solutions, review Appendix H.

Manikin Decontamination Procedure

During practice sessions, the manikin's face and the inside of its mouth must be cleaned after use by each participant.

For some manikins, this requires the following procedures:

1. Dry the manikin's face with a clean 4" x 4" gauze pad.
2. Wet a second clean gauze pad with decontaminating solution.
3. Squeeze excess solution from the pad.
4. Scrub the manikin's face and the inside of its mouth vigorously with the soaked pad (being careful not to tear the mouth).
5. Place the wet pad over the manikin's mouth and nose and wait 30 seconds.
6. Discard the pad and dry the manikin's face with a third clean gauze pad.

Tell participants that to keep the manikins' faces clean and free from dirt, they should not place the manikins facedown. Participants should also be asked to wash their hands and remove lipstick before practice on a manikin.

Manikin Decontamination After Class

As soon as possible after the end of each class session in which manikins are used, all manikins should be properly cleaned. Manufacturer's recommendations should be followed regarding disassembly. The parts should be scrubbed with warm soapy water, rinsed, and decontaminated with a solution of liquid household chlorine bleach and water (1/4 cup of bleach to one gallon of water). Vigorous scrubbing with soap and water is as important as scrubbing with bleach. Disposable gloves and protective eyewear should be worn while manikins are being decontaminated.

To decontaminate the manikins after class, you will need, besides the decontamination solution and gauze pads, a baby bottle brush, soap and water, basins or buckets, nonsterile disposable gloves, and any other supplies that may be recommended by the manikin manufacturer. The manikin's body, hair, and clothes should be washed periodically to ensure that the manikins are clean.

Cleaning the Resuscitation Masks After Class

Manufacturer's instructions for cleaning the resuscitation masks should be followed after each use.

Usually, the disposable one-way valve on the resuscitation mask can be cleaned and reused after practice on a manikin. For use on a victim, the disposable one-way valve should not be reused.

The resuscitation mask and one-way valve may be cleaned after training by first vigorously scrubbing in warm soapy water and rinsing with clean water. Both are then submerged for 10 minutes in a solution of water and liquid chlorine bleach (1/4 cup of liquid chlorine bleach to one gallon of tap water). They are then rinsed with clean water and allowed to dry. The mask should not be pasteurized, boiled, or steamed (autoclaved).

Other Equipment

Suggested and required equipment is listed at the beginning of each lesson in the course outlines and in Appendix G. Make sure all equipment is ready and in working order before your course begins. If your facility does not have the needed equipment, check with the local Red Cross unit to see if they have it available and follow their procedures

for reserving it. Some local units have a
rental fee. If you have signed an *Authorized
Provider Agreement* (Form 6575), it may
cover the use of the equipment.

3 how to run practice sessions

during the practice sessions, participants are learning and perfecting skills. You must decide how best to design the practice sessions. The sessions should include direction and instruction, ample practice time, instructor reinforcement, corrective feedback, and encouragement to ensure participants' success. Plan the practice sessions to reinforce learning objectives.

In general, practice sessions will involve instructor-led practice and reciprocal (partner) practice. During the practice sessions, you are responsible for—

- Demonstrating a skill and/or guiding students through it.
- Keeping the practice sessions running smoothly.
- Providing sufficient time for all participants to practice the skill.
- Identifying errors promptly and providing feedback to help participants improve their skills.
- Encouraging participants to improve their skills.
- Checking each student for critical skill competency.
- Ensuring a safe environment during the practice sessions.

Orienting Participants to Practice Sessions

Orienting participants to the practice sessions will help them get started more quickly and practice more efficiently. Participants will practice in groups of two or three, and in some cases, more (depending on space and

supplies). Some practice sessions require participants to practice on other participants. Others, such as CPR and rescue breathing, require practice only on a manikin. Emphasize to participants that for personal safety, they do not practice these skills on each other.

How Participants Learn Skills

To acquire skills efficiently, participants should be supervised during practice sessions. They may need more attention during the first practice session. Carefully planning the first session and commending participants for good performance sets a positive tone for later sessions. The skills may be new to participants, and they may frequently require one-on-one attention. The following list of characteristics applies to skills and the way participants learn them:

- Course skills are complex. Participants often have some difficulties when they first begin.
- Skills are learned by practice. Refinements in technique take time, and immediate success in demonstrating the skill is unlikely.
- Skills require a defined sequence of movements. Participants should follow this sequence to perform the skills correctly.
- Learning times for each skill differ, since some skills are easier than others.
- Participants have different learning rates. Take individual differences into account when teaching the course.
- Skills are quickly forgotten. Regular practice improves retention of skills.

Practice With A Partner (Reciprocal Practice)

Practice with a partner has been included to give participants experience in providing care for a real person. One participant acts as the victim while another provides care. Participants change roles so that each person in the group has a chance to practice the skill.

During partner practice, be sure participants take the following precautions so that they do not get hurt:

■ Participants should not engage in horseplay, which can lead to injury.

■ **Tell participants that they should not make mouth-to-mouth contact with a partner, should not give actual rescue breaths, and should not perform actual abdominal thrusts or chest compressions during the CPR skills practice sessions.**

Instructor-Led Practice

Instructor-led practice, or drill, can be used for speeding up skill practice. It is particularly useful for introducing new skills that build on previously learned skills, for example, adding chest compressions to rescue breathing to perform CPR, or the skill of rescuing a submerged victim once participants know how to do a feet-first surface dive.

When you lead the practice, position the participants so that you can see everyone. If the participants are practicing on manikins, the manikins' heads should be pointing in the same direction, and all the participants should be in the same position next to the manikins. If the participants are practicing on partners, being able to see everyone allows you to judge skill competency as well as ensure participant safety.

Guide participants through each step of a skill, and have participants do each step together as a group, or in small groups, one step at a time. For most skills, allow the participants additional time to continue practicing on their own.

Helping Participants Practice Correctly

You should watch for errors participants make while practicing. Try to correct problems as soon as possible so that participants will practice the skill correctly. While you are working closely with one participant, check others with an occasional glance. Correct any major problems you notice to keep participants from continuing to practice incorrectly. Encourage participants to ask questions if they are unsure how to perform any part of a skill. Stay in the practice area throughout the practice session to help participants who need assistance.

A positive learning environment is important. Participants perform best when they are kept informed of their progress. When they are practicing correctly, provide positive feedback. If they are practicing incorrectly, provide specific corrective feedback. Before saying what they are doing wrong, tell them what they are doing correctly. Then tactfully help them correct their errors.

Other strategies for corrective feedback include the following:

■ If the error is simple, explain directly and positively how to correct the skill. Be specific when providing feedback. For example, if the participant is having trouble getting the chest to rise during rescue breathing, you might say, "Your hand position is good, but you should tilt the head back farther. That will open the airway more so your breaths can go in more easily."

- You may have to show the participant what he or she should be doing. For the previous example, you might have to tilt the manikin's head yourself to show the participant how far back the manikin's head should be to open the airway.
- It may help to tell the participants why they should perform a skill in a certain way. This may help them remember to perform the skill correctly. For example, if a participant continues to forget to check the pulse before giving chest compressions, you might remind the participant that the victim may have a pulse and therefore not need chest compressions.
- If a participant has an ongoing problem with technique, carefully observe what he or she is doing. Give exact instructions for performing the technique the correct way, and lead the participant through the skill. It may be helpful to the participant to repeat the steps back to you to help reinforce them correctly.

Throughout this process, you should continue to remind the participants of both what they are doing right and what they are doing wrong. Use phrases like "Your compressions are very smooth, but they should be a little deeper," or "You are doing a good job getting to the victim, but you need to support the victim securely to keep his or her face out of the water during the rescue." Help participants focus on the "critical" aspects for each skill, which, when performed incorrectly, may be life-threatening.

Teaching to Objectives

The Americans with Disabilities Act (PL 101–336) has led to an increasing awareness that people with disabilities and other conditions can excel as lifeguards. The skills they need to prevent injury or to save a life may need modification, but the result is the same.

Instructors must now focus on the abilities needed to successfully complete an objective as opposed to perfecting every individual skill. For example, a person with one arm may not be able to perform a front crawl or breaststroke approach stroke. However, he or she may be able to perform a modified sidestroke to reach a victim in distress. If the "objective" is for the lifeguard to reach a victim, the person with one arm will fully satisfy that objective even though he or she has not performed a conventional approach stroke in the process. As another example, the person may not be able to support the head and neck in the standard way for in-line stabilization, but if the person is able to hold the victim's head in-line, the objective is met.

Physically Challenged Participants

As an American Red Cross instructor, you may be asked to present courses to a class that includes one or more physically challenged participants. Physically challenged participants include those who are deaf or hard of hearing or legally blind, lack full use of limbs, or have breathing difficulties or other physical problems. In some instances, entire classes may be composed of this special group. When the physically challenged individual can meet the stated course objectives, he or she should receive a course completion certificate.

The following instructor considerations can help the physically challenged individual succeed in class:
- Instructors can adapt their teaching to these individuals.
- There is no one strategy for teaching participants who have physical limitations.

- Methods of recognizing the limitations include —
  - Instructor observation of participants.
  - Participants' statements.

Helping Participants Overcome Physical Challenges

To help the participant overcome a physical challenge, you may modify the delivery of course materials as follows:

- Increase the amount of time you spend with each participant.
- Allow frequent rests.
- Help participants modify the techniques necessary for successful skill completion. For example, a participant with one arm could be instructed to seal the nose with his or her cheek while using his or her arm and hand to do the head-tilt/chin-lift in rescue breathing. Another example would be allowing a participant who is unable to get on the floor to perform skills on a manikin placed on a table or other platform.

Refer to Appendix F, The Americans With Disabilities Act — Course Modification Guide, for more information on teaching physically challenged individuals.

Emphasize the value of information and skills learned, regardless of whether or not participants earn course certificates.

Lifeguarding Rescue Skills Information

Using the Lifeguarding Skills Checklist

The Lifeguarding Skills Checklist (Appendix M) is a tool for documenting a participant's progress and skills evaluation results. The Lifeguarding Skills Checklist should be reproduced by the instructor for each class and the copies taken to poolside. Note the spaces for listing participants' names, as well as the listing of skills.

Use this form to check off skills as participants complete them. Occasionally, a participant does not understand why he or she did not complete the course requirements. The skills checklist is useful in such situations because it enables an instructor to identify exactly what skills have been completed. An instructor may also use this form to track class attendance.

The Lifeguarding Skills Checklist has the following components:

- **Skill Areas**
  These are general functions, such as entries and rescues, that have multiple specific skills listed with each.

- **Specific Skills**
  These are skills that are demonstrated, practiced, and evaluated, such as stride jump and compact jump, under the skill area of entries. Although there may be alternative methods, specific skills provide the safest and most effective means to perform an action relating to a particular skill sequence. By teaching all specific skills, you give participants options as to which method they would prefer to use in a particular situation. For example, even though it is not the only method to enter the water from a height, the compact jump is an effective way to enter the water from a height.

  Instructors should record participants' results with a check when a skill is successfully completed and a zero if it is not successfully completed. All of these skills are not necessarily required to complete the course requirements and receive certification.

■ **Critical Skills**

These are skills that must be successfully performed by a participant to complete the course requirements and receive certification. Critical skills are based on the objective of the skill area. Refer to the Lifeguarding Critical Skills Chart (Appendix N) in this instructor's manual.

For example, under the skill area of "entries" you will find the specific skills of stride jump and compact jump. A participant may not be able to perform either of those specific skills, but may be able to enter the water in some other safe way. It is not essential that a rescuer enters the water in a specific manner during a rescue, only that he or she can enter the water safely. Therefore, it is possible a that participant cannot perform the stride jump and compact jump entries, but still meets the critical skill of "entering the water." This participant may continue the course and still receive certification, since he or she is capable of performing that function of a lifeguard during a rescue.

Critical skills are the shaded areas on the Lifeguarding Skills Checklist. Instructors should mark the appropriate box with a "P" (pass) if the skill is successfully completed and an "F" (fail) if not successfully completed. Participants must successfully perform all critical skills to complete course requirements and receive certification.

Conducting In-Water Demonstrations and Skills Practice Sessions

Often participants depend on demonstrations rather than words to understand the concepts and movements involved in performing a skill. Remember that, "A picture is worth a thousand words."

The rescue skills performed in lifeguarding have multiple actions occurring simultaneously. If a skill is only demonstrated from one side or angle, the secondary actions may be missed and the total picture will be incomplete. This is particularly true for skills that involve actions both above and below water. For example, in demonstrating how to turn a victim faceup using a head and chin support, participants may clearly see the rescuer's hand and arm position above water, but may not notice the rescuer's bottom arm or leg action. Since supporting the victim and avoiding unnecessary movement are important when performing the rescue, the rescuer's underwater actions are significant elements in the total skill.

Instructors should focus on the "total picture" concept when demonstrating skills. Demonstrations should be performed as slowly as possible without losing the integrity of the skill. Whenever possible, all skills should be demonstrated in exactly the same manner from the front, back, and both sides. This allows participants to see all sides and angles of a sequence. In some cases, this may not be possible, such as with an entry from a lifeguard stand. However, the more participants can see, the more they will conceptualize a skill. Whenever possible, the skill should first be demonstrated on land.

A key element in mastering a motor skill is practice. Instructors should keep in mind that the more participants have the opportunity to practice, the better their skill performance and retention will be.

Practice sessions provide an immediate opportunity to put the "total picture" into practice. However, participants cannot be expected to instantly be able to perform a skill correctly. Therefore, instructors should break down skills into parts so that they can lead participants through the correct progression for each skill. For example, with a land practice for the head and chin support, an instructor may have the participants stop their movement after they have placed their hands and arms on the victim. This will allow the instructor to evaluate their hand and arm placement and make corrections before they proceed to the next step. This method is very effective for reinforcing correct actions.

Common Participant Errors in Rescue Skills

The following list of common errors will help you when you are watching participants work through the practice sessions. The list is intended to help you assist students in performing the skill in a way that provides mechanical advantage and ease of learning. The list is not intended to be a list of critical errors or criteria for passing the skill. The criterion for passing a skill is successful completion of the critical skills listed in the Lifeguarding Skills Checklist (Appendix M).

Entering the Water
- Leaning too far forward or backward, resulting in loss of rescue tube
- Failing to hold the rescue tube securely, resulting in loss of tube
- Failing to hold excess line of rescue tube in one hand

Approaching the Victim
- Improper position of the rescue tube, resulting in tube slipping out or slow progress through the water

Active Victim Rescue
- Failing to approach from the rear whenever possible
- Not reaching far enough under victim's armpits, resulting in the inability to keep victim's mouth above water while progressing to safety

- The rescuer failing to keep his/her head out of the way when pulling the victim onto the rescue tube, resulting in injury

Multiple Victim Rescue
- Failure to adequately support one victim, resulting in the inability to keep both victims' mouths above the surface of the water

Passive Victim Rescue
- Failing to use body weight appropriately to roll the victim faceup

Submerged Victims
- Failing to remove the rescue tube if water is too deep
- Forgetting to maintain control of the line in order to pull yourself and the victim to the surface
- Not approaching the victim from the rear

Victim Removal
- Lifting with the back instead of the legs
- Not working as a team when two rescuers are lifting
- Not grasping the victim securely
- Not lifting upward and then stepping back in order to get the victim's body out of the water and onto the deck

Spinal Injury Techniques
- Failing to firmly hold the victim's back and chest with forearms while supporting the head with hands
- Twisting the victim's body when turning the victim faceup
- Not holding the victim's arms securely against the head when performing the head splint technique

Backboarding and Removal From the Water
- Not working as a team to minimize movement of the victim
- Securing the head before the body

- Placing the chest strap over the arms instead of under the armpits
- Not securing the straps adequately, resulting in movement of the victim during removal from the water
- Allowing the victim to achieve a vertical position during removal, resulting in movement of the victim and possible further injury

First Aid and CPR Skills Information

In Lesson 3 of the Lifeguard Training course, you should do the following:

- Review with participants the information on first aid and infectious disease on pages xiv–xv of the *CPR for the Professional Rescuer* participant's manual. Tell participants that if they have any of the health conditions listed on these pages, they should request a separate manikin. They also should refrain from physical activity if it is detrimental to their health and check with their doctor if in doubt.
- Before the first practice session, you should tell participants to do the following:
  - Remove jewelry as well as lipstick.
  - Place jewelry in a safe place such as a purse or deep pocket.
  - Have clean hands.
  - Refrain from smoking, using smokeless tobacco products, eating, chewing gum, or drinking during the practice sessions.
  - Review Health Precautions and Guidelines for the Professional Rescuer on pages xiv–xv in the *CPR for the Professional Rescuer* participant's manual.

Use of Skill Summaries and Skill Sheets

Skill summaries are included in the *Lifeguarding Today* participant's manual for first aid skills and skill sheets are in *CPR for the*

Professional Rescuer participant's manual for CPR skills that participants will practice and be checked on. These skill summaries and skill sheets identify the critical steps required to adequately perform each skill, and each critical step is illustrated. Directions for performing each step are next to the illustrations.

Some skill sheets have decision points. These points, in bold type, describe what care should be provided when certain conditions are found. For example, during the check for consciousness in the primary survey, if the victim is not breathing or the rescuer cannot tell, the rescuer should position the victim on his or her back (if necessary) and open the victim's airway, which are the next steps on the skill sheet. By reacting to various conditions, participants are better able to understand how to use a skill in an actual emergency situation.

Practice on a Manikin

Participants must practice on a manikin to learn the complete procedures for rescue breathing, first aid for an unconscious victim with an obstructed airway, and CPR. Participants must successfully demonstrate these skills on a manikin to receive an American Red Cross course completion certificate.

Having the manikins out of their cases at the beginning of class can help save valuable class time. If you take the manikins out before class, cover each face with a shield or piece of gauze to keep it clean. If you keep the manikins in their cases until the beginning of the practice session, allow a few minutes to get them out at the beginning of the session.

Common Participant Errors in CPR and First Aid

The following list of common errors will help you when you are watching participants work through the CPR and first aid practice sessions. The list is not intended to be a list of critical errors or a criterion for passing the skill. **The criterion for passing a skill is successful completion of the steps listed on the skill summaries and skill sheets.**

Checking for Consciousness

Not using a combination of tapping and shouting

Positioning the Victim

Not supporting the victim's head and neck when rolling the victim
Not rolling the victim as a single unit

Opening the Airway

■ Not tilting the head back far enough to open the airway
■ Forgetting to lift the chin
■ Applying pressure on the soft parts under the chin when lifting the chin (wrong finger placement)
■ Closing the mouth when lifting the chin
Placing the hand under the neck instead of lifting the chin

Checking for Breathing

Not placing the ear close enough to the mouth and nose of the victim
Not looking at the chest when checking for breathing
■ Not checking long enough for breathing

Breathing Into the Victim

■ Not pinching the nose
Not making an adequate mouth-to-mouth seal, causing air to leak out around the mouth when breaths are given
■ Giving breaths too quickly or forcefully. Each breath should be delivered slowly (for about 1 1/2 seconds) until the chest gently rises.
■ Not watching the chest rise and fall

Checking the Pulse

■ Not keeping the airway open while checking the pulse
■ Checking for the pulse in the wrong place; for example, pressing on the windpipe when checking the carotid pulse
■ Using the thumb to check the pulse
■ Not checking the pulse for 5 to 10 seconds

Complete Airway Obstruction (Conscious Victim)

■ Not determining that the victim is choking
■ Not locating the correct hand position for giving abdominal or chest thrusts
■ Not keeping the elbows out when pretending to give abdominal thrusts

Complete Airway Obstruction (Unconscious Victim)

■ Not retilting the head and repeating rescue breath attempts
■ Checking the pulse before the obstruction is cleared and the rescuer is able to breathe air into the victim
■ Not locating the correct hand position to give abdominal/chest thrusts or back blows
■ Forgetting the foreign body check/finger sweep step

CPR

■ Kneeling in the wrong position or place beside the victim
■ Not properly locating hand/finger position for compressions
■ Not relocating the proper hand position for compressions when the hands lose contact with the chest
■ Placing the palm rather than the heel of the hand on the breastbone when giving compressions

Controlling External Bleeding

- Failing to apply direct pressure
- Failing to apply a dressing before bandaging
- Failing to anchor the bandage securely before wrapping
- Wrapping the bandage too loosely
- Failing to elevate the wound above the level of the heart
- Placing the hand in the wrong position when locating the pressure points

Splinting

- Failing to immobilize the joints above and below the fracture site
- Failing to check circulation by checking color and temperature of a limb before and after splinting
- Placing splinting materials directly over the injured area

4 program planning

his chapter discusses program planning for lifeguarding instructors who are program administrators. Usually, lifeguarding instructors teach courses in programs set up and administered by someone else. Sometimes, however, you may be responsible for setting up a program. The following sections can help you to do so.

Role of the Red Cross Unit

Your local Red Cross unit may have a Health and Safety director who supervises the swimming and water safety, lifeguarding, first aid, and CPR courses. If not, the unit manager can refer you to the volunteer or staff person who handles the lifeguarding program.

Your unit's Health and Safety committee and/or Water Safety committee is an important resource for you. Water Safety committees usually encompass the areas of swimming, water safety and lifeguarding. Many units have committees but some may not. Both committees may include representatives of community groups concerned with safety, such as schools, recreation departments, youth groups, and service organizations. Most Red Cross units have active lifeguarding instructors on the committee and, if possible, representatives from the unit's other safety committees. This committee helps develop the health and safety goals for the unit.

Authorized Provider Agreement

Before starting a new program, you will need to enter into an Authorized Provider Agreement with your local Red Cross unit. The purpose of the Authorized Provider

Agreement is to maintain quality control and corporate control of Red Cross materials, to improve understanding between the Red Cross and providers and their expectations of each other, and to improve the American Red Cross internal system for delivery of instructional services and materials. An Authorized Provider may be an individual or a facility who provides American Red Cross courses. If the facility is the Authorized Provider, there is no need for each individual instructor to become one.

Working With the Community

Community-service activities include promoting water safety by offering demonstrations, talks, videos, and displays, and by distributing educational materials through public information outlets. Since community support is essential to a successful program, investigate ways to advertise your program in the community. Your local Red Cross unit can often be helpful with this. There are several marketing brochures and posters available through local Red Cross units and Mosby Lifeline. The following brochures and posters can be used as tools to market classes and to provide information to participants about additional programs and products.

Lifeguard Training brochure (Stock No. 654125)—This brochure concentrates on detailed information on the Lifeguard Training course. Its focus is to target and interest potential Lifeguard Training candidates. It also describes the Waterpark Lifeguarding and Waterfront Lifeguarding modules, training modules of the Lifeguarding program that lifeguard candidates may be interested in taking. This brochure also lists products that lifeguarding classes may be interested in purchasing to demonstrate their new affiliation.

Head Lifeguard brochure (Stock No. 654126)—This brochure explains the concept and philosophy of the Head Lifeguard course. The brochure is designed to interest both lifeguard candidates and current lifeguards by showing them additional career opportunities. It is important that they know there is a career development track within the American Red Cross Lifeguarding program.

Community Water Safety brochure (Stock No. 654127)—This brochure describes the Community Water Safety course and its goals of creating a safer aquatic atmosphere for the general public. This marketing tool is targeted to the general public and can be used to stimulate interest in the course and/or the book. Making these brochures available to lifeguard candidates would provide them with useful information and educate them about programs that are available for the general public through the American Red Cross.

Aquatic Examiner Program brochure (Stock No. 654128)—This brochure describes the purpose and philosophy of the Aquatic Examiner Program and is designed to relate this information to facility managers and owners. It provides lifeguard candidates with information about a Red Cross service that they may not currently know about but may encounter in the future.

Aquatics Catalog (Stock No. 654129)—This comprehensive catalog includes all American Red Cross aquatic programs and products such as the Learn-to-Swim program, Aqua Fitness, and Lifeguard Training. Other programs that are necessary to fulfill aquatic requirements are also highlighted, such as

CPR for the Professional Rescuer. This catalog can be used as a resource for product and program information for the lifeguard candidate or lifeguard throughout his or her lifeguarding career.

Aquatics Marketing Posters (Stock No. 654120)—This set of posters includes a poster of the cover of Lifeguarding Today, a Lifeguard Training recruitment poster, a Head Lifeguard course promotion poster, and a Waterpark Lifeguarding and Waterfront Lifeguarding promotional poster. This poster set is designed to assist local Red Cross units and aquatic facilities to market and promote programs, and recruit candidates for basic and instructor level courses.

Safety Poster Package (Stock No. 654121)—This set of posters includes a Spinal Injury Prevention poster, a "What to do in an Aquatic Emergency" poster, an Adult Lifesaving Steps poster, and an Infant and Child Lifesaving Steps poster. These posters are great to use as safety reminders in public pool areas.

Registration

To start a new program, you must develop procedures and policies for registration. To determine how many and what type of Lifeguarding and/or Water Safety classes to offer, consider the size of the facility, the deck and water areas, the availability of periods in the day for younger and older populations, the number of instructors available, budget, and the number of programming hours available. Once you decide on your program, prepare a chart of Lifeguarding and Water Safety classes that includes the dates, times, locations, and fees.

Staffing

Staffing the program is your next concern. Decide early in the planning process who will hire, supervise, and evaluate staff. Many programs have an on-site program coordinator and instructors, instructor aides, and lifeguards. All personnel should be oriented to the specific facility and its emergency action plan(s).

Budgeting

Prior to your budget planning, contact your local Red Cross unit about authorized provider fees and enter into an Authorized Provider agreement. Fees and charges should be based on local standards and in cooperation with your local Red Cross unit. Be sure to plan for scholarship funding so that no one is kept from participating because of financial problems or accommodations. Your organization may consider fund-raising events to increase resources.

Records and Reports

Records and reports are critical to authorized providers and the local Red Cross unit. When you meet with the local unit, develop a list of required records and reports. Red Cross records and reports are standardized throughout the country, and your attention to detail in completing them speeds the certification process.

Your local Red Cross unit can advise you of the local policies and procedures for submitting these documents. Work closely with your local unit to meet the deadlines. With prior written permission from your local Red Cross unit, schools, camps, and similar institutions may submit the Course Record (6418) with the top portion completed and an attached list (such as a grade book, handwritten roster, or computer printout) of participants' names and grades.

5 class safety

As an American Red Cross lifeguarding instructor, you must make your teaching environment as safe as possible. In many cases, you will have to make others aware of the importance of safety for the organization and/or the facility. Your primary goal as an instructor is to ensure the safety of participants. Participants expect and deserve a safe and healthy learning environment. If it is not safe, your participants may become distracted, be afraid to participate, or even be at risk of injury. In addition, if you become distracted because of hazardous conditions, your program and participants will suffer. Some state recreational bathing and health codes require certain standards be met before the course begins. These may include requirements for lifeguards, safety equipment, and proper water chemistry. You should know the requirements for your state and local jurisdictions. Regardless of whether these regulations exist, you must provide for the safety of the participants in your classes.

Factors Affecting Injury Prevention

Effective injury prevention starts with *your* awareness that hazards may be present. Safety awareness is necessary for recognizing hazards so that these conditions can be corrected or controlled. Many other factors also affect the safety of your program, as discussed in the following sections.

Supervision

During your lessons, you are observing participants, making suggestions, and evaluating individual performance. You cannot keep a watchful eye on everyone at all times. Since any aquatics class not properly supervised faces potential hazards, all participants must be accounted for throughout each lesson. *Adequate supervision must be maintained at all times.* A qualified lifeguard should be on duty at all times during all lessons. This will—

- Improve instruction by letting the instructor concentrate on teaching.
- Increase the safety of participants.
- Provide an additional trained person to respond in an emergency.

Instructor Preparation

You can improve your program by being thoroughly prepared. Careful preparation includes considering possible hazards and managing safety concerns before the program starts. Often you can foresee hazards and eliminate or control them long before participants step into the water.

Assistant Instructors and Instructor Aides

Co-instructors, assistant instructors, and instructor aides can help decrease risks by giving more supervision and reducing the instructor–participant ratio. They also increase participation and learning by providing more attention to individual participants. However, an assistant or instructor aide is not a substitute for having a lifeguard on duty.

The key element when using additional staff is to define their roles and responsibilities clearly. This helps eliminate confusion and lapses in supervision. Remember, you have the ultimate responsibility for your participants' safety. Be sure your instructor aides have been trained according to the guidelines in Chapter 12.

To determine your staffing needs, consider the different ages of participants, the program's level, and the individual abilities of participants in that program. If your program has a large number of participants, it may require additional staffing or increased supervision by lifeguards.

Participants

The participants themselves greatly affect how you minimize hazards in the class. Be sure your participants know and follow the facility's and program's rules and regulations. Explain and enforce all rules and regulations consistently. At all times, safety is your primary concern.

Safety Equipment and Instructional Aids

Your instructor training has taught you how to use safety equipment and instructional aids. You should request and receive an orientation on the location and use of the equipment in any facility where you teach. Always check instructional aids before you use them to ensure they are safe.

Teaching Environment

The teaching environment may involve hazards you need to eliminate or minimize. Hazards in permanent or semi-permanent structures cannot easily be altered, such as the natural hazards of a pool or lake, deck areas, and permanent equipment such as diving boards. Be alert for potential hazards. Document and report your concerns to the facility manager and/or program administrator, and retain a copy for your records.

Adjust your program to reduce such risks to your participants if you cannot completely eliminate them. Some conditions, such as poor water conditions and weather situations like electrical storms, may require temporary adjustments or suspending a class. Note these conditions on the *Course Record* (Form 6418).

Facility Policies and Procedures

Besides being prepared to teach, you should be prepared to react appropriately in a serious emergency. Know the facility's emergency action plan to ensure your safety and that of your participants. Know the location of emergency equipment, telephones, first aid supplies, and additional personnel. Be sure you know where emergency phone numbers are posted, including these for police, EMS personnel, fire fighters, poison control, security, and facility management. You do not have time to find this information when an emergency occurs.

All facility policies and procedures, including how to activate the emergency action plan, should be in writing and available to you. You should have your own copy, and it is *your* responsibility to know how the plan pertains to you and your classes. Be sure your duties and responsibilities are clearly documented to avoid misunderstandings.

Costs Related to Safety

It costs money to supply lifeguards in addition to instructors, to provide enough proper equipment for participants, and to maintain the facility correctly and safely. However, not minimizing hazards effectively may be far more costly in the long run. Budgetary concerns do not justify poor safety practices. Inadequate safety procedures can lead to injury and lawsuits, both of which can be extremely expensive.

By staying alert for potential hazards, you are taking a big step toward providing a safe teaching environment. Before you teach your classes, personally inspect the instructional area and every piece of equipment you will use. Maintaining recommended instructor–participant ratios also decreases risks.

The American Red Cross as a Safety Resource

Your local Red Cross unit may also have safety information and resources provided by national headquarters. One such example is the Aquatic Examiner Program (AEP). This program is a service designed to help the management of an aquatic facility achieve a safer and more professional operation. Your local Red Cross unit may also have safety equipment and instructional aids you can use. Before you start your program, find out what support your local unit can provide.

6 course completion

Criteria for Course Completion

On successful completion of an American Red Cross Lifeguarding program course or module, participants receive a course completion certificate. The criteria for completion of the courses and modules of the Lifeguarding program are in the administration section of each course outline and in Appendix E, Course Fact Sheets.

Participants should be told the requirements when they enroll for a course and again during the course introduction.

Course Certification

Many agencies, organizations, and individuals look to the American Red Cross for formal training resulting in certification. Red Cross certification means that on a particular date an instructor verified that a course participant could do the following:

- Demonstrate competency in each critical skill taught in a course. Competency is defined as being able to perform each critical skill correctly and without guidance.
- Correctly answer at least 80 percent of the questions on a final written examination.

Achieving course certification does not imply any future demonstration of the skill or knowledge at the level achieved on the particular date.

Criteria for Grading Participants

The *Course Record* (Form 6418) and the *Course Record Addendum* (Form 6418A) require that you enter a grade of pass, fail, incomplete, or audit for each participant. The correct grade is assigned by these criteria:

- "Pass" (P) is entered for a participant who has passed all the required course skills, the final skills test, and the final written test, if applicable.
- "Fail" (F) is entered for a participant who has not passed all the required course skills and the final skills test or the written test at the completion of the course.
- "Incomplete" (I) is entered for a participant who could not complete the course because of certain circumstances, such as an illness or death in the family. A grade of Incomplete should be given only when arrangements have been made for the participant to complete the training. These arrangements should be noted on the *Course Record* (Form 6418) in the section for instructor's comments.
- "Audit" should be entered as the final grade for a participant who has chosen the self-evaluation option for testing. This should not be substituted for a Fail for a participant who attempts certification but is unable to pass the completion requirements. This participant does not receive a course completion certificate.

Reporting Procedures

At the conclusion of the course, you must accurately complete, sign, and promptly turn in to your Red Cross unit the American Red Cross *Course Record* (Form 6418) and *Course Record Addendum* (Form 6418A) to receive course completion certificates. You should keep a copy for your records and give a copy to the institution or organization where the course was conducted. Your local Red Cross unit may require you to complete other forms, such as an equipment log sheet. Report problems with equipment to your Red Cross unit if you used its equipment.

Awarding Certificates

Discuss with your local Red Cross unit the procedures for obtaining American Red Cross course completion certificates for participants in your courses. Be sure to follow approved procedures. Sign the certificates before giving them to the participants. If you receive certificates after the course is over, make arrangements to get them to the participants. You may wish to ask your participants to give you a stamped, self-addressed envelope at the beginning of the course.

Course Evaluation

Receiving feedback from participants is important in any evaluation. Participants should have an opportunity to tell you what they thought about the course by completing evaluation forms in every course you teach. This information gives you useful feedback about the course and your instruction, and it helps you and the Red Cross maintain courses of highest quality.

A Participant Course Evaluation form is found in the back of the participant's manual (Appendix Q, in this manual contains an example of this form). Additional copies of the Participant Course Evaluation form are available from your local Red Cross unit. Use this evaluation at the end of each course. Submit completed Participant Course Evaluation forms to your local American Red Cross unit. You may want to submit them the same time you submit your completed course record.

Instructor's Evaluation

To continue to improve its courses, the American Red Cross needs your help. After you teach a course the first and second time, use the feedback from participants to help you complete the Lifeguarding Program Instructor Evaluation form. This form is at the back of this instructor's manual (Additional copies of this evaluation form are available from your local Red Cross unit). Return the completed evaluation to—

American Red Cross National Headquarters
Health and Safety Course Evaluations
431 18th Street, N.W.
Washington, DC 20006

We also invite you to share your thoughts and suggestions about the courses at any time by sending in additional evaluation forms or by writing to the above address.

Instructor Self-Assessment

You may find it useful to use the Lifeguarding Instructor Self-Assessment in Appendix R in this instructor's manual to rate your instructional skills.

section b: teaching tools

when disinfecting man - wear
goggles + gloves

3 yrs lifeguard training - certified

has to teach 1 every 3 yrs to remain

- course evaluation form - know how did
  regu LGT
  17 yrs.

course record needs to be handed in 10 day

precourse - swim 500   36 total
            tread water with   including

6 participates

not intended to be complete

4 ft shallow] - pool
9 ft deep]

community water safety - no requirements
provided incl with general info
book comunity water

only need to demonstrate critical skills

The purpose of the Lifeguard Training course is to teach lifeguards the skills and knowledge needed to prevent and respond to aquatic emergencies. The course content and activities prepare lifeguard candidates to recognize emergencies, respond quickly and effectively to emergencies, and prevent drownings and other incidents. The course also teaches other skills an individual needs to become a professional lifeguard.

Administrative Notes

The following points apply to this course:

Prerequisites

To be eligible for the Lifeguard Training course, the candidate must be 15 years of age on or before the start of this precourse session. The candidate must also successfully complete the following swimming prerequisites:

- Swim 500 hundred yards continuously, using each of the following strokes for at least 100 yards each: crawl stroke, breaststroke, and sidestroke. Participants choose their stroke(s) for the remaining 200 yards. There is no time requirement for this skill.
- Submerge to a minimum depth of 7 feet, retrieve a 10-pound object, and return with it to the surface. There is no time requirement for this skill.
- Tread water for 2 minutes using legs only. Participants cross their arms across their chest and place their hands under their armpits.

Course Length

This course is designed to be taught in a minimum of 33 hours (Participants spend an additional 1 1/2 hours in a precourse session.). This time includes time for lifeguarding, CPR, and first aid skills practice; class activities; and the showing of three videos. This course has nine 3-hour sessions, one 3 1/4 hour session, and one 2 3/4 hour session.

Since the times allotted in the lesson plans do not include relief breaks, you may have to build additional time into the course.

Class Size

It is recommended that there be one instructor for every 10 participants in the class. If the class has more than 10 participants, you should have a co-instructor or aide. Close supervision is necessary to ensure effective practice and the safety of participants. Furthermore, you can run a class more efficiently if you keep the class reasonably small, and you are less likely to exceed the allotted time periods for various activities.

Facilities

Classroom Space

The lessons in the Lifeguard Training course require classroom space suitable for discussion, video viewing, first aid and CPR skills practice, and taking final written exams. The classroom should be conveniently located for participants. It should also be equipped with the necessary teaching aids and materials.

Swimming Area

A pool is suggested for skills practice and testing. The pool should have the following dimensions:

- The shallow end of the pool should be a maximum of 4 feet deep.
- The deep end of the pool should be a minimum of 9 feet deep.
- The pool should be a minimum of 30 feet wide and 60 feet long.

If a waterfront or waterpark facility is used, it should be an open-area free from surf or obstructions and with sufficient space and depth for skills practice and testing.

An adequate number of lifeguards with no duties other than supervising the class should be present during all water sessions.

Equipment and Supplies

At the beginning of each lesson is a list of required equipment and supplies. A master list of equipment for the course is found in Appendix G. Make sure all the equipment is ready and in working order before you teach the course.

All participants should have a copy of *Lifeguarding Today* (Stock No. 654110) and *CPR for the Professional Rescuer* (Stock No. 652048) participant's manual. The following videos are required for this course: *Lifeguarding Today* (Stock No. 654114), *CPR for the Professional Rescuer* (Stock No. 652051), and *Community First Aid* (Stock No. 652035).

Testing and Certificates

On successful completion of the course, participants receive two certificates: one for American Red Cross Lifeguard Training (Cert. 653460), which is valid for three years, and the second for American Red Cross CPR for the Professional Rescuer (Cert. 653214), which is valid for one year.

Note: The Lifeguard Training certificate includes certification in first aid.

To receive the two course completion certificates for the American Red Cross Lifeguard Training course, the participant must—

■ Demonstrate competency in each critical skill taught in the course. (See the Lifeguarding Skills Checklist, Appendix M and the Lifeguarding Critical Skills Chart, Appendix N. For more information on critical skills, see Chapter 3.)

■ Successfully complete the two final skills scenarios.

■ Correctly answer at least 80 percent of the written examination questions (for the Lifeguard Training exam, which includes questions on first aid, and for the CPR for the Professional Rescuer exam— 40 correct out of a total of 50 total questions for each exam).

For more information on awarding certificates, completing records, and conducting course evaluations, see Chapter 6.

Course Outlines

Lifeguard Training Course Outline

Precourse Session

Activity	Approximate Time
Introduction to Precourse Session	10 minutes
Verification of Age Prerequisite	5 minutes
Break	10 minutes
Prerequisite Swimming Skills Test	60 minutes
Closing	5 minutes
Counseling After Precourse Session	As needed
Precourse Session, Total Time	**1 hour, 30 minutes**

Lesson 1 — The Professional Lifeguard

Activity	Approximate Time
Introduction to the Course	15 minutes
Introduction to Lifeguarding	10 minutes
Characteristics of a Professional Lifeguard	10 minutes
Benefits of Regular Exercise	5 minutes
Appearance and Behavior	10 minutes
Responsibilities of a Professional Lifeguard	20 minutes
Professionalism	10 minutes
Interacting With the Public	20 minutes
The Safety Team	20 minutes
Responsibilities of Management	20 minutes
Prevention of Aquatic Injuries	10 minutes
Communication as an Injury Prevention Strategy	25 minutes
Closing	5 minutes
Lesson 1, Total Time	**3 hours**

Lesson 2 — Preventing Aquatic Injury

Activity	Approximate Time
Review of Previous Material	5 minutes
Patron Surveillance	55 minutes
Facility Surveillance	45 minutes
Basic Responsibilities of a Lifeguard in an Emergency	5 minutes
Emergency Action Plans	15 minutes
Contacting EMS	5 minutes
Communication	5 minutes
Break	10 minutes
In-Water Activity: Victim Recognition	30 minutes
Distressed Swimmer	(5 minutes)
Active Drowning Victim	(5 minutes)
Passive Drowning Victim	(5 minutes)
Surveillance	(15 minutes)
Closing	5 minutes
Lesson 2, Total Time	**3 hours**

Lesson 3 — CPR for the Professional Rescuer Part 1

Activity	Approximate Time
The Professional Rescuer	15 minutes
Review of Legal Considerations	5 minutes
Human Body Systems	15 minutes
Disease Transmission	10 minutes
Emergency Action Principles	15 minutes
Skill Practice: Primary Survey	25 minutes
Recognizing Breathing Emergencies	5 minutes
Caring for Breathing Emergencies	15 minutes
Skill Practice: Rescue Breathing (Adult, Child, Infant)	30 minutes
Airway Obstruction	10 minutes
Skill Practice: Obstructed Airway	30 minutes
Closing	5 minutes
Lesson 3, Total Time	**3 hours**

Lesson 4 — CPR for the Professional Rescuer Part II

Activity	Approximate Time
Airway Obstruction for Infants	10 minutes
Skill Practice: Obstructed Airway	30 minutes
Resuscitation Mask	10 minutes
Skill Practice: Resuscitation Mask	30 minutes
Bag-Valve-Mask Resuscitator (BVM)	10 minutes
Skill Practice: Bag-Valve Mask	30 minutes
Recognizing a Heart Attack	15 minutes
Cardiac Arrest	15 minutes
Skill Practice: Adult CPR	40 minutes
Closing	5 minutes
Lesson 4, Total Time	**3 hours, 15 minutes**

Lesson 5 — CPR for the Professional Rescuer Part III

Activity	Approximate Time
Child CPR	10 minutes
Skill Practice: Child CPR	15 minutes
Infant CPR	10 minutes
Skill Practice: Infant CPR	15 minutes
Two-Rescuer CPR	10 minutes
Skill Practice: Two-Rescuer CPR	35 minutes
Special Resuscitation Situations	20 minutes
Written Examination	45 minutes
Closing	5 minutes
Lesson 5, Total Time	**2 hours, 45 minutes**

Lesson 6 — Rescue Skills Part I

Activity	Approximate Time
Review of Previous Material	5 minutes
General Rescue Procedures	10 minutes
Use of the Rescue Tube	5 minutes
Rescue Skills	20 minutes
Break	10 minutes
Skill Practice: Getting To Know The Rescue Tube	35 minutes
Positioning the Rescue Tube	(5 minutes)
Entries	(15 minutes)
Approaches	(15 minutes)
Skill Practice: Rescue Skills	90 minutes
Extension Assist From the Deck	(10 minutes)
Swimming Extension Rescue	(15 minutes)
Active Victim Rear Rescue	(25 minutes)
Multiple-Victim Rescue	(20 minutes)
Passive Victim Rear Rescue	(20 minutes)
Closing	5 minutes
Lesson 6, Total Time	**3 hours**

Lesson 7 — Rescue Skills Part II

Activity	Approximate Time
Review of Previous Material	5 minutes
Rescue Skills	10 minutes
Break	10 minutes
Skill Practice: Rescue Skills	75 minutes
Feet-First Surface Dive	(15 minutes)
Submerged Victim Rescue	(35 minutes)
Removal From the Water	(25 minutes)
Skills Review	75 minutes
Review of Skills	(25 minutes)
Putting It All Together	(50 minutes)
Closing	5 minutes
Lesson 7, Total Time	**3 hours**

Lesson 8 — First Aid

Activity	Approximate Time
Injuries	5 minutes
Soft Tissue Injuries	10 minutes
Caring for Wounds	10 minutes
Skill Practice: Controlling Bleeding	20 minutes
Shock	5 minutes
Special Situations	5 minutes
Burns	10 minutes
Musculoskeletal Injuries	20 minutes
Skill Practice: Immobilizing Muscle, Bone, and Joint Injuries	35 minutes
Special Situations	10 minutes
Sudden Illness	30 minutes
Caring for Children	5 minutes
Caring for the Elderly	5 minutes
Putting It All Together	5 minutes
Closing	5 minutes
Lesson 8, Total Time	**3 hours**

Lesson 9 — Spinal Injury Management

Activity	Approximate Time
Overview	5 minutes
Anatomy and Function of the Spine	5 minutes
Recognizing Spinal Injury	10 minutes
Caring for Spinal Injury	30 minutes
Break	10 minutes
Skill Practice: In-Line Stabilization Techniques	50 minutes
Skill Practice: Using a Backboard (Shallow Water)	65 minutes
Closing	5 minutes
Lesson 9, Total Time	**3 hours**

Lesson 10 — After An Emergency

Activity	Approximate Time
Review of Previous Material	5 minutes
Responsibilities Related to the Facility	30 minutes
Responsibility to Yourself	15 minutes
Break	10 minutes
Putting It All Together—Shallow Water Spinal Injury Management Skills Review	20 minutes
Caring for Spinal Injury in Deep Water	5 minutes
Skill Practice: In-Line Stabilization Techniques (Deep Water)	30 minutes
Skill Practice: Using A Backboard (Deep Water)	60 minutes
Closing	5 minutes
Lesson 10, Total Time	**3 hours**

Lesson 11 — Final Written Exam and Final Skills Scenarios

Activity	Approximate Time
Review of Course Material	15 minutes
Final Written Exam	45 minutes
Break	10 minutes
Final Skills Scenarios	90 minutes
Break	10 minutes
Closing	10 minutes
Lesson 11, Total Time	**3 hours**

Precourse Session

Length:	1 1/2 hours
Equipment/Supplies:	Lifeguarding Skills Checklist (Appendix M); 10-pound object (a diving brick, a weight, or a diving belt with plastic coated weights), one per every five participants.
Goal:	To determine the eligibility of prospective participants to enroll in the Lifeguard Training course.

INTRODUCTION TO PRECOURSE SESSION

Time: 10 minutes

Activity:

Explain to prospective participants that this session is designed to evaluate their swimming skills. They have to successfully complete the following swimming prerequisites to enroll in the Lifeguard Training course:

1. Swim 500 hundred yards continuously, using each of the following strokes for at least 100 yards each:
   - Crawl stroke (commonly referred to as freestyle)
   - Breaststroke
   - Sidestroke

   Prospective participants choose their stroke(s) for the remaining 200 yards.

   Note: There is no time requirement for this skill. Prospective participants must show only that they can swim 500 yards using the above strokes without stopping, regardless of the amount of time it takes them to complete the swim.

2. Submerge to a minimum depth of 7 feet, retrieve a 10-pound object, and return with it to the surface.
3. Tread water for 2 minutes using legs only. Prospective participants cross their arms across their chest, placing the hands under the armpits.

These prerequisites determine whether prospective participants have the basic swimming abilities to complete the lifeguarding skills in the Lifeguard Training course.

VERIFICATION OF AGE PREREQUISITE

Time: 5 minutes

Activity:

Tell prospective participants that to enroll in the Lifeguard Training course they must be fifteen (15) years of age on or before the start of this precourse session.

Check the eligibility of each prospective participant to enroll in the course by checking their proof of age, which can be a driver's license, birth certificate, or passport.

If an individual does not meet the age requirement for enrollment into the course, suggest that the individual enroll in the next available lifeguard training course once he or she meets the age requirement or take the option of auditing the course without participating.

BREAK

Time: 10 minutes

Before having the prospective participants break to change into their swimsuits for the prerequisite swimming skills test, orient them to the locker rooms and the pool area where they are to meet.

PREREQUISITE SWIMMING SKILLS TEST

Time: 60 minutes

Activity:

Organize prospective participants for the prerequisite swimming skills test. Test each participant on the following skills. Participants must be able to demonstrate each skill satisfactorily in order to enroll in the course. Check the skills off on the Lifeguarding Skills Checklist (Appendix M) once they have completed them.

1. Swim 500 hundred yards continuously, using each of the following strokes for at least 100 yards each:
   - Crawl stroke
   - Breaststroke
   - Sidestroke

   Prospective participants choose their stroke(s) for the remaining 200 yards.

> **TEACHING TIP:**
>
> To maximize the time for this skill, divide the participants into groups and assign the groups to lanes. Have the groups circle swim. Tell them to keep to the right and remain in one lane as they turn and continue swimming.

2. Submerge to a minimum depth of 7 feet, retrieve a 10-pound object, and return with it to the surface.

Note: The 10-pound object can be a diving brick, a weight, or a diving belt with plastic coated weights.

3. Tread water for 2 minutes using legs only. Prospective participants cross their arms across their chest, placing the hands under the armpits.

With adequate practice and study, individuals who complete these prerequisite swimming skills should be able to successfully complete the Lifeguard Training course.

CLOSING

Time: 5 minutes

| **Activity:** | Respond to any questions from the participants. |
| **Assignment Prior to the First Class** | Read Chapters 1, 2, 3, and 4 in *Lifeguarding Today*. |

COUNSELING AFTER PRECOURSE SESSION

Time: As needed

On an individual basis, advise all participants that entry into the Lifeguard Training course is strictly limited to those who have successfully completed the swimming skills prerequisites. Not having the appropriate skill level could pose a safety threat to that participant and to others in the class.

For individuals who do not meet these prerequisites, suggest appropriate developmental training opportunities or the option to audit the class without participating. Indicate the specific skills that the individual needs to improve for the individual to be eligible to take the Lifeguard Training course in the future. Advise each individual as to the American Red Cross course appropriate for his or her level of skills. Direct individuals to contact their local unit of the American Red Cross for more information.

Lesson 1

The Professional Lifeguard

Class Assignment prior to this lesson: Read Chapters 1, 2, 3, and 4 of *Lifeguarding Today*.

Length: 3 hours

Equipment/Supplies: Name tags; course roster; course outline; participant's manuals; video — *Lifeguarding Today,* VCR and monitor; chalkboard or newsprint (flip chart); chalk or markers

Goal: Participants will become aware of the roles, characteristics, and responsibilities of a professional lifeguard and of guidelines for interacting with the public. In addition, participants will become familiar with the lifeguard's role in facility operations and aquatic injury prevention.

Objectives

After completing this lesson, participants should be able to—

1. List six characteristics of a professional lifeguard.
2. List six benefits of regular exercise.
3. List three reasons why a professional lifeguard's appearance and behavior are important.
4. List the five primary and the four secondary responsibilities of a professional lifeguard.
5. Describe six legal considerations that shape the role of the professional lifeguard.
6. Explain the importance of ongoing professional development for lifeguards.
7. Describe five benefits of being a professional lifeguard.
8. Describe four steps for responding to patrons' inquiries.
9. Describe seven steps for handling patrons' suggestions or concerns.
10. Describe what to do when a patron is uncooperative.
11. Describe four ways to help prevent and prepare for a violent situation.
12. List two aspects of cultural behavior relevant to lifeguarding situations.
13. Describe four ways to accommodate patrons with disabilities.
14. List three general categories of disabilities.
15. Describe the people who may be on a safety team.
16. List two ways in which a bystander can help in an emergency.
17. List two benefits of being part of a safety team.
18. Describe five responsibilities of management for ensuring the safety of everyone at a facility.
19. Explain the importance of three regulations that affect facility operations.
20. List three ways in which management can support lifeguards' professional development.

21. Describe the three strategies a lifeguard uses for preventing injuries.	23. Explain the four-step process for verbally communicating with patrons about risky behavior.
22. List the three parts of the communication strategy for injury control.	24. List at least three unsafe practices you should watch for and prohibit.

INTRODUCTION TO THE COURSE

Time: 15 Minutes

Activity:

Name Tags

Course Roster

Course Outline

1. **Instructor and Participant Introductions**
   - Introduce yourself and welcome participants to the American Red Cross Lifeguard Training course.
   - Have participants introduce themselves by sharing their names and their reasons for taking this course and their expectations. Name tags can be used.
   - Give a brief description of your background and credentials. Identify yourself as an American Red Cross instructor, and explain that this course is one of many offered by the American Red Cross. Ask the participants to write their full names and addresses on the course roster so that you can complete the *American Red Cross Course Record* (Form 6418 and 6418A).

2. **Orientation to the Location**
   - Point out the locations of fire exits, telephones, restrooms, and drinking fountains, and explain facility rules, if any.
   - Ask participants to wear comfortable clothing or a swimsuit that will enable them to participate in skill practice sessions.

3. **Course Schedule**
   - Distribute a course outline that includes dates and times of class meetings, lesson content, and class assignments.
   - Skill practice sessions and examinations should be clearly identified.

4. **Course Description**
   - Share the following goal statement with the class:

     The purpose of this course is—
     To teach lifeguards the skills and knowledge needed to prevent and respond to aquatic emergencies. The course content and activities will prepare you to recognize emergencies, respond quickly and effectively to emergencies, and

prevent drownings and other incidents. It also teaches you the other skills you need to become a professional lifeguard.

5. **How Participants Will Learn**
   ■ Briefly explain that participants will learn through lectures, discussions, reading, group activities, and skill practice. Some lessons are supported by audiovisual material, such as video segments.

6. **Participant's Manuals**

   ■ Identify the participant's manuals for this course, *American Red Cross Lifeguarding Today* and *American Red Cross CPR for the Professional Rescuer,* and lead the participants through them. Instruct the participants how best to use the manuals to master the course content. Point out the following features:

Lifeguarding Today	*CPR for the Professional Rescuer*
■ Objectives	■ Objectives
■ Key Terms	■ Key Terms
■ Sidebars	■ Main Ideas
■ Skill Summaries	■ Sidebars
■ Study Questions	■ Figures and Tables
■ Appendixes	■ Review Questions
■ Glossary	■ Skill Sheets
	■ Appendixes
	■ Glossary

The participant's manuals for this course are required reading.

7. **Course Completion Requirements**
   ■ Describe the American Red Cross requirements for successful course completion. To successfully complete this course, the participant must—
   ■ Correctly demonstrate the skills taught in the course.
   ■ Successfully complete the final skills scenarios.
   ■ Correctly answer at least 80 percent of the written examination questions (Lifeguard Training—40 correct out of a total of 50 questions and CPR for the Professional Rescuer—40 correct out of a total of 50 total questions).

Note: If there are academic requirements or state or local requirements beyond the minimum course completion requirements set by the American Red Cross, explain them to participants at this time.

INTRODUCTION TO LIFEGUARDING

Time: 10 minutes

Video:

Tell participants that you are going to show a short video segment of lifeguards talking about what it takes to be a lifeguard. Show the introductory video segment. (approx. 6 minutes)

Activity:

Ask participants to describe the image of the lifeguard commonly held by the public. Encourage a discussion on how that image may differ from a lifeguard's actual role and responsibilities as shown in the video segment.

CHARACTERISTICS OF A PROFESSIONAL LIFEGUARD

Time: 10 minutes

Primary Points:

Lifeguarding Today pages 5 & 6

Personal characteristics associated with a professional lifeguard include—
- Reliability.
- Maturity.
- Courtesy and consistency.
- Positive attitude.
- Health and fitness.

Activity:

Ask participants to give specific examples of why each of these characteristics is important for a professional lifeguard. These points and behaviors should be emphasized throughout the course.

BENEFITS OF REGULAR EXERCISE

Time: 5 minutes

Primary Points:

Lifeguarding Today pages 6 & 7

- Staying healthy and physically fit is part of being a professional lifeguard because it helps ensure the attentiveness, strength, and stamina necessary to prevent and respond to emergencies.
- Regular exercise improves your ability to—
  - Respond quickly to any situation.
  - Perform the most strenuous rescues.
  - Stay alert.
  - Cope with stress and fatigue.
  - Stay healthy.
  - Feel good.

APPEARANCE AND BEHAVIOR

Time: 10 minutes

Primary Points:

Lifeguarding Today
pages 9 & 10

- A lifeguard should have a professional appearance, because it—
  - Instills confidence in patrons, co-workers, and facility managers.
  - Reinforces facility rules by setting an example of proper behavior.
  - Reinforces the lifeguard's professional attitude.
- The image you project reflects your attitude and training. It also reflects on your facility.
- Some guidelines to help you look professional include—
  - Wear your uniform only during your lifeguarding shift.
  - Keep yourself well groomed.
  - Always keep your rescue equipment with you, positioned for immediate response.
  - Keep essential personal gear on or near you at all times.
  - Sit or stand erect at your lifeguarding station.
  - Keep interactions with others short.
  - Keep your eyes on your area of responsibility at all times.
  - Transfer equipment carefully.
  - Observe all facility rules and policies.
  - Eat only when on break or off duty.

RESPONSIBILITIES OF A PROFESSIONAL LIFEGUARD

Time: 20 minutes

Primary Points:

Lifeguarding Today
page 10

The primary responsibilities of the professional lifeguard include—
- Preventing injuries by minimizing or eliminating hazardous situations and behaviors.
- Enforcing all facility rules and regulations.
- Recognizing and responding quickly and effectively to all emergency situations.
- Administering first aid or CPR in an emergency.
- Informing other lifeguards and facility staff when more help or additional equipment is needed.

Activity:

Emphasize the primary responsibilities of a lifeguard. Ask participants to give examples of ways in which a lifeguard may display these five responsibilities.

Secondary Responsibilities

Primary Points:

Lifeguarding Today
page 11

Secondary responsibilities of professional lifeguards include—
- Educating patrons about facility rules and regulations.
- Helping patrons locate a missing person.
- Completing required records and reports on schedule and submitting them to the proper person or office.
- Doing maintenance or other tasks assigned by your supervisor.

Note: Perform your secondary responsibilities only when you are not responsible for patron surveillance.

Activity:

In addition to identifying primary and secondary responsibilities, have participants identify other responsibilities that a lifeguard may be asked to perform. List these responsibilities on the chalkboard or newsprint and discuss why these tasks should never prevent a lifeguard from meeting his or her primary responsibilities.

Legal Considerations

Primary Points:

Lifeguarding Today
pages 11 & 12

Legal considerations that shape the roles and responsibilities of a professional lifeguard include—
- Duty to act.
- Standard of care.
- Negligence.
- Good Samaritan laws.
- Consent.
- Refusal of care.
- Abandonment.
- Confidentiality.
- Record keeping.

Activity:

Review the meaning of each legal consideration and have participants discuss how each one could affect the role of a lifeguard. Discuss the following scenario:

> An 8-year-old child enters the water from a 1-meter board and swims to the bottom of the pool. She does not surface. A lifeguard makes a rescue and with the assistance of other lifeguards removes the child from the water. When she is on the pool deck, it becomes clear that the child is having a seizure. The lifeguards place her on her side to help keep her airway clear. Later she vomits but otherwise appears to be fine once the seizure has passed.
>
> The lifeguard did not immediately notify EMS personnel because he wanted to see first whether the child needed help. The camp

counselor who brought the child to the pool with a group now comes up to the lifeguard and says that the child is prone to seizures, but she appears to be alright now and the group is leaving. The counselor wants to take the child with the others, and you let her go.

The lifeguard failed to call 9–1–1 and then failed to advise the counselor that anyone who has a seizure in the water should be evaluated by more advanced medical personnel. Later that day, the child is hospitalized for complications from the near-drowning incident.

Ask the following questions with participants and discuss their answers:
- Did the lifeguard have a duty to act?
- Did the lifeguard abandon care of the child?
- Should the lifeguard keep a record of the incident? If so, why?
- Do you think the child's parents have grounds for legal action against the lifeguard or the facility? If so, why?
- If you were this lifeguard, what would you have done to avoid the possibility of legal action?

Note: Answers to these questions may vary. These questions are intended merely to get the participants thinking about how these legal considerations could affect a lifeguard.

PROFESSIONALISM

Time: 10 minutes

Primary Points:

Lifeguarding Today
pages 12 & 13

Staying Professional

Ongoing professional development is important for lifeguards, since it is a means of enhancing an individual's ability to prevent and respond to an emergency situation. You can take advantage of professional development opportunities by—
- Attending various aquatic and emergency response workshops.
- Becoming a member of an aquatic association.
- Reading related literature and periodicals.
- Attending in-service training sessions offered at your facility.
- Pursuing further training in aquatics or emergency response.

Benefits of Being a Professional Lifeguard

Primary Points:

Lifeguarding Today
page 13

The many benefits associated with being a professional lifeguard include—
- Knowing your actions can save a life.
- Being prepared to respond effectively to emergencies.
- Gaining discipline and decision-making skills that can remain with you for life.
- Earning the respect and appreciation of peers and patrons.
- Feeling good about yourself and your accomplishments.

INTERACTING WITH THE PUBLIC

Time: 20 minutes

Primary Points:

Lifeguarding Today
pages 18 & 19

The lifeguard must be able to respond to inquiries and handle suggestions and concerns. It is important to be courteous, but the specific way you respond to an inquiry or handle questions or concerns depends on your duties at the time. When interacting with a patron while you are conducting surveillance—
- Continue to scan your area of responsibility.
- Acknowledge the patron, quickly explaining that you cannot look at him or her while talking.
- Politely answer or instruct the patron, keeping the response brief.
- If you cannot answer in a few seconds or the patron needs more assistance, refer him or her to another staff member who is not engaged in surveillance.

Handling Suggestions and Concerns

Primary Points:

Lifeguarding Today
page 20

If you are not involved in surveillance, give the patron your full attention when handling suggestions and concerns. To do this, you should be polite, make eye contact while speaking, and—
- Listen attentively and without interruptions.
- Repeat the patron's suggestion or concern back to him or her to make sure you understand.
- Thank the patron for bringing the concern to your attention.
- If the concern alerts you to a dangerous situation, such as a broken ladder, try to remedy it or keep patrons from that area until a repair is made.
- Document the suggestion or concern as soon as possible.
- If necessary, ask someone on staff to follow up with the patron to let him or her know what is being done.

Activity:

1. Give the following scenario to the participants:

    It is a warm summer afternoon and you are one of three lifeguards on duty at a large outdoor facility. As the result of the good weather, many patrons are enjoying the pool. You are actively engaged in the surveillance of your assigned area.

    A patron approaches your lifeguard stand from the side and asks you about the Learn-to-Swim program offered at your facility in the morning.

2. Ask participants to explain how they would handle the situation. Answers will vary but should include the following points:
    - Acknowledge the patron.
    - Do not stop scanning your area of responsibility.
    - Let the patron know that you cannot look at him or her, but you are listening.
    - Continue to scan your area of responsibility while answering the patron's question.
    - Keep the response brief.
    - If you are unable to answer the question or if the patron needs more help, refer the patron to the head lifeguard, the facility manager, or another staff member on break.

Addressing Uncooperative Patrons

Primary Points:

Lifeguarding Today
page 20

When addressing uncooperative patrons, the lifeguard should remember the following points:
- Be certain that the patron is able to hear and understand what you are saying.
- Follow your facility's procedures for addressing uncooperative patrons.
- If necessary, contact the head lifeguard or facility manager for help as soon as possible.

Dealing With Violence

Primary Points:

Lifeguarding Today
pages 20 & 22

The potential for violence exists at any facility. To help prevent or prepare for a violent situation—
- Make sure everyone is aware of facility rules.
- Establish your authority at the facility.
- Know your patrons.
- Have a plan established to deal with violent incidents.
- If you suspect that a violent incident is about to happen, notify the head lifeguard or facility manager immediately.

Working With Diverse Cultures

Primary Points:

Lifeguarding Today
pages 22 & 23

While cultural background does not dictate an individual's aquatic ability, there are aspects of cultural behavior that may potentially influence a lifeguarding situation. These aspects include—

■ Dress—different cultures have different standards for what clothing and body coverage is appropriate. For example, some religions and cultures prohibit exposure of the body. Therefore, some patrons may come into a facility wearing long-sleeve shirts and trousers. On the other hand, certain cultures accept partial or total nudity or changing clothes in public view at aquatic facilities.

■ Communication—as a result of language differences, a patron may be unable to understand written rules or spoken directions from the lifeguard.

Accommodating Patrons With Disabilities

Primary Points:

Lifeguarding Today
page 23

Making facilities safe and accessible for people with disabilities may require you and your facility to make accommodations. Accommodations may include—

■ Policies.
■ Procedures.
■ Programs.
■ Facility features such as ramps, hand rails, and devices to get patrons in and out of the water.
■ Adapting rescue skills.
■ Special communication techniques.
■ Adjusting patron surveillance.

General Categories of Disabilities

Primary Points:

Lifeguarding Today
page 23–25

There are three general categories of disabilities. Patrons may be disabled in one or more of these areas:

Sensory Function—includes hearing, sight, and touch. Effects of impairment may include—

■ Difficulty communicating.
■ Balance problems.
■ Difficulty reading signs and markings.
■ Lack of sensation of touch or pain.

Mental Function—includes intelligence and the capacity to reason and process information. Effects of impairment may include—

■ Difficulty understanding and remembering rules.
■ Difficulty understanding explanations and directions.
■ Difficulty interacting with others.

Motor Function—involves the brain's ability to direct physical activity. Some conditions that inhibit motor function include—

- **Paralysis**—Permanent loss of feeling and movement.
- **Cerebral palsy**—A central nervous system dysfunction in which a person has little or no control of the muscles.
- **Muscular dystrophy**—A hereditary disease characterized by progressive deterioration of muscles, leading to disability, deformity, and loss of strength.
- **Multiple sclerosis**—A progressive disease characterized by patches of hardened tissue in the brain or spinal cord, which can result in muscle weakness, vision difficulties, slurring of words, and loss of bladder control.
- **Loss of a limb**—Missing or nonfunctioning arms or legs.

THE SAFETY TEAM

Time: 20 minutes

Primary Points:

Lifeguarding Today
page 30

The safety team is the network of people in the facility and the EMS system who can respond and assist in an emergency.

Members of the safety team may include—
- Lifeguards.
- Facility management.
- Staff members:
  - Swimming instructors.
  - Security guards.
  - Concession employees.
- Bystanders.
- EMS professionals:
  - Police.
  - Fire fighters.
  - Medical personnel.

Activity:

Ask participants to identify situations in which assistance from members of the safety team is crucial and explain how interaction between groups works in various situations. Encourage participants to think of other safety team members they can include besides lifeguards. The following are possible situations:

Situation	Other Possible Safety Team Members
Observing someone stealing another person's belongings	Facility manager, facility security guard, police
A patron is found unconscious in the locker room	Facility manager, maintenance or custodial personnel, bystanders, medical personnel
Crowd control during an emergency	Facility manager, cashier, staff members, bystanders

Bystander Assistance in an Emergency

Primary Points:

Lifeguarding Today page 32

Bystanders can help in an emergency situation by providing the lifeguard with valuable assistance. The bystander may:
- Assist with providing first aid and CPR (**Note**—*For safety, bystanders should not handle the victim if care for bleeding is required or if other bodily fluids are involved, but they could assist by getting first aid supplies*).
- Provide crowd control.
- Relay messages to other team members.
- Get equipment or supplies.
- Call for additional assistance.

Activity:

1. Ask participants to list possible bystander behaviors that would interfere with rescue efforts during an emergency (for example, crowding in on a lifeguard while he or she is giving care, becoming hysterical, upsetting others, or refusing to leave the water).
2. From the list provided, have participants develop ideas to help alleviate potential problems and encourage positive and helpful behavior from the bystander.
3. List behaviors or actions that a bystander could engage in to help the lifeguard, such as getting supplies, calling 9–1–1, providing information as a witness of an incident, or holding back other bystanders from crowding in during an emergency.

Benefits of Being Part of a Safety Team

Primary Points:

Lifeguarding Today page 32

As a lifeguard, there are benefits associated with being a member of a safety team. These include—
- Having backup, regardless of how difficult a situation may be.
- Enhancing safety through a cooperative effort.

■ Gaining greater opportunity for professionalism, friendship, team spirit, and fun by working with others.

RESPONSIBILITIES OF MANAGEMENT

Time: 20 minutes

Primary Points:

Lifeguarding Today
pages 21 28

Management is responsible for ensuring the safety of everyone at a facility. Specific areas of responsibility include—

■ Warning patrons and staff about actual and potential dangers. This is done by—
  ■ Posting warning signs, such as "No Diving."
  ■ Providing safe facility design, such as depth markings.
  ■ Outlining rules for facility use.
  ■ Providing staff with written and verbal information.
  ■ Supplying staff with protective equipment.
■ Addressing unsafe conditions such as—
  ■ Physical hazards:
    ■ Hole in a fence.
    ■ Broken ladders.
    ■ Broken glass.
    ■ Loose or missing tiles.
  ■ Chemical hazards:
    ■ Chemicals used to disinfect and clarify the pool water.
    ■ Pesticides.
    ■ Office supplies.
■ Complying with all federal, state, and local regulations by —
  ■ Providing the Hazard Communication Standard, which specifies management's responsibilities to—
    ■ Prevent illness and injury as a result of exposure to hazardous chemicals.
    ■ Provide employees with information about chemicals present in the workplace to which they may be exposed.
    ■ Maintain a file of information on all chemicals at the facility.
  ■ Providing information about the Bloodborne Pathogens Standard
  ■ Protecting the civil rights of patrons and employees.
■ Keeping records on facility operations and employees, including—
  ■ Employee schedules and time sheets.
  ■ Health, sanitation, and maintenance records.
  ■ Daily attendance logs.

- In-service training records.
- Water conditions.
- Incident and injury reports.
- Assisting after an emergency by—
  - Closing and reopening the pool.
  - Interacting with the media.
  - Coordinating reporting procedures.
  - Helping with stress-related problems.

Complying With Regulations

Primary Points:

Lifeguarding Today
pages 36 & 37

Federal regulations may affect facility operations and the job of a lifeguard. These include—

- **The Hazard Communication Standard**. This regulation requires employers to provide employees with the following information:
  - Which hazardous chemicals are present in the facility
  - Where those chemicals are located within the facility
  - What specific dangers these chemicals pose
  - How to identify chemical hazards in the facility
  - How to protect them and others from being exposed to hazardous chemicals
  - What to do if they and others are exposed to such hazards
- **Bloodborne Pathogens Standard**. This regulation was developed to reduce the risk of disease transmission.
  - This standard helps protect you from contact with bodily fluids that might contain bloodborne pathogens.
  - Management must help protect you from being exposed to pathogens in and around the facility by providing you with protective equipment. They must also provide you with training to let you know what to do if exposure occurs.
- **Civil Rights Laws**. These laws protect your civil rights, as well as those of patrons.
  - **Americans with Disabilities Act**. This act requires that people with disabilities have access to many kinds of opportunities and services.
  - **Equal Employment Opportunity Commission (EEOC)**. The commission's policies require that management recruit, hire, and treat employees fairly and impartially.

Activity:

1. Ask participants to identify situations in which lifeguards might encounter bloodborne pathogens.
2. Ask participants to identify how a lifeguard might be exposed to dangerous chemicals.

Supporting Lifeguard Professional Development

Lifeguarding Today
pages 38–40

Management has a role in supporting the professional development of lifeguards. This support may be provided through the following:

■ A policy and procedures manual
■ Orientation and in-service training at the facility
■ Support after an emergency
■ Opportunities for training in areas beyond the lifeguard's everyday duties
■ Opportunities for recognition

PREVENTION OF AQUATIC INJURIES

Time: 10 minutes

Primary Points:

Lifeguarding Today
page 44

■ Aquatic injury prevention is a part of your facility's risk management program.
■ Risk management is identifying, eliminating, or managing all dangerous conditions that can cause injuries and result in financial loss.
■ An injury is physical harm caused when the body is subjected to an external force.
■ Understanding how injuries are caused helps you know how to prevent them by—
  ■ Increasing your awareness of risks and hazards.
  ■ Helping patrons avoid risky behaviors.
  ■ Developing an attitude of safety at your facility.
■ Evidence shows that most injuries can be prevented.
■ The two most serious injuries you want to prevent are drowning and spinal injuries.
■ Drowning occurs when a person suffocates while in the water.
■ Most diving-related spinal injuries occur in shallow water (usually in 5 feet of water or less).

COMMUNICATION AS AN INJURY PREVENTION STRATEGY

Time: 25 minutes

Primary Points:

Lifeguarding Today
page 46

Communication as an injury prevention strategy has three aspects:
■ Informing patrons about the potential for injury
■ Educating patrons about the consequences of inappropriate behavior
■ Enforcing rules and regulations that prevent injury

Informing Patrons About the Potential for Injury

Primary Points:

Lifeguarding Today
pages 46–50

- Patrons are informed about risks that could cause injury by signs that state warnings, tell how to use equipment, or list rules and regulations.
- Safety signs and rules should be placed at appropriate locations around the facility.
- The signs should be easy to understand and should include pictures, when possible.
- Signs should be easily visible.
- Health Department Regulations
  - Health regulations can help prevent injuries and disease transmission by setting standards for pool design, construction, operation, maintenance, and management. The following are typical rules established by health departments or other local agencies:
    - Patrons must shower with soap before entering the water and wash their hands with soap after using the rest room.
    - Swimming caps are required.
    - Spitting, spouting water, and blowing one's nose in the water are not allowed.
    - Food, drinks, and smoking are allowed only in designated areas.
    - Pets are not allowed in the facility.
    - Street shoes and clothing are not allowed on the deck.
    - No more than the maximum number of patrons are allowed in the facility at one time.
    - Swimmers must wear appropriate swimming attire.
    - First aid equipment can be used only by authorized personnel.
- Facility Rules and Regulations
  - Rules are designed for the health and safety of patrons and facility staff.
  - General rules of conduct give patrons guidelines for how to behave and can help them enjoy the facility without endangering themselves or others.
  - These rules should be posted in plain view inside the facility and at its entrance so that you and your patrons can refer to them easily.
- Equipment and Structures
  - Additional rules govern the use of specific equipment and structures.

- These rules include governance of diving boards, towers, and water slides.

Discussion of the rules a facility might have.
1. Divide the participants into three groups.
2. Have participants refer to page 11 of *Lifeguarding Today* for the listing of typical facility rules.
3. Assign each group four rules from this list.
4. Have each group come up with the purpose of each of these rules and how they would enforce them.
5. Have each group identify a leader to report their results back to the class.
6. Reassemble the class after about 5 minutes. Have each group's leader present their results.

Educating Patrons About the Consequences of Inappropriate Behavior

Primary Points:

Lifeguarding Today
page 50

- Patrons arriving at a facility may at first be unfamiliar with some of its features or just excited to be there. They may not read signs or pay attention to rules.
- The following is a quick four-step process to prevent a patron from engaging in risky behavior:
  1. Get the patron's attention by alerting him or her to the hazard.
  2. Explain what the hazard or danger is.
  3. Explain how the patron might be injured.
  4. Say what to do to avoid being injured.

Enforcing Rules and Regulations

Primary Points:

Lifeguarding Today
page 50

- Enforcing rules helps prevent injuries and will lead to safer attitudes among patrons.
- Be consistent and fair.
- Use a method in accordance with facility policies.
- Have repeat offenders (children) sit out of the water for a set time.
- Have off-duty lifeguards read and explain the rules to children who repeatedly break them.
- Avoid arguing with adults, but make your point clearly.
- Call the facility manager or head lifeguard to help with situations involving adults.
- Treat teenagers and adults with respect.
- If someone keeps breaking the rules, you may have to expel the person.
- Law enforcement personnel may need to be called in some circumstances.

CLOSING

Time: 5 minutes

Activity:

1. Respond to any questions from the participants.
2. Tell participants to bring their swimsuits to the next class session.

Assignment:

Read Chapters 5 and 6 of *Lifeguarding Today,* and complete the study questions at the end of each chapter.

Lesson 2

Preventing Aquatic Injury

Class Assignment prior to this lesson: Read Chapters 5, 6, and 7 of *Lifeguarding Today.*

Length: 3 hours

Equipment/Supplies: Video —*Lifeguarding Today;* VCR and monitor; Facility Floor Plans (Appendix J); Facility Safety Checklist (Appendix K); chalkboard or newsprint (flip chart), chalk or markers

Goal: Participants will become familiar with the surveillance techniques a lifeguard is required to have and how these techniques can help prevent injury at the facility. Participants will also become familiar with the function of an emergency action plan and how to take appropriate action in an emergency.

Objectives

After completing this lessson, participants should be able to—

1. Explain the four elements of effective surveillance.

2. Describe four behaviors to watch for that indicate a swimmer is in distress or is drowning.

3. Describe the characteristics of a distressed swimmer.

4. Describe four characteristics of the instinctive drowning response.

5. Describe the characteristics of a passive drowning victim.

6. List at least four possible causes of passive drowning.

7. Explain how hyperventilation can affect the drowning process.

8. Explain how to prevent hyperthermia.

9. List the three elements of the RID factor as a cause of drowning.

10. Describe four factors that can influence effective scanning.

11. Describe how to relieve a lifeguard at a ground-level station and at an elevated station.

12. Explain total coverage and zone coverage.

13. Explain at least five ways for improving surveillance at competitive events and instructional/therapeutic activities.

14. Explain the three-part safety check used for facility surveillance.

15. Describe the five areas of the facility that must be regularly inspected for safety.

16. List the types and causes of injuries that can occur in the four areas of the pool environment.

17. Explain the guideline for determining when to allow patrons to return to the water after a thunderstorm.
18. Explain what an emergency action plan is.
19. Describe the lifeguard's four basic responsibilities in an emergency.
20. Describe at least seven situations in which EMS should be contacted.
21. Describe the five steps involved in calling EMS.
22. Describe three types of communication often used at aquatic facilities.

REVIEW OF PREVIOUS MATERIAL

Time: 5 minutes

Primary Points:

Review

■ Being a professional lifeguard means being fully prepared for this challenging and important work.
■ Some characteristics of a lifeguard include—
  ■ Reliability.
  ■ Maturity.
  ■ Courtesy and consistency.
  ■ Positive attitude
  ■ Health and fitness.
  ■ Good grooming.
■ When interacting with patrons, always be positive and courteous.
■ The operation of a safe and healthful facility is a team effort.
■ Other people can help support you in your role as a lifeguard. These people include professionals and bystanders, both inside and outside the facility.

PATRON SURVEILLANCE

Time: 55 minutes

Video:

Show the video segment: "Patron Surveillance." (approx. 18 minutes)

Primary Points:

Lifeguarding Today page 54

The most important responsibility for a lifeguard is patron surveillance. Patron surveillance requires a lifeguard to maintain a close watch over patrons using a facility.
■ Effective surveillance has four elements:
  ■ Recognizing how distressed swimmers and drowning persons behave

- Using appropriate scanning techniques to identify patrons in trouble in the water
- Proper stationing of lifeguards
- Knowing your area of responsibility

Victim Recognition

Primary Points:

Lifeguarding Today
page 55

- The four behaviors to watch for that indicate a swimmer is in distress or is drowning are—
  - Breathing.
  - Arm and leg action.
  - Body position.
  - Locomotion—whether the patron is making progress in the water.

Characteristics of a Distressed Swimmer

Primary Points:

Lifeguarding Today
page 55, Table 5.1;
page 56

For a variety of reasons, such as exhaustion, cramp, or sudden illness, a swimmer can become distressed.

- The characteristics of a distressed swimmer include—
  - The ability to continue breathing and call for help.
  - The ability to float, scull, or tread water; the ability to wave for help.
  - A horizontal, vertical, or diagonal body position, depending on the means of support.
  - Little or no forward progress.
- If a distressed swimmer is not rescued, he or she can become an active drowning victim.

Characteristics of an Active Drowning Victim

Primary Points:

Lifeguarding Today
page 55, Table 5.1;
pages 56 & 57

The instinctive drowning response is the universal behavior that an active drowning victim exhibits.

- The instinctive drowning response has four characteristics. An active drowning person—
  - Struggles to breathe and cannot call out for help.
  - Extends arms to the sides, pressing down; and has no supporting kick.
  - Has a vertical body position in the water.
  - Has no forward movement, and struggles 20–60 seconds before submerging.

Characteristics of a Passive Drowning Victim

A passive drowning victim is a face-down unconscious victim who is submerged or is at or near the surface of the water.

Lifeguarding Today page 55, Table 5.1; pages 58 & 59

■ A passive drowning can occur from a variety of conditions such as—
  ■ A heart attack or stroke.
  ■ A seizure.
  ■ A head injury.
  ■ Hyperventilation
    ▪ Hyperventilation is the act of taking deep breaths in rapid succession and forcefully exhaling in order to swim long distances underwater.
    ▪ This practice lowers the carbon dioxide level in the body. The level of carbon dioxide in the body signals the body to breathe.
    ▪ With decreased carbon dioxide in the body, the blood vessels in the brain constrict, decreasing blood flow, which can cause dizziness, unconsciousness, and possibly seizures.
  ■ Hyperthermia
    ▪ Hyperthermia is more likely to occur at facilities that have spas.
    ▪ A person's body core temperature becomes higher than normal.
    ▪ Higher body temperature causes a person to become weak, dizzy, and sometimes become confused or unconscious.
  ■ Use of alcohol or drugs.
■ The characteristics of a passive drowning victim include—
  ■ No breathing.
  ■ No arm or leg action.
  ■ A face-down body position, either submerged or at the surface.
  ■ No locomotion.

Activity:

1. Ask participants to discuss the difference between a distressed swimmer and an active drowning victim. Answers may differ but should include the differences in breathing, arm and leg actions, body position in the water, and locomotion (Table 2–1).

Table 2–1 *Characteristics of Distressed Swimmers and Drowning Victims Compared to Swimmers*

Behaviors	Swimmer	Distressed Swimmer	Active Drowning Victim	Passive Drowning Victim
Breathing	Rhythmic breathing	Can continue breathing and call for help	Struggles to breathe; cannot call out for help	Not breathing
Arm and Leg Action	Relatively coordinated movement	Floating, sculling, or treading water; can wave for help	Arms to sides, pressing down; no supporting kick	None
Body Position	Horizontal	Horizontal, vertical, or diagonal, depending on means of support	Vertical	Face-down submerged or near surface
Locomotion	Recognizable progress	Little or no forward progress; less and less able to support self	None; has only 20–60 seconds before submerging	None

The RID Factor as a Cause of Drowning

Primary Points:

Lifeguarding Today pages 61 & 62

Swimming-related drownings (distressed swimmer and active drowning victims) in areas where lifeguards are on duty result from three causes, summarized as the RID factor:

- **Recognition**
  - The failure of the lifeguard to recognize the instinctive drowning response or a swimmer who is in distress
- **Intrusion**
  - Performing secondary duties instead of the lifeguard's primary responsibility of patron surveillance
    - Secondary duties include maintenance or recreational functions, such as sweeping the deck or coaching swimmers
- **Distraction**
  - Behavior that affects the lifeguard's ability to properly supervise patrons, such as prolonged observation of troublemakers or talking with other lifeguards and patrons

Drowning may result from any one element of the RID factor or a combination of them.

Proper Scanning

Primary Points:

Lifeguarding Today
pages 62–65

Scanning is a visual technique used by lifeguards to properly observe and monitor patrons participating in water activities.

- When scanning, you want to—
  - Look for signals that indicate a person needs help.
  - Use peripheral vision to detect the characteristics of distressed swimmers and drowning victims.
  - Use frontal vision to closely examine a person's behavior.
  - Limit your scanning to a defined area of responsibility.
  - Scan back and forth from point to point, rapidly glancing at all movements of the people in your area.
  - Be aware of conditions that affect visibility when scanning, such as blind spots and glare off the water's surface.
- The effectiveness of scanning can be influenced by—
  - The type and location of lifeguard stations.
  - Your area of responsibility.
  - Fatigue.
  - The variety of patrons to be monitored.

Lifeguard Stations

Primary Points:

Lifeguarding Today
pages 65–68

A lifeguard can supervise patrons from lifeguard stands or from the deck.

- **Elevated stations**
  - A lifeguard stand can provide a lifeguard with an excellent position from which to scan his or her area of responsibility.
- **Ground-level stations**
  - The purpose of a ground-level station is to have the lifeguard close to patrons.
  - A ground-level station may be a walking patrol, a fixed location on deck, or a station in the water near a play structure.
- **Lifeguard rotations**
  - Periodic rotations from one station to another, plus relief breaks, help keep a lifeguard alert during surveillance.
  - To relieve a lifeguard at an elevated station—
    - Take a position next to the stand, and begin scanning the area of responsibility. Signal the other lifeguard to come down.
    - Once on deck, the lifeguard takes a position next to the stand and resumes surveillance.
    - Climb up in the stand and establish a scanning pattern. Signal the outgoing lifeguard to leave.
  - To relieve a lifeguard at a ground-level station—
    - Walk to the side of the lifeguard to be relieved, and begin scanning.

- Establish a scanning pattern, and signal the outgoing lifeguard to leave.

Note: These rotation examples assume that both lifeguards have rescue equipment. If only one lifeguard has rescue equipment, the following procedure should be used:
- *The incoming lifeguard assumes a scanning position.*
- *The lifeguard who is being relieved passes the rescue equipment to the incoming lifeguard and prepares to come down off the stand and assume a scanning position.*
- *The rotation is complete when the incoming lifeguard is in position and is scanning the pool.*

Area of Responsibility

Primary Points:

Lifeguarding Today
page 68

The head lifeguard or the facility manager establishes a lifeguard's area of responsibility. This area of responsibility may include total coverage or zone coverage.
- **Total coverage**
  - Used at single-lifeguard facilities
  - Only one lifeguard with small number of patrons and swimmers present
  - Lifeguard scans entire area of the facility
- **Zone coverage**
  - A facility is divided into separate areas of responsibility (zones) for each lifeguard station.
  - Areas may be designated by ladders, lane lines, lifelines, visual markers, or by the shape of pool.
  - Zones should overlap each other.

Identifying Zones

Activity:

Facility Floor Plans,
Lifeguarding IM
Appendix J

1. Divide participants into groups of four.
2. Pass out one copy of a floor plan to each group.
3. Designate the number of lifeguards available for that facility (2, 3, 4, 5, etc.).
4. Have participants identify the location of each lifeguard and the lifeguard's zone of coverage.
5. Have participants identify hazardous areas within each zone.
6. Have each group explain why it positioned the lifeguards in the locations identified and why it decided on the zone assigned to each lifeguard.
7. Compare all plans and discuss differences and similarities.

Surveillance During Special Activities

Special activities include competitive events, such as swim meets, and instructional/therapeutic activities, such as exercise programs.

Primary Points:

Lifeguarding Today
page 69

- To effectively provide surveillance for competitive events, a lifeguard should—
  - Be familiar with the rules and regulations for the events to be guarded.
  - Plan rescues before an incident occurs.
  - Have swimmers follow rules set for lane activity.
- To effectively provide surveillance for instructional/therapeutic activities, the following points need to be considered—
  - Different precautions may be necessary depending on the age and abilities of participants.
  - Infants and children must be accompanied and watched by a parent.
  - Patrons may become nauseated and fatigued during exercise programs.

Activity:

1. Ask participants to identify special work conditions that would be present during a special event, such as a competitive swim meet.
2. Ask participants why it is important that a lifeguard be present during—
   - Instructional activities.
   - Therapeutic activities.

FACILITY SURVEILLANCE

Time: 45 minutes

Primary Points:

Lifeguarding Today
page 74

- Facility surveillance is a method of preventing injuries caused by hazards in the facility environment.
- One way to prevent injuries is to eliminate as many hazards at the facility as possible and to minimize any unavoidable hazards.

Safety Checks

Primary Points:

Lifeguarding Today
pages 74 & 75

The safety check is your primary method of facility surveillance.

- When you find an unsafe condition, if possible, correct it before the facility opens.
- If the hazard involves moveable equipment, remove the piece of equipment.

- If the condition is serious, you may have to close the pool or keep patrons away from the area.
- There are three safety checks that can be completed during the day.

  1. Opening Safety Check (before facility opens)
  - Walk around the entire area to make sure all safety equipment is properly placed and in working order.
  - Check the following equipment:
    - Rescue tubes
    - Backboards, including straps and head immobilizers
    - First aid station
    - Telephones
    - Lights
    - Public address system
    - Deck, pool, locker rooms

  2. On-Duty Safety Checks (during the day)
  - Make sure your surveillance area is covered.
  - Conduct ongoing checks of the facility for hazards. This may include checking showers, changing areas, deck, and swimming areas.
  - Check for objects such as food, soda cans, or other debris that may accumulate in the pool area.
  - Monitor weather conditions.

  3. Closing Safety Check (end of the day)
  - Make sure no one is in the pool or anywhere else in the facility.
  - Check—
    - Pool.
    - Locker room.
    - Shower area.
    - Playground.
    - Eating areas.
  - After the closing inspection, complete the daily log.
    - Identify that the area is clear and you have made the safety check.
    - Record what steps were taken to correct unsafe conditions.
    - Sign the log.

Specific Areas To Inspect for Safety

There are five areas of the facility with which you are concerned:

- **Area 1: The Deck**
  - Begin your safety check with the deck.
  - Three main potential hazards are—
    - Entrance areas.
    - Flooring materials.
    - Deck obstructions.
  - Check for loose and broken tiles and slippery surfaces.
  - Keep decks clear of equipment, personal belongings, or other material that could create a hazardous area.
- **Area 2: The Pool**
  - Your safety check of the pool will include the following items:
    - Ladders and steps—Make sure they are secured properly and that the steps are not chipped.
    - Drain covers—Check to see that they are firmly secured.
    - Lifeline(s)—Check to see that lifelines are tight enough to support an adult.
      Also check that the floats are visible and no more than a few feet apart.
    - Water clarity—The water should be clear. The main drain should be visible from the deck.
    - Water temperature—Check that the water is within the proper range for the population using the pool.
      - Warmer water is more enjoyable and less hazardous to patrons
      - Patrons may develop hypothermia in colder water or hyperthermia in a spa.
- **Area 3: Recreational Equipment**
  - Your safety check of recreational equipment will include a check of the following items:
    - Diving boards—Check to see that steps or stairs are secure and not slippery. Also check to see that—
      - Railings are secure and have no sharp edges.
      - The board does not have algae or any bare spots.
      - There are no loose bolts.
      - No cracks exist on the board.
      - The fulcrum is in good working order (movable fulcrums).
    - Starting blocks—Check to see that they are secure. "No diving" signs, cones, or covers should be placed on permanent starting blocks when they are not being used under the direct supervision of an instructor or diving coach.

- Play structures—Use the guidelines supplied by the manufacturer when checking play structures. These guidelines may include checking—
  - All nonmoving parts of permanent play structures.
  - Ladders, frames, and platforms for loose bolts or connections.
  - That inflatable structures have correct air pressure.
- Water slides—Check to see that joints have no gaps, cracks, or sharp edges. Also check to see that sufficient water keeps the surface of the slide wet. For removable slides, check to see that the water depth is sufficient.

■ **Area 4: Chemical Storage Areas**
- Do not enter such areas unless you have the special training required.
- Make sure doors are locked.
- Report any suspicious odors immediately.

■ **Area 5: Showers, Locker Rooms, and Restrooms**
- Check to make sure all areas are clean and hazard free.

Safety Check

Activity:

Facility Safety Checklist, *Lifeguarding IM* Appendix K

1. Divide participants into groups of four.
2. Provide each group with a safety checklist.
3. Assign each group a section on the facility safety checklist they are to inspect. These sections include: deck; pool; recreational equipment and play structures; and showers, locker rooms, and rest rooms. (For the safety of the participants, the section on chemical storage is not assigned.)
4. Have participants perform a safety check on the aquatic facility at which this course is being taught.
5. Allow 10 minutes for the groups to perform their inspection of their section of the facility.
6. After 10 minutes, reassemble the groups and have each group present the results of its section of the checklist.
7. Discuss each section with input from all groups.

Incident and Injury Chart

Primary Points:

Lifeguarding Today pages 83 & 84

- The incident and injury chart can be used to help facility management prevent injury by indicating on a diagram where injuries occur at a facility.
- The information that the incident and injury chart provides can help management prevent future injuries by identifying trouble areas in the facility. Management than corrects the condition by—
  - Necessary maintenance.

- Installing safety equipment.
- Scheduling extra lifeguards.
- Reassigning lifeguards for better supervision.
- Taking other necessary steps.

Weather Conditions

Primary Points:

Lifeguarding Today
pages 84–86

Weather conditions can affect the safety of swimmers in all facilities. Since weather conditions vary throughout the country, you should know what conditions to look for at your facility and follow your facility's guidelines for inclement weather.

The following is basic information about weather conditions:

- **Cloud formations**
  - Clouds high and hazy usually indicate that a storm may arrive within hours.
  - Large clouds with cauliflower-like tops signal an imminent thunderstorm.
  - Rolling, dark clouds indicate that bad weather may arrive.
  - Fleecy white clouds indicate that good weather is approaching.
- **Lightning**
  - Lightning kills more people in this country than do tornadoes, floods, or hurricanes.
  - Storms with lightning often occur during July and August.
  - There are no set rules for when you should clear patrons from water because of an impending storm, but a generally safe practice is to clear the water at the first sound of thunder.
    - Your facility may have guidelines for responding to thunder and lightning.
  - Keep everyone away from windows.
  - Do not allow anyone to take a shower during a thunderstorm. Water and metal can conduct the electricity of lightning.
  - Do not use the telephone except for emergencies.
  - Keep away from tall isolated trees or objects.
- **Heavy rain and hail**
  - Heavy rain and hail can be dangerous, since it can prevent a lifeguard from seeing the bottom of the pool.
  - Clear patrons from the water and take shelter.
- **Tornadoes**
  - A "tornado watch" indicates that tornadoes are possible.
  - A "tornado warning" means that a tornado has been sighted and everyone should take shelter immediately.

- **High wind**
  - High wind can produce wave action that reduces visibility.
  - Increases chances of hypothermia, especially for children and the elderly.
- **Fog**
  - Fog can occur anytime as a result of special weather conditions, such as a cold front.
  - You may have to close the facility.
- **Weather conditions and indoor facilities**
  - Indoor facilities are safe from most weather problems; however, they may still be affected by some weather conditions, such as lightning and power failure.
  - Every facility should have some type of portable or emergency lighting equipment.

Activity:

Ask participants to identify weather hazards that might prompt closing the facility. List responses on newsprint or chalkboard.

BASIC RESPONSIBILITIES OF A LIFEGUARD IN AN EMERGENCY

Time: 5 minutes

Primary Points:

Lifeguarding Today
page 90

A lifeguard has four basic responsibilities in an emergency:
- To keep patrons safe by ensuring all zones are covered at all times
- To rescue and give first aid or CPR to a victim, or help another lifeguard provide care
- To make sure EMS is called when necessary
- To ensure the victim gets the best possible care until EMS arrives, then help EMS personnel as needed

EMERGENCY ACTION PLANS

Time: 15 minutes

Primary Points:

Lifeguarding Today
page 90

Emergency action plans are written plans that detail how staff and management should respond in an emergency.
- Emergency action plans are usually developed by facility management and sometimes by the head lifeguard, often with input from appropriate outside agencies, such as police and fire departments.
- Large facilities may have several plans, each one for a specific emergency.
- Small facilities may have only a few plans that cover many situations.

- Plans vary among facilities because of different local rules and ordinances.
- Lifeguards should practice plans during in-service training.
- Lifeguards should know what the emergency plan(s) are for their facility before they begin their first shift as a lifeguard.
- If the facility does not have a plan, the lifeguard can offer to help develop one.

Features of an Emergency Action Plan

An emergency action plan should cover—
- What all staff should do in emergency.
- When to call EMS and what to say.
- First aid procedures.
- Communications systems used at the facility.
- Reports to be filled out after the emergency.
- How to work with the public and the media after an emergency and who is the designated spokesperson for the facility.

Plans may also include—
- A floor plan of the facility showing hazardous areas.
- Equipment—what is used, where it is, whom to tell about needed repairs, and what has to be in place to reopen the water area if it has been cleared.

The Lifeguard's Initial Actions in an Emergency

- Recognize an emergency has occurred.
- If more than one lifeguard is in the facility, signal other lifeguards to cover for you.
- When you leave your station, your zone must be covered by other lifeguards.
- Backup coverage should be planned for the facility depending on its size, shape, and staffing.
- Check that the scene is safe to enter.
- Reach the victim and assess the victim's condition. If the victim is unconscious or has been submerged, signal for EMS to be called, or if the victim is conscious, bring the victim to safety and have someone call EMS.
- If the victim's condition is life-threatening, give necessary care and call EMS immediately, if someone has not already called.
- If victim's condition is not life-threatening, give necessary care.

■ **Primary Points:**

Lifeguarding Today
page 91

■ **Primary Points:**

Lifeguarding Today
pages 91–93

The Single Lifeguard Facility

Primary Points:

Lifeguarding Today
pages 93–96

Effective communication and education of patrons is especially important in the event of an emergency. The following is an emergency action plan for a single-lifeguard facility:

■ Lifeguard recognizes that person needs help and acts.
■ Lifeguard contacts victim and moves victim to safety.
■ Lifeguard assesses victim's condition. If victim is unconscious or not breathing, call EMS and provide necessary care.
■ Chain of command is notified.
■ Witnesses are interviewed.
■ The lifeguard completes an incident report.
■ Equipment is checked.
■ Staff discussion of the incident.
■ Any appropriate corrective action is taken by the facility management and the lifeguard.

Activity:

Lifeguarding Today
pages 94 & 95

Review the three flow charts in the *Lifeguarding Today* participant's manual showing emergency action plans for single-lifeguard, two-lifeguard, and multi-lifeguard facilities.

On newsprint or chalkboard, write the following headings: single-lifeguard, two-lifeguard, and multi-lifeguard. Have participants note the areas in which the three plans differ from each other. List these differences under the appropriate heading.

CONTACTING EMS

Time: 5 minutes

Primary Points:

Lifeguarding Today
pages 96 & 97

■ The telephone number for EMS and the information the dispatcher will need should be posted next to every telephone in the facility.
■ EMS must be called if the victim—
  ■ Is unconscious.
  ■ Has a head injury.
  ■ Is bleeding severely.
  ■ Has an obstructed airway.
  ■ Has had a seizure in the water or under other circumstances requiring EMS to be called as described in Chapter 10 of *Lifeguarding Today.*
  ■ Has critical burns.
  ■ Has a suspected fracture.
  ■ Has a suspected spinal injury.
  ■ Has a certain or suspected sudden illness as described in Chapter 10 of *Lifeguarding Today.*

■ EMS should be called for any near-drowning victim or any victim who has received rescue breathing or CPR regardless of how well the victim appears to have recovered. Otherwise, if the victim's condition is not life-threatening, the lifeguard caring for the victim can decide whether the victim's condition warrants calling EMS.

The steps for calling EMS—
1. Call the emergency number (9–1–1 in most areas).
2. Give the dispatcher the necessary information.
3. Describe who will be meeting EMS personnel and where they will meet.
4. Do not hang up until the dispatcher hangs up.
5. Return and report to the lifeguard caring for the victim.

COMMUNICATION

Time: 5 minutes

Primary Points:

Lifeguarding Today pages 97–100

Every facility has a communications system that all staff must use. Signals vary among facilities, although certain ones are common. Methods of communication include the use of—
■ **Whistles.** Commonly used whistle signals are—
  ■ One short blast to get the attention of a swimmer.
  ■ Two short blasts to get the attention of another staff member.
  ■ Three short blasts to activate the emergency action plan.
  ■ One long blast to clear the water.
■ **Hand signals.** These signals are often used in conjunction with whistle signals. Commonly used hand signals are—
  ■ Pointing directly at an individual to get his or her attention.
  ■ Holding one arm straight out palm facing the individual to tell someone to stop or stay in place.
  ■ Hand with fist held high indicates assistance is needed.
  ■ Placing hand on top of head and patting twice indicates "cover my area."
  ■ Placing hand on head or showing thumbs up or giving the OK sign indicates situation under control.
■ **Equipment signals.** Two commonly used equipment signals are—
  ■ Hold rescue tube vertically over head and move it from side to side to signal assistance is needed.
  ■ Hold rescue tube horizontally over the head to signal the situation is under control.

■ Other means of communication may include—
  ■ Bull horns.
  ■ Public address systems.
  ■ Electric buzzers.
  ■ Telephones.
  ■ Flags (commonly used at waterfronts).

BREAK

Time: 10 minutes

Participants should change into swimsuits and prepare to participate in the in-water activity.

In-Water Activity: Victim Recognition

Time: 30 minutes

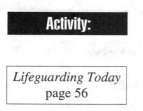

Lifeguarding Today
page 56

Distressed Swimmer (5 minutes)

Explain and demonstrate the actions of a distressed swimmer. Assign partners or ask participants to find a partner.

1. Have participants simulate the actions of a distressed swimmer. One partner is in the water simulating a distressed swimmer while the other is on the deck observing. Guide participants through the following actions of a distressed swimmer:
   ■ Continues breathing and calls for help.
   ■ Floats, sculls, or treads water (tell participant in the water to chose one); can wave for help (Fig. 2–1).

Figure 2–1

- The body position may be horizontal, vertical, or diagonal, depending on means of support (each participant will chose one position).
- Makes little or no forward progress; less and less able to support self.

2. Have participants perform the simulation and then change places with their partners and repeat the simulation. Have participants practice this simulation until they have an understanding of the actions of a distressed swimmer.

Active Drowning Victim (5 minutes)

Activity:

Lifeguarding Today
pages 56 & 57

Explain and demonstrate the actions of an active drowning victim. Assign partners or ask participants to find a partner.

1. Have participants simulate the actions of an active drowning victim. One partner is in the water simulating an active drowning victim, while the other is on the deck observing. Guide participants through the following actions of an active drowning victim:
   - Struggles to breathe; cannot call out for help (Fig. 2–2)

Figure 2–2

   - Arms are to the sides, pressing down; has no supporting kick
   - The body position is vertical
   - Does not move forward; has only 20 to 60 seconds before submerging

2. Have participants perform the simulation and then change places with their partners and repeat the simulation. Have participants practice this simulation until they have an understanding of the actions of an active drowning victim.

Passive Drowning Victim (5 minutes)

Activity:

Lifeguarding Today
pages 58 & 59

Explain and demonstrate the actions of a passive drowning victim. Assign partners or ask participants to find a partner.

1. Have participants simulate the actions of a passive drowning victim. One partner is in the water simulating a passive drowning victim, while the other is on the deck observing. Guide participants through the following actions of a passive drowning victim:
    - Not breathing
    - Has no arm or leg movement
    - Is face-down submerged or near the surface
2. Have participants perform the simulation and then change places with their partners and repeat the simulation. Have participants practice this simulation until they have an understanding of the actions of a passive drowning victim.

Surveillance (15 minutes)

Activity:

1. Confidentially assign participants a number. Explain that on hearing that number called, he or she is expected to act like a distressed swimmer or an active or passive drowning victim.
2. Select one participant to play the role of a lifeguard. Explain to the participants that if they are selected to be the lifeguard during this activity, they will be assigned a zone for which to perform surveillance.

Note: You may want to briefly review how to scan properly. Also, the zone you assign the lifeguard may be limited based on the amount of space available to you at the facility.

3. Ask the remaining participants to enter the water in the zone assigned to the lifeguard and engage in "normal" recreational activities for the facility. This could include lap swimming, playing, or diving off a diving board.

Note: Be sure to write down or remember the number you assigned the participant in the lifeguard role to avoid calling that number while that participant is acting as the lifeguard.

4. After several minutes, call out a number. The participant whose number was called will then simulate his or her choice of a distressed swimmer, an active drowning victim, or a passive drowning victim.

5. The lifeguard has to identify the victim. For this activity, have the lifeguard point at the victim once he or she recognizes the emergency. Let the lifeguard know if he or she identified the correct participant as the victim.
6. Ask the lifeguard to identify what type of victim the participant simulated.
   - If the lifeguard answers correctly, ask him or her what characteristics led him or her to identify the victim as in distress, active, passive.
   - If the lifeguard does not answer correctly, provide the correct answer. Briefly review the characteristics of that type of victim.
7. Select another participant to be the lifeguard. Repeat this activity.

CLOSING

Time: 5 minutes

Activity:

1. Respond to any questions from the participants.
2. Tell participants to wear comfortable clothes for dry land skills practice in the next class session.

Assignment:

Read Chapters 1, 2, 3, and 4, of *CPR for the Professional Rescuer,* and complete the review questions at the end of each chapter.

Lesson 3 CPR for the Professional Rescuer Part I

Class Assignment prior to this lesson:	Read Chapters 1, 2, 3, 4 and 5 of *CPR for the Professional Rescuer.*
Length:	3 hours
Equipment/Supplies:	Video—*CPR for the Professional Rescuer;* VCR and monitor; Skill Sheets: "Primary Survey," "Rescue Breathing for an Adult," "Rescue Breathing for an Infant," "Care for an Unconscious Adult/Child with an Obstructed Airway," "Care for a Conscious Adult/Child with an Obstructed Airway"; Participant Progress Log (Appendix L); adult and infant manikins, 1 manikin for every two or three participants (child manikins optional); decontamination supplies; blankets or mats
Goal:	Participants will become familiar with the EMS system and with the roles and responsibilities of professional rescuers within the EMS system. They will become familiar with the structures, functions, and interdependence of specific body systems, and they will gain a basic understanding of disease transmission and how to protect against it. They will also learn how and when to perform a primary survey and how to respond to a breathing emergency in an adult, in a child, and in an infant.

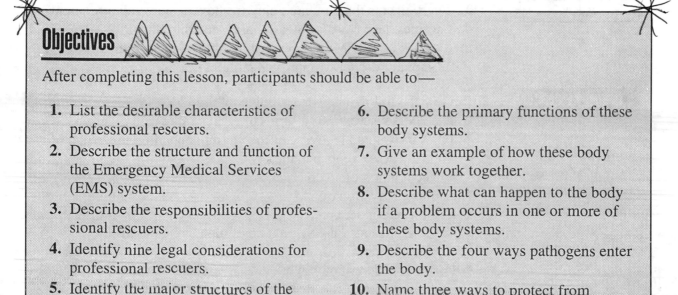

Objectives

After completing this lesson, participants should be able to—

1. List the desirable characteristics of professional rescuers.
2. Describe the structure and function of the Emergency Medical Services (EMS) system.
3. Describe the responsibilities of professional rescuers.
4. Identify nine legal considerations for professional rescuers.
5. Identify the major structures of the respiratory, circulatory, and nervous systems.
6. Describe the primary functions of these body systems.
7. Give an example of how these body systems work together.
8. Describe what can happen to the body if a problem occurs in one or more of these body systems.
9. Describe the four ways pathogens enter the body.
10. Name three ways to protect from disease transmission when giving care.

11. Describe the four emergency action principles.

12. Explain why you do a primary survey in every emergency situation.

13. Describe and demonstrate how to do a primary survey.

14. List the signs and symptoms of respiratory distress.

15. Make appropriate decisions about care when given an example of an emergency requiring a primary survey.

16. Describe how to care for a victim of respiratory distress.

17. Explain when to provide rescue breathing.

18. Describe how to provide rescue breathing.

19. List three causes of an obstructed airway.

20. Describe and demonstrate how to care for an unconscious adult and child victim with an obstructed airway.

21. Describe and demonstrate how to care for a conscious adult and child victim with an obstructed airway.

22. Demonstrate rescue breathing for an adult, a child, and an infant.

23. Make appropriate decisions about care when given an example of an emergency in which a person is not breathing.

THE PROFESSIONAL RESCUER

Time: 15 minutes

| Video: |

Tell participants that you are going to show a short video segment that defines the roles of professional rescuers in the emergency medical services (EMS) system. Show the video segment: "The Professional Rescuer." (approx. 8 minutes)

| Primary Points: |

Review the following primary points of the video:
- The EMS system links a series of events in a chain of survival. The survival and recovery of the victim depend on this chain of events. These events include—
  - Recognition of an emergency.
  - Early activation of EMS.
  - First responder care.
  - More advanced prehospital care, such as by paramedics.
  - Hospital care.
- For the EMS system to work effectively, prompt response is vital.

REVIEW OF LEGAL CONSIDERATIONS

Time: 5 minutes

Primary Points:

CPR: PR
pages 10–14

A lifeguard, being a professional rescuer, needs to be aware of the following legal considerations—

Note: This information was covered in Lesson 1 but is briefly being reviewed here to remind participants of the legal considerations that affect their duties as a lifeguard and as a professional rescuer.

- **Duty to act.** Most professional rescuers have a duty to act in an emergency.
- **Standard of care.** The public expects a certain standard of care from a professional rescuer. If your actions do not meet the standards set for you, you may be successfully sued if your actions harm another person.
- **Negligence.** Negligence is the failure to follow a reasonable standard of care, thereby causing injury to someone. A person could be negligent by acting wrongly or failing to act at all.
- **Good Samaritan laws.** Most states have Good Samaritan laws, which protect people providing emergency care. These laws differ from state to state. You should be familiar with your state's laws.
- **Consent.** Before you provide care, you must obtain the victim's consent. You must—
  - Identify yourself.
  - State your level of training.
  - Explain what you think may be wrong.
  - Explain what you plan to do.

  A parent or guardian, if present, must give consent to care for a minor unless a life-threatening condition exists. If the victim is unconscious or too confused or upset to grant care, the law assumes the victim would grant consent if able to do so. This is called implied consent.
- **Refusal of care.** If a person refuses care, even if his or her condition is serious, you should honor the request. If possible, have someone witness the refusal. Document it; some EMS systems have a "Refusal of Care" form you can use in such situations.
- **Abandonment.** Once you have started emergency care, you are legally obligated to continue that care until a person with equal or higher training relieves you. If you stop care before that happens, you can be legally responsible for the abandonment of a person in need.

- **Confidentiality.** When providing care, protect the victim's confidentiality. Never discuss the victim or the care you gave with anyone except law enforcement personnel or personnel caring for the victim.
- **Record keeping.** Always document the care you provide as soon as possible. Your record may be helpful to others providing care. Your record is also a legal document and will support what you saw, heard, and did at the scene of the emergency.

Note: Since laws vary from state to state, you may want to advise participants to become familiar with the laws of their state. Also, the sidebar, "A Right to Choose," in Chapter 1, pages 12 and 13 of the participant's manual, describes another set of issues with legal implications. Participants should become familiar with these also, since they may have to deal with them at some time.

HUMAN BODY SYSTEMS

Time: 15 minutes

Primary Points:

CPR: PR
page 19

- Knowing how the respiratory, circulatory, and nervous systems normally function will help you understand what happens when these systems fail.
- When body systems fail, physical signs and symptoms appear. These are often your first indication that something is wrong.

Video:

Show the video segment: "Human Body Systems." (approx. 10 minutes)

Primary Points:

Review the following primary points of the video:
- Body systems have unique structures and functions.
- **Respiratory system:** (nose, mouth, epiglottis, trachea, lungs, bronchi, alveoli, diaphragm; brings oxygen into the body in inhaled air, exchanges oxygen with carbon dioxide, and removes carbon dioxide from the body in exhaled air).
- **Circulatory system:** (arteries, veins, capillaries, heart; pumps oxygen-rich blood throughout the body, carries oxygen-poor blood back to the heart).
- **Nervous system:** (brain, spinal cord, nerves; regulates all body functions, including respiratory and circulatory systems).
- Body systems work together to keep the body healthy. They do not work independently.

- Injury or illness rarely affect only one body system. For example, if the heart stops beating, breathing will stop. If the body is deprived of oxygen, brain cells will begin to die within 4 to 6 minutes.

DISEASE TRANSMISSION

Time: 10 minutes

Primary Points:

CPR: PR
pages 30–45

- Diseases are caused by microorganisms called pathogens.
- Pathogens enter the body in four ways:
  - By direct contact with an infected person's body fluids, such as blood or saliva
  - By indirect contact—touching an object with contaminated body fluids on it
  - By inhaling infected droplets in the air
  - By being bitten by an infected animal or insect
- Herpes, meningitis, tuberculosis, hepatitis, and HIV, the virus that causes AIDS, are serious diseases that must be of concern to professional rescuers.
- You can protect yourself from disease transmission by following certain precautions when giving care, such as wearing protective coverings—gloves and masks, using a resuscitation mask for rescue breathing—getting appropriate immunizations, and following certain work control practices that change the way a task is carried out. Examples of work control practices include—
  - Not trying to bend or recap any needles.
  - Removing soiled protective clothing as soon as possible.
  - Washing hands thoroughly immediately after providing care.
  - Cleaning and disinfecting all equipment and work surfaces possibly soiled by blood or other body fluids.
- If you think you have been exposed to an infectious disease, it is your responsibility to notify your supervisor immediately. You should receive medical evaluation, counseling, and postexposure care.

Note: The American Red Cross has a module to supplement the information on disease transmission in this course. ***Preventing Disease Transmission*** *is a 2-hour module geared toward individuals whose jobs involve "reasonable anticipation" of exposure to blood or other body fluids that could cause infection.*

A participant booklet (Stock No. 652053), instructional outline (Stock No. 652054), and 20-minute video (Stock No. 652055) are *available. For further information on the **Preventing Disease Transmission** module or to find out how you can qualify to deliver this module, contact your local unit of the American Red Cross.*

EMERGENCY ACTION PRINCIPLES

Time: 15 minutes

Primary Points:

CPR: PR
page 50

- The four emergency action principles are—
  - Survey the scene.
  - Do a primary survey.
  - Summon additional personnel if necessary.
  - Do a secondary survey.

The Primary Survey

Video:

Show the video segment: "Primary Survey." (approx. 5 minutes)

Primary Points:

Review the following primary points of the video:
- The primary survey identifies life-threatening conditions.
- The four items to check in the primary survey are—
  - Consciousness.
  - Airway.
  - Breathing.
  - Circulation (pulse and severe bleeding).
- The primary survey can be done with the victim in the position in which you find him or her. If, however, you are unsure whether a face-down victim is breathing, position the victim on his or her back.
- A person who is speaking or crying is conscious, has an open airway, is breathing, and has a pulse.
- Sometimes the tongue is blocking the airway. The head-tilt/chin-lift technique opens the airway by moving the tongue away from the back of the throat.
- Open the airway to check for breathing.
- If the victim is not breathing but has a pulse, perform rescue breathing.
- A person who makes no sound and fails to respond to stimulation may be unconscious and may not be breathing or have a pulse.

SKILL PRACTICE: PRIMARY SURVEY

Time. 25 minutes

Skill Sheet
CPR: PR
pages 60–62

Blankets or Mats

Activity:

Skill Sheet
CPR: PR
pages 60–62

Positioning the Victim Faceup

1. Ask participants to take skill sheets with them to the practice area.
2. Assign partners or ask participants to find a partner.
3. Tell participants that they will practice positioning a victim, using their partner to simulate a face-down, unconscious victim.
4. Guide participants through the skill.
5. Have participants perform the skill several times and then change places with their partners and repeat the practice. Have participants practice the skill until they feel comfortable performing it. Check off the participants' skills on the Participant Progress Log (Appendix L) as you watch them practice.
6. Answer any questions.

Primary Survey

1. Tell the participants that they will practice the primary survey on an unconscious but breathing victim.

Note: Participants will tilt the head back and lift the chin to open the victim's airway. Then they will check for breathing. Since the victim is breathing, the rescuer does not need to check the carotid pulse but will check for severe bleeding.

2. Have participants practice performing a primary survey on an unconscious victim who is not breathing.

Note: In this situation, participants should be told that they would give 2 slow breaths for the nonbreathing person and then do a pulse check and bleeding check. The nonbreathing adult victim is likely to be pulseless.

3. Guide participants through the skill. Have participants locate their own carotid pulse and then locate their partner's carotid pulse.
4. Have participants perform the skill several times and then change places with their partners and repeat the practice. Have participants practice the skill until they feel comfortable performing it. Check off the participants' skills as you watch them practice.
5. Answer any questions.

RECOGNIZING BREATHING EMERGENCIES

Time: 5 minutes

Primary Points:

CPR: PR
pages 66 & 67

Respiratory Distress

- Someone having trouble breathing is said to be in respiratory distress.
- Causes of breathing emergencies include—
  - Heart attack or heart disease.
  - Lung disease, such as emphysema.
  - Asthma.
  - Injury to the chest or lungs.
  - Allergic reactions to food, drugs, and insect bites or stings.
  - Drowning or near drowning.
  - Electrocution.
  - Poisoning.
  - Shock.
- Signs and symptoms of respiratory distress are—
  - Gasping for air.
  - Unusually fast or slow breathing.
  - Unusually shallow or deep breathing.
  - Unusually noisy breathing.
  - Painful breathing.
  - Dizziness.
  - Feeling short of breath.
  - Tingling in the hands or feet.
  - Moist, pale, bluish, or flushed skin.

CARING FOR BREATHING EMERGENCIES

Time: 15 minutes

Primary Points:

CPR: PR
page 68

Care for Respiratory Distress

- Position the victim in a sitting position.
- Attempt to reduce heat if the room is hot and stuffy.
- Administer supplemental oxygen when it is available.

Primary Points:

CPR: PR
page 68

Respiratory Arrest

- Respiratory distress, if uncared for, can turn into respiratory arrest.
- Respiratory arrest is a life-threatening condition in which breathing stops.
- It is commonly caused by injury, illness, or choking.

■ In respiratory arrest, body systems will fail because of lack of oxygen.

Care for Respiratory Arrest

Primary Point:

CPR: PR, page 68

■ Rescue breathing is the care you provide for a person who is in respiratory arrest but has a pulse.

Video:

Show the video segment: "Rescue Breathing." (approx. 9 minutes)

Primary Points:

Review the following primary points of the video:
■ Start by checking a victim's consciousness, then the ABCs.
■ Sometimes the tongue is blocking the airway. The head-tilt/chin-lift technique opens the airway by moving the tongue away from the back of the throat.
■ Open the airway to check for breathing. If the victim is not breathing, give 2 breaths. Blow in slowly until the chest rises.
■ Check for a pulse. If a pulse is present but the victim is still not breathing, continue rescue breathing.
■ For adults, give 1 breath every 5 seconds. For children and infants, give 1 breath every 3 seconds.
■ Give rescue breathing for 1 minute, then recheck the pulse.
■ For an infant, make a seal with your mouth over both the nose and mouth when you give breaths.

SKILL PRACTICE: RESCUE BREATHING (ADULT, CHILD, INFANT)

Time: 30 minutes

Primary Points:

Skill Sheet
CPR: PR
pages 86–92

1. Briefly review the "Health Precautions and Guidelines for the Professional Rescuer."
2. Explain that participants will practice rescue breathing on a manikin.
3. Demonstrate how to properly clean the manikin after use. Tell participants to keep the manikin on its back at all times in order to keep the face clean.

Adult and Infant Manikins
(Child manikins optional)

4. Ask the participants to take their skill sheets to the practice area.
5. Assign partners or ask participants to find a partner.
6. Guide participants through the skill.
7. Have participants perform the skill several times and then change places with their partners and repeat the practice. Have

participants practice the skill until they feel comfortable performing it. Check off the participants' skills as you watch them practice.

8. Answer any questions.

AIRWAY OBSTRUCTION

Time: 10 minutes

Primary Points:

> *CPR: PR*
> pages 73–75

- Airway obstruction is the most common respiratory emergency.
- There are two types of airway obstruction: anatomical and mechanical.
- An obstruction is called anatomical if the airway is blocked by an anatomical structure such as the tongue or swollen tissues of the mouth and throat.
- The most common cause of obstruction in an unconscious person is the tongue, which drops to the back of the throat and blocks the airway.
- An obstruction is called mechanical if the airway is blocked by a foreign object, such as a piece of food, a small toy, or fluids such as vomit, blood, mucus, or saliva. Someone with a mechanical obstruction is said to be choking.
- A person who is choking may have either a complete or a partial airway obstruction.
- A person with a partial airway obstruction can still move air to and from the lungs, which enables him or her to be able to cough in an attempt to dislodge the object.
- A person with a complete airway obstruction is unable to speak, breathe, or cough.

First Aid for Airway Obstruction

Video:

Show the video segment: "Clearing an Obstructed Airway—Adult and Child." (approx. 9 minutes)

Primary Points:

Review the following primary points of the video:
- The head-tilt/chin-lift technique opens the airway by moving the tongue away from the back of the throat. If the airway is blocked by a foreign object, attempt to remove it by giving abdominal thrusts (Heimlich Maneuver).
- Care for a child's obstructed airway in the same way as for an adult, but give the thrusts with less force.

SKILL PRACTICE: OBSTRUCTED AIRWAY

Time: 30 minutes

Activity:

Skill Sheet
CPR: PR
page 96

Conscious Adult and Child

1. Ask participants to take skill sheets with them to the practice area.
2. Explain that participants will practice on their partner how to care for a conscious victim whose airway is obstructed, but they will not give actual abdominal thrusts.
3. Have participants stand in a line or semi-circle with their partner behind them.
4. Guide participants through the skill.
5. Have participants perform the skill several times and then change places with their partners and repeat the practice. Have participants practice the skill until they feel comfortable performing it. Check off the participants' skills as you watch them practice.
6. Answer any questions.

Activity:

Skill Sheet
CPR: PR
pages 93–95

Unconscious Adult and Child

1. Assign partners or ask participants to find a partner.
2. Tell the participants that they will use a manikin to practice first aid for an unconscious adult and an unconscious child whose airway is obstructed.
3. Guide the participants through the skill.
4. Have participants perform the skill several times and then change places with their partners and repeat the practice. Have participants practice the skill until they feel comfortable performing it. Check off the participants' skills as you watch them practice.

CLOSING

Time: 5 minutes

Activity: Respond to any questions from the participants.

Assignment: Review Chapter 5, and read Chapters 6 and 7 of the *CPR for the Professional Rescuer* participant's manual. Complete the review questions at the end of each chapter.

Lesson 4

CPR for the Professional Rescuer Part II

Class Assignment prior to this lesson: Review Chapter 5, and read Chapters 6 and 7 of the *CPR for the Professional Rescuer* participant's manual.

Length: 3 hours, 15 minutes

Equipment/Supplies: Video — *"CPR for the Professional Rescuer";* VCR and monitor; Skill Sheets: "Care for an Unconscious Infant with an Obstructed Airway," "Using a Resuscitation Mask for Rescue Breathing," "Using a Bag-Valve-Mask Resuscitator for Rescue Breathing (Two-Rescuer)"; "CPR for an Adult"; Participant Progress Log (Appendix L); adult and infant manikins, one manikin for every two or three participants; decontamination supplies; resuscitation masks; bag-valve masks; blankets or mats

Goal: Participants will become familiar with how to care for an infant with an obstructed airway and with the advantages of using the resuscitation mask and the bag-valve-mask resuscitator (BVM) to ventilate a nonbreathing victim. Participants will also become familiar with the signs and symptoms of a heart attack/cardiac arrest, how to care for victims who experience them, and how to identify and reduce risk factors for cardiovascular disease.

Objectives

After completing this lesson, participants should be able to—

1. Describe how to care for an unconscious infant with an obstructed airway.

2. Describe how to care for a conscious infant with an obstructed airway.

3. Demonstrate how to care for an unconscious infant with an obstructed airway.

4. Demonstrate how to care for a conscious infant with an obstructed airway.

5. Identify at least three advantages of using breathing devices.

6. Describe how to use a resuscitation mask to ventilate a nonbreathing person.

7. Demonstrate on a manikin how to use a resuscitation mask to ventilate a nonbreathing person.

8. Describe how to use a bag-valve-mask resuscitator to ventilate a nonbreathing person.

9. Demonstrate on a manikin how to use a bag-valve-mask resuscitator to ventilate a nonbreathing person.

10. Make appropriate decisions about care when given an example of an emergency in which a person is not breathing.

11. List at least four signs and symptoms of a heart attack.

12. Describe how to care for a heart attack victim.

13. Identify the primary sign of cardiac arrest.

14. Describe the purpose of CPR.

15. List the conditions under which a rescuer may stop CPR.

16. Identify risk factors for cardiovascular disease that can be controlled.

17. Describe and demonstrate how to give CPR to an adult.

18. Make appropriate decisions about care when given an example of an emergency in which a person is in cardiac arrest.

AIRWAY OBSTRUCTION FOR INFANTS

Time: 10 minutes

| Video: |

Show the video segment: "Clearing an Obstructed Airway: Infant." (approx. 7 minutes)

| Primary Points: |

Review the following primary points of the video:
- Care for infants who are choking includes a combination of chest thrusts and back blows. Abdominal thrusts are not used because of their potential for causing injury.
- To support the infant during back blows and chest thrusts, place the infant on your arm and support the head and neck while holding the infant's jaw with your thumb and fingers.

SKILL PRACTICE: OBSTRUCTED AIRWAY

Time: 30 minutes

Note: Tell the participants that because the airway obstruction techniques are so similar, it will not be necessary to practice the conscious infant technique. Therefore, there is no skill sheet for Airway Obstruction (Conscious Infant).

Airway Obstruction (Unconscious Infant)

*Skill Sheet
CPR: PR
pages 97–100*

1. Ask the participants to take their skill sheets with them to the practice area.

2. Assign partners or ask participants to find a partner.

Infant manikins

Blankets or mats

3. Explain that participants will use a manikin to practice first aid for an unconscious infant whose airway is obstructed.
4. Guide participants through the skill.
5. Have participants perform the skill several times and then change places with their partners and repeat the practice. Have participants practice the skill until they feel comfortable performing it. Check off the participants' skills on the Participant Progress Log (Appendix L) as you watch them practice.
6. Answer any questions.

RESUSCITATION MASK

Time: 10 minutes

Primary Points:

CPR: PR
pages 104–106

■ Two advantages of the resuscitation mask:
  1. It can be used on breathing and nonbreathing victims.
  2. It reduces the possibility of disease transmission by providing a barrier between the rescuer and the victim.
■ Masks should meet certain criteria to be most effective. They should—
  ■ Be made of transparent, pliable material that allows you to make a tight seal.
  ■ Have a one-way valve for releasing exhaled air.
  ■ Have a standard 15mm or 22mm coupling assembly.
  ■ Have an inlet for the delivery of supplemental oxygen.
  ■ Work well under a variety of environmental conditions.
  ■ Be easy to assemble and use.

Video:

Show the video segment: "Using a Resuscitation Mask."
(approx. 6 minutes)

Primary Points:

Review the following primary points of the video:
■ Using the mask is a simple skill. Place the mask on the victim's face and—
  ■ Tilt the head back.
  ■ Lift the jaw.
  ■ Open the mouth.

SKILL PRACTICE: RESUSCITATION MASK

Time: 30 minutes

Activity:

Skill Sheet
CPR: PR
pages 111 & 112

1. Ask participants to take skill sheets with them to the practice area.
2. Assign partners or ask participants to find a partner.
3. Using manikins, have participants begin with the primary survey. When participants get to the "Check Breathing" step, tell them the victim is not breathing.

Note: Participants should apply the mask and give two breaths, check for a pulse and breathing, then provide rescue breathing through the resuscitation mask.

4. Watch as participants practice, focusing on four steps:
   - Tilting the victim's head back
   - Lifting the jaw with both hands
   - Keeping the mouth open with the thumbs
   - Ventilating only until the chest rises

Adult manikins
Resuscitation masks

5. Have participants perform the skill several times and then change places with their partners and repeat the practice. Have participants practice the skill until they feel comfortable performing it. Check off the participants' skills as you watch them practice.
6. Answer any questions.

BAG-VALVE-MASK RESUSCITATOR (BVM)

Time: 10 minutes

Primary Points:

CPR: PR
pages 106 & 109

- There may be times when you have to use a bag-valve mask (BVM) or are asked to assist with one.
- The bag has three pieces:
  - Self-inflating bag
  - One-way valve
  - The mask, which is very similar to the resuscitation mask
- Using the mask reduces the possibility of disease transmission.
- The BVM delivers 21 percent oxygen (the surrounding air).

Note: Only when a BVM is used in conjunction with supplemental oxygen is a reservoir attached to the bag.

- Because it is difficult for one person to maintain a proper seal and head position, using the BVM is recommended as a two-rescuer skill. One rescuer holds the mask in place; the other squeezes the air from the bag into the victim's lungs.

Show the video segment: "Using a Bag-Valve Mask."
(approx. 4 minutes)

SKILL PRACTICE: BAG-VALVE MASK

Time: 30 minutes

Activity:

Skill Sheet
CPR: PR
pages 113 & 114

Bag-Valve-Masks

1. Ask participants to take skill sheets with them to the practice area.
2. Assign partners or ask participants to find a partner.
3. Using manikins, have participants begin with the primary survey. When participants get to the "Check Breathing" step, tell them the victim is not breathing.

Note: Participants should give two breaths using the BVM, check for a pulse and breathing, then continue ventilations using the BVM.

4. Watch as participants practice, focusing on four steps:
   - Tilting the victim's head back
   - Lifting the jaw with both hands
   - Keeping the mouth open with the thumbs
   - Ventilating slowly, only until the chest rises
5. Have participants perform the skill several times and then change places with their partners and repeat the practice. Have participants practice the skill until they feel comfortable performing it. Check off the participants' skills as you watch them practice.
6. Answer any questions.

RECOGNIZING A HEART ATTACK

Time: 15 minutes

Activity:

1. Remind participants that when the heart is deprived of oxygen, heart muscle in the affected area dies. The result may be a heart attack.
2. Tell participants that they are now going to view a video on heart attack. Tell them to note carefully the signs and symptoms of heart attack and the care provided.

Video:

Show the video segment: "Recognizing a Heart Attack."
(approx. 12 minutes)

Note: *Point out to participants that when the woman calls 9–1–1, she does not give the location of the building. This is because the number is "enhanced" 9–1–1. The location of the call is automatically registered on the dispatcher's computer and appears on the screen.*

Primary Points:

Review the following primary points of the video:
- Signs and symptoms of a heart attack:
  - Persistent chest pain
  - Nausea
  - Sweating
  - Looking and feeling ill
  - Shortness of breath (breathing difficulty)
- Heart attack is usually the result of cardiovascular disease (CVD)—disease of the heart and blood vessels.
- Cardiovascular disease is the leading cause of death for adults in the United States.
- Certain factors increase a person's chances of developing cardiovascular disease. These are called risk factors. Some risk factors cannot be changed:
  - Men have a higher risk for cardiovascular disease than women.
  - Having a history of cardiovascular disease in your family increases your chances of developing it.
- Many risk factors can be controlled:
  - Do not smoke.
  - Get sufficient exercise.
  - Keep body weight at an appropriate level.
  - Eat a diet low in fats.
  - Be aware of high blood pressure and take steps to control it.
- Participants should review the Healthy Heart IQ in Chapter 7 of their manual to determine how many of these risk factors apply to them.

CARDIAC ARREST

Time: 15 minutes

Primary Points:

CPR: PR
pages 123–125

- Cardiac arrest is the condition in which the heart stops beating or beats too weakly to circulate blood effectively.
- Cardiac arrest can be caused by cardiovascular disease, drowning, electrocution, suffocation, poisoning, respiratory arrest, and injuries causing severe blood loss.

- A victim in cardiac arrest is unconscious, not breathing, and without a pulse.
- Some cardiac arrests are very sudden. The victim does not show any signs and symptoms of heart attack before the arrest.
- To give the victim a chance of survival, CPR must be started promptly, followed by early defibrillation and early advanced cardiac care.
- Tell participants to read Appendix A, Automated External Defibrillation (AED) in their manual.

| Video: | Show the video segment: "Adult CPR." (approx. 6 minutes) |

| Primary Points: | Review the following primary points of the video: |

- Giving ventilations places oxygen in the blood and chest compressions help move the oxygen-rich blood throughout the body.
- CPR is only stopped when—
  - Another trained rescuer takes over.
  - If you are exhausted and unable to continue.
  - If the victim's heart starts beating.
  - If the rescue becomes unsafe.
  - If more advanced personnel order you to discontinue the attempt.

SKILL PRACTICE: ADULT CPR

Time: 40 minutes

| Activity: |

Skill Sheet
CPR: PR
pages 141–144

Adult Manikins

1. Ask participants to take skill sheets with them to the practice area.
2. Assign partners or ask participants to find a partner.
3. Using manikins, review locating proper hand position and giving compressions (Fig. 4–1).
4. When participants have mastered these techniques, add giving rescue breaths alternately with sets of compressions.
5. Instruct participants to practice CPR, beginning with the primary survey.
6. Have participants perform the skill several times and then change places with their partners and repeat the practice. Have participants practice the skill until they feel comfortable performing it. Check off the participants' skills as you watch them practice.
7. Answer any questions.

ADULT

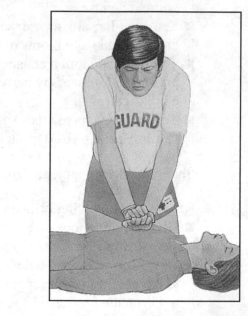

HAND POSITION:	Two hands on lower $\frac{1}{2}$ of sternum
COMPRESS:	$1\frac{1}{2}$–2 inches
BREATHE:	Slowly until chest gently rises (about 1.5 seconds per breath)
CYCLE:	15 compressions 2 breaths
RATE:	15 compressions in about 10 seconds

Figure 4–1

CLOSING

Time: 5 minutes

Activity:

Respond to any questions from the participants.

Assignment:

Review Chapter 7, and read Chapter 8 of the *CPR For the Professional Rescuer* participant manual. Complete the review questions at the end of the chapter.

Lesson 5 — CPR for the Professional Rescuer Part III

Class Assignment prior to this lesson: Review Chapter 7, and read Chapter 8 of the *CPR for the Professional Rescuer* participant's manual.

Length: 2 hours, 45 minutes

Equipment/Supplies: Video — *"CPR for the Professional Rescuer";* VCR and monitor; Skill Sheets: "CPR for a Child," "CPR for an Infant," "Two-Rescuer CPR—Beginning Together"; "Two-Rescuer CPR—Changing Positions"; Participant Progress Log (Appendix L); adult, child, and infant manikins; decontamination supplies; blankets or mats; copies of exams CPR for the Professional Rescuer A and B and answer sheets for each participant (Appendix S); pencils

Goal: Participants will become familiar with how to perform infant, child, and two-rescuer CPR. Participants will also become familiar with four special situations requiring modification of emergency care procedures and with the care to give for them.

Objectives

After completing this lesson, participants should be able to—

1. Describe and demonstrate how to give CPR to a child and an infant.

2. Make appropriate decisions about care when given an example of an emergency in which a person is in cardiac arrest.

3. Identify four special situations that require modifying emergency care procedures.

4. Describe the procedures for giving emergency care to victims of—
   - Near drowning.
   - Electric shock and lightning strike.
   - Traumatic injury.
   - Hypothermia.

5. Describe the guidelines for performing CPR in difficult situations or locations.

CHILD CPR

Time: 10 minutes

Primary Points:

CPR: PR
pages 130–133

- Unlike adults, children do not often initially suffer a cardiac emergency. Instead, they suffer a respiratory emergency that results in a cardiac emergency.
- One way to prevent cardiac emergencies in infants and children is to prevent injuries that lead to cardiac emergencies. Another is to make sure that infants and children receive proper medical care. A third is to recognize the early signs of a respiratory emergency. These signs include—
  - Agitation.
  - Drowsiness.
  - Change in skin color (to pale, blue, or gray).
  - Increased difficulty breathing.
  - Increased heart and breathing rates.

Video:

Show the video segment: "Child CPR." (approx. 6 minutes)

SKILL PRACTICE: CHILD CPR

Time: 15 minutes

Activity:

Skill Sheet
CPR: PR
pages 145–148

Child manikins

Blankets or mats

1. Ask participants to take skill sheets with them to the practice area.
2. Assign partners or ask participants to a find partner.
3. Using manikins, review locating proper hand position and giving compressions (Fig. 5–1).
4. Guide participants through the skill.
5. Have participants perform the skill several times and then change places with their partners and repeat the practice. Have participants practice the skill until they feel comfortable performing it. Check off the participants' skills on the Participant Progress Log (Appendix L) as you watch them practice.
6. Answer any questions.

CHILD

HAND POSITION:	One hand on lower $^1/_2$ of sternum
COMPRESS:	$1-1^1/_2$ inches
BREATHE:	Slowly until chest gently rises (about 1.5 seconds per breath)
CYCLE:	5 compressions 1 breath
RATE:	5 compressions in about 3 seconds

Figure 5–1

INFANT CPR

Time: 10 minutes

Primary Points:

CPR: PR
pages 133–135

- The rate of chest compressions for an infant is faster than for an adult or child.
- Two or three fingers are used to compress the chest.
- As in child CPR, the rescuer compresses the chest 5 times and ventilates once.

Video:

Show the video segment: "Infant CPR." (approx. 4 minutes)

SKILL PRACTICE: INFANT CPR

Time: 15 minutes

Activity:

Skill Sheet
CPR: PR
pages 149–152

Infant manikins

1. Ask the participants to take skill sheets with them to the practice area.
2. Assign partners or ask participants to find a partner.
3. Using manikins, review locating proper hand position and giving compressions (Fig. 5–2).
4. Guide participants through the skill.
5. Have participants perform the skill several times and then change places with their partners and repeat the practice. Have participants practice the skill until they feel comfortable performing it. Check off the participants' skills as you watch them practice.
6. Answer any questions.

TWO-RESCUER CPR

Time: 10 minutes

Video:

Show the video segment: "Two-Rescuer CPR." (approx. 6 minutes)

Primary Points:

Review the following primary points of the video:
- In two-rescuer CPR, the ratio of compressions to breaths is 5 to 1.
- When two rescuers begin CPR together, the first rescuer does a primary survey and the second rescuer gets into position to give chest compressions.
- When CPR is in progress by one rescuer and a second rescuer arrives, that rescuer should ask whether advanced medical personnel have been summoned. If they have, the second rescuer can then assist the first rescuer in giving two-rescuer CPR.

CHILD

HAND POSITION:	One hand on lower $\frac{1}{2}$ of sternum
COMPRESS:	$1-1\frac{1}{2}$ inches
BREATHE:	Slowly until chest gently rises (about 1.5 seconds per breath)
CYCLE:	5 compressions 1 breath
RATE:	5 compressions in about 3 seconds

Figure 5–1

INFANT CPR

Time: 10 minutes

Primary Points:

*CPR: PR
pages 133–135*

- The rate of chest compressions for an infant is faster than for an adult or child.
- Two or three fingers are used to compress the chest.
- As in child CPR, the rescuer compresses the chest 5 times and ventilates once.

Video:

Show the video segment: "Infant CPR." (approx. 4 minutes)

SKILL PRACTICE: INFANT CPR

Time: 15 minutes

Activity:

Skill Sheet
CPR: PR
pages 149–152

Infant manikins

1. Ask the participants to take skill sheets with them to the practice area.
2. Assign partners or ask participants to find a partner.
3. Using manikins, review locating proper hand position and giving compressions (Fig. 5–2).
4. Guide participants through the skill.
5. Have participants perform the skill several times and then change places with their partners and repeat the practice. Have participants practice the skill until they feel comfortable performing it. Check off the participants' skills as you watch them practice.
6. Answer any questions.

TWO-RESCUER CPR

Time: 10 minutes

Video:

Show the video segment: "Two-Rescuer CPR." (approx. 6 minutes)

Primary Points:

Review the following primary points of the video:
- In two-rescuer CPR, the ratio of compressions to breaths is 5 to 1.
- When two rescuers begin CPR together, the first rescuer does a primary survey and the second rescuer gets into position to give chest compressions.
- When CPR is in progress by one rescuer and a second rescuer arrives, that rescuer should ask whether advanced medical personnel have been summoned. If they have, the second rescuer can then assist the first rescuer in giving two-rescuer CPR.

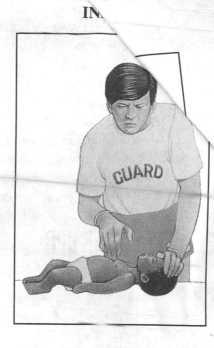

HAND POSITION:	Two fingers on lower $\frac{1}{2}$ of sternum
COMPRESS:	$\frac{1}{2}$–1 inch
BREATHE:	Slowly until chest gently rises (about 1.5 seconds per breath)
CYCLE:	5 compressions 1 breath
RATE:	5 compressions in about 3 seconds

Figure 5–2

This can be done without interrupting the flow of CPR. The second rescuer enters immediately after the first rescuer has completed a cycle of 15 compressions and 2 breaths.

- The second rescuer gets into position at the chest and finds the correct hand position. The first rescuer checks the pulse. If there is no pulse, the second rescuer begins compressions.

■ If a rescuer becomes tired, he or she can change positions with the other rescuer. When the rescuers change, the rescuer at the victim's head completes 1 breath and then moves to the chest. The rescuer at the chest completes 5 compressions and then moves to the head. Both rescuers move quickly into position without changing sides.

SKILL PRACTICE: TWO-RESCUER CPR

Time: 35 minutes

Activity:

Skill Sheet
CPR: PR
pages 153–157

Adult manikins

1. Ask participants to take skill sheets with them to the practice area.
2. Assign partners or ask participants to find a partner.
3. Guide participants through two rescuers beginning CPR together.
4. Have participants perform the skill several times and then change places with their partners and repeat the practice. Have participants practice the skill until they feel comfortable performing it. Check off the participants' skills as you watch them practice.
5. When participants have mastered these techniques, review two rescuers changing positions.
6. Have participants practice this skill until they are comfortable in performing it. Check off participants' skills as you watch them practice.
7. Answer any questions.

SPECIAL RESUSCITATION SITUATIONS

Time: 20 minutes

Activity:

1. Tell participants that certain situations require the professional rescuer to modify the care he or she normally uses. The most common special situations are—
   - Near drowning.
   - Electric shock and lightning strike.
   - Traumatic injury.
   - Hypothermia.

They will also need to learn what to do if they need to give CPR in certain difficult locations and situations.

Near Drowning

Primary Points:

CPR: PR
pages 159–160

- A person who has been submerged for more and than 2 or 3 minutes will suffer from lack of oxygen and need emergency care.
- A rescuer should get to the victim as soon as possible without risking personal safety.
- Use rescue equipment, such as a rescue tube or rescue board, to help in the rescue.
- If you suspect head or spine injury, support the victim's head and neck and immobilize the victim onto a backboard or surfboard before removing from the water. If you need to turn the victim, support the head, neck, and trunk and turn as a unit. Provide emergency care.
- Check airway, breathing, and circulation. Provide care based on the victim's condition. If you are unable to adequately ventilate the victim, do the Heimlich Maneuver to clear any obstruction and continue your attempts to ventilate.
- Regardless of speed of recovery, every near-drowning victim needs follow-up care at a medical facility.

Electric Shock

Primary Points:

CPR: PR
page 161

- Electric shock causes between 500 and 1,000 deaths each year in the United States. An additional 5,000 people receive emergency treatment. Electric shock can cause serious burns and also paralyze the breathing muscles, causing cardiac arrest.
- The severity of an electric shock is affected by—
  - Duration of contact with the source of the electricity.
  - Strength of the current.
  - Environmental conditions.
- Immediately after a severe shock, the victim may not be breathing and may be without a pulse.
- Never approach the victim until the source of the electricity is turned off.
- As soon as it is safe, check the victim's airway, breathing, and pulse. Start rescue breathing or CPR at once if necessary.

Lightning

Primary Points:

CPR: PR
page 161

- Lightning acts as a direct current that interrupts the heart rhythm.
- Victims who suffer immediate cardiac arrest are those most likely to die.
- Victims can be resuscitated even if some time has passed before attempts are made.
- Lightning strike can cause severe fractures, including spinal fracture, and severe burns.

Traumatic Injury

Primary Points:

CPR: PR
page 161

- Survival rates from cardiac arrest as the result of trauma are extremely poor.
- The victim must be transported as soon as possible to a trauma center, where he or she will receive specialized treatment.
- Suspect head or spine injury in a trauma victim, especially a victim of a fall from a height, a motor vehicle accident, or a diving or skiing accident. Be sure the head and neck are stabilized before you open the airway.

Hypothermia

Primary Points:

CPR: PR
page 162

- In hypothermia, the entire body cools and body temperature drops below 95° Fahrenheit (35° C). In severe hypothermia, body temperature is below 86° Fahrenheit (30° C).
- The victim will die if not given care.
- A growing concern in the United States is the number of people dying each year from cold exposure. These fatalities are associated with the increasing number of homeless and older adults.
- Signs and symptoms of hypothermia include —
  - Shivering.
  - Numbness.
  - Apathy.
  - Decreasing level of consciousness.
  - Erratic heartbeat.
  - Rigid muscles.
- If the victim is not breathing, begin rescue breathing. The pulse may be hard to find, so check the victim's pulse for at least 45 seconds and as long as one minute. If the victim has no pulse, begin CPR.
- The victim should be transported to a medical facility at once and should continue to be given CPR on the way.

- Prevent further heat loss by removing any wet clothing and protecting the victim from wind or cold.
- Warm the body gradually by wrapping the victim in blankets or dry clothing.
- Handle the victim gently. Rough handling and rapid rewarming can cause dangerous heart rhythms.

CPR in Difficult Situations and Locations

Primary Points:

CPR: PR
pages 162 & 163

- Use the following guidelines if you find yourself having to perform CPR in certain situations.
  - Only move a victim from a cramped or busy location if it is unsafe or impractical to perform CPR.
  - If a victim has to be transported up or down a flight of stairs, perform CPR at the head or foot of the stairs. Then, using a predetermined signal, interrupt CPR, move quickly to the next level, and resume CPR. Try not to interrupt CPR for more than 30 seconds.
  - Do not interrupt CPR while a victim is being transferred to an ambulance or into the emergency department. With a high litter or bed, you may have to kneel beside the victim on the bed or litter or stand on a stool next to the bed or litter rails to get sufficient height to adequately compress the chest.

WRITTEN EXAMINATION

Time: 45 minutes

Activity:

**CPR: PR Exam
(Appendix S)**
Answer Sheets
Pencils

1. Tell participants that they will now take a 50-question examination. They will have 40 minutes to complete the exam and must answer at least 40 questions correctly to pass. They may not use their participant's manual to find the answers.
2. Hand out an examination and answer sheet to each participant.
3. Tell participants to write only on the answer sheet, mark answers clearly, and use pencil only in case they want to erase or change an answer.
4. Tell them to check their answers before handing their exams in.
5. Tell them to come to you or raise one hand when they have finished the exam or have any questions.
6. Score the exams. The answer keys for both exams are at the end of this instructor's manual.

Note: As participants hand in their answer sheets and exams, quickly grade each exam and return it to the correct participant so he or she can review any missed questions. If time allows, discuss with the class any exam items that were a problem. Collect all answer sheets and exams before the participants leave the class. If a participant fails the exam, ask him or her to see you after class to schedule a retest.

CLOSING

Time: 5 minutes

| Activity: | Respond to any remaining questions from the participants. |
| Assignment: | Read Chapter 8 of *Lifeguarding Today*. Complete the study questions at the end of the chapter. |

Lesson 6   Rescue Skills Part I

Class Assignment prior to this lesson: Read Chapter 8 of *Lifeguarding Today*.

Length: 3 hours

Equipment/Supplies: Video—*Lifeguarding Today;* VCR and monitor; rescue tubes (one rescue tube per two or three participants); Lifeguarding Skills Checklist (Appendix M)

Goal: Participants will become familiar with the seven steps of a rescue. They will learn how to use a rescue tube, how to enter the water, how to approach a victim, how to rescue a victim at or near the surface, and how to perform a multiple-victim rescue.

Objectives

After completing this lesson, participants should be able to—

1. List the seven steps that are part of any rescue.
2. List three reasons for using rescue equipment when performing a rescue.
3. Explain when to use a stride jump entry and when to use a compact jump.
4. Demonstrate two methods of entering the water.
5. Explain when to use an extension assist from the deck.
6. Demonstrate an extension assist from the deck.
7. Demonstrate two ways to approach a victim with equipment.
8. Demonstrate the swimming extension rescue.
9. Demonstrate the active victim rear rescue.
10. Demonstrate the multiple-victim rescue.
11. Demonstrate the passive victim rear rescue.

REVIEW OF PREVIOUS MATERIAL

Time: 5 minutes

Primary Points:

Review

- As a lifeguard, you are a professional rescuer and have a duty to respond when someone needs emergency care.
- Some skills that you may perform as a professional rescuer may include—
  - Rescue breathing.
    - Rescue breathing consists of giving breaths to a nonbreathing victim who has a pulse.

- Care for an obstructed airway.
  - If a victim's airway is blocked by a foreign object, attempt to remove the object by giving abdominal thrusts (Heimlich Maneuver).
- CPR.
  - CPR consists of giving breaths and chest compressions to a nonbreathing victim without a pulse.

Note: Remember there are some differences in the way rescue breathing, care for an obstructed airway, and CPR are performed for adults, infants, and children.

- Two-Rescuer CPR.
  - With a second rescuer, one person can perform compressions while the other gives breaths.
- Use of a resuscitation mask.
  - The use of a resuscitation mask reduces the possibility of disease transmission by providing a barrier between the rescuer and the victim.

GENERAL RESCUE PROCEDURES

Time: 10 minutes

Primary Points:

Lifeguarding Today
page 104

The seven steps of a water rescue are as follows:
1. **Activate the facility's emergency action plan.** On recognizing an emergency, alert other lifeguards and staff so that they can provide backup coverage, give additional help, and call EMS personnel when appropriate.
2. **Enter the water.** Choose the best entry based on the following factors—water depth, height from which the entry is made, and facility design.
3. **Approach the victim.** Swim to the victim to make contact. Slow your approach before contacting the victim. This prepares you to get into a good swimming position to tow the victim to safety.
4. **Perform an appropriate rescue.** Determine the victim's condition before making contact. Check to see if the victim is a distressed swimmer, an active drowning victim, or a passive drowning victim, and whether the victim is located at the surface or submerged. Make contact and perform the appropriate rescue for the situation.

5. **Move the victim to safety.** Move the victim to the side of the pool or dock or to shallow water.
6. **Remove the victim from the water.** Get help when lifting the victim from the water.
7. **Provide emergency care as needed.** Depending on the victim's condition; CPR, rescue breathing, or first aid may be needed until EMS personnel arrive.

USE OF THE RESCUE TUBE

Time: 5 minutes

Primary Points:

Lifeguarding Today
page 105

- The rescue tube is the most commonly used piece of equipment in lifeguarding.
- The rescue tube is a foam-filled floating support 45 to 54 inches long. Attached to it are a tow line and shoulder strap, varying in total length from 4 to 6 feet.
- The rescue tube provides safety for the lifeguard and the victim. It also—
  - Provides flotation for the victim and the lifeguard.
  - Reduces the amount of energy the lifeguard needs to move the victim to safety.
  - Reduces the chance of the victim grasping the lifeguard.

TEACHING TIP:

You may want to have a rescue tube available to show the participants.

RESCUE SKILLS

Time: 20 minutes

Show the video segment: "Rescues—Part 1." (approx. 14 minutes) Stop the tape after the skill "Passive Victim Rear Rescue."

Review the following primary points of the video:
- When faced with an emergency, follow the seven steps of a water rescue.
- The rescue tube is a lifeguard's primary piece of equipment. Be sure to always wear the rescue tube properly.

- To enter the water with the rescue tube, use either a stride jump or compact jump.
- When approaching a victim, you can use either a modified crawl or breaststroke.
- To rescue a victim, you can use one of the following techniques:
  - Extension Assist From the Deck
  - Swimming Extension Rescue
  - Active Victim Rear Rescue
  - Multiple-Victim Rescue
  - Passive Victim Rear Rescue

BREAK

Time: 10 minutes

Participants should change into swimsuits and prepare for the in-water skills practice.

SKILL PRACTICE: GETTING TO KNOW THE RESCUE TUBE

Time: 35 minutes

Activity:

Lifeguarding Today
page 105

Positioning the Rescue Tube (5 minutes)

Demonstrate how to properly position the rescue tube for immediate response. Reinforce the following points:

1. Put the strap of the rescue tube over your shoulder and head.
2. Standing — Position the tube across your stomach (Fig. 6–1).

Figure 6–1

Sitting in a lifeguard chair — Position the tube across your thighs (Fig. 6 2).

Figure 6-2

Note: In some situations, it may not be practical for a lifeguard in a lifeguard chair to have the rescue tube positioned for immediate response. For example, a tall lifeguard stand requires the lifeguard to climb down before entering the water. The rescue tube may be positioned on the stand.

Entries (15 minutes)

Stride Jump

Primary Point:

Activity:

Lifeguarding Today pages 106 & 107

Rescue Tubes

The stride jump with a rescue tube is used only in water at least 5 feet deep and only from a height of 3 feet or less above the water.

Explain and demonstrate the stride jump entry with a rescue tube. Guide participants through the following steps:

1. Squeeze the rescue tube high against the chest with the ends under the armpits. Hold the excess line in one hand (Fig. 6–3, A).
2. Leap into the water with one leg forward and the other back. Lean slightly forward. Keep chest forward of hips when entering the water (Fig. 6–3, B).
3. When entering the water, squeeze or scissor legs together for upward thrust (Fig. 6–3, C).
4. Have participants practice the skill until they feel comfortable. Check off the participants' skills on the Lifeguarding Skills Checklist (Appendix M) as you watch them practice.

Figure 6–3, A

Figure 6–3, B

Figure 6–3, C

Compact Jump

Primary Point:

The compact jump with a rescue tube is used to enter the water from a height greater than 3 feet into water that is at least 5 feet deep. It can also be used from the deck into water less than 5 feet deep.

Activity:

Explain and demonstrate the compact jump entry with a rescue tube. Guide participants through the following steps:

1. Squeeze rescue tube high against the chest with the ends under the armpits. Hold the excess line in one hand.
2. Jump out away from the deck or dock. Keep knees bent and feet together and flat (Fig. 6–4).

Lifeguarding Today page 108

Figure 6–4

SAFETY TIP:

A person using the compact jump can be injured by hitting the bottom of the pool. Therefore, make sure participants do not point their toes or enter the water with straight legs! Also emphasize that the participants must hold the excess line to keep it from getting caught in the lifeguard chair or other equipment.

3. The buoyancy of rescue tube will bring the participant back to the surface.
4. Have participants practice the skill until they feel comfortable. Check off the participants' skills as you watch them practice.

Approaches (15 minutes)

Primary Point:

Lifeguarding Today
page 108

The most effective swimming stroke for reaching a nearby victim is a modified crawl or breaststroke (Figs. 6–5, A and B).

Figure 6–5, A

Figure 6–5, B

Explain and demonstrate the modified crawl and breaststroke approaches. Guide participants through the following steps:

1. Have participants enter the water. After entry, the rescue tube should be under the armpits or torso as you swim toward a victim with your head up.

2. Keep the rescue tube in control at all times. If it slips out from under the arms or if the distance to the victim is great, let the rescue tube trail behind (Fig. 6–6).

Figure 6–6

3. When you get close to the victim, slow your approach (Fig. 6–7). This puts you in a good swimming position before making contact with the victim and prepares you to support the victim with the rescue tube.

Figure 6–7

4. Have participants practice both the modified crawl and breast-stroke until they feel comfortable performing them. Check off the participants' skills as you watch them practice.

SKILL PRACTICE: RESCUE SKILLS

Time: 90 minutes

Primary Points:

Lifeguarding Today
pages 105 & 106

Activity:

Extension Assist From the Deck (10 minutes)

Explain to the participants that if a distressed swimmer is close to the side of the pool, they can extend a rescue tube to him or her. Extending a tube may not work with a drowning victim, since he or she might not be able to grasp it. For a drowning victim, they must use a different rescue that will be covered later.

Explain and demonstrate the extension assist from the deck. Assign partners or ask participants to find a partner. Guide participants through the following steps:
1. Remove the rescue tube's shoulder strap from your shoulder.
2. Hold the shoulder strap in one hand and extend the rescue tube to the victim. Talk to the victim to calm him or her (Fig. 6–8, A). Tell the victim to grasp and hold the rescue tube for support.

Figure 6–8, A

3. When the victim grasps the rescue tube, slowly pull him or her to safety (Fig. 6–8, B).

Figure 6–8, B

4. Have participants perform the skill several times and then change places with their partners and repeat the practice. Have participants practice the skill until they feel comfortable performing it. Check off the participants' skills as you watch them practice.

Swimming Extension Rescue (15 minutes)

Primary Point:

The swimming extension rescue is a simple rescue used for a distressed swimmer.

Activity:

Explain and demonstrate the swimming extension rescue. Guide participants through the following steps:

1. Approach the victim from the front. Slow your approach as you near the victim (Fig. 6–9, A).

Lifeguarding Today
page 114

Figure 6–9, A

2. Extend the end of the rescue tube to the victim. Tell the victim to grasp the rescue tube, hold it for support, and kick if he or she can (Fig. 6–9, B).

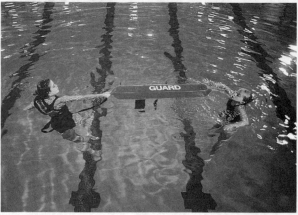

Figure 6–9, B

3. Move the victim to safety (Fig. 6–9, C).

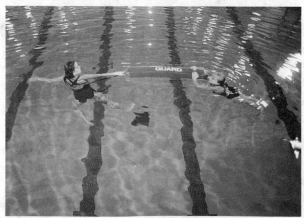

Figure 6–9, C

4. Have participants perform the skill several times and then change places with their partners and repeat the practice. Have participants practice the skill until they feel comfortable performing it. Check off the participants' skills as you watch them practice.

Active Victim Rear Rescue (25 minutes)

Primary Point:

Activity:

Lifeguarding Today
page 115

The active victim rear rescue can be used for either a distressed swimmer or an active drowning victim. Approaching from the rear is safest for you.

Explain and demonstrate the active victim rear rescue. Guide participants through the following steps:

1. Approach the victim from the rear. Slow your approach as you near the victim (Fig. 6–10, A).

Figure 6–10, A

2. Reach under the victim's armpits and grasp the shoulders (Fig. 6–10, B).

Figure 6–10, B

Squeeze the rescue tube between your chest and the victim's back (Fig. 6–10, C).

Figure 6–10, C

3. Lean back and pull the victim onto the rescue tube. Use the rescue tube to support the victim with his or her face out of the water. Talk to the victim to calm him or her (Fig. 6–10, D).

Figure 6–10, D

SAFETY TIP:

Keep your head to one side as you reach for and support the victim to prevent being hit by the victim's head if it comes back toward you.

4. Move the victim to safety using a kick you feel comfortable with.
5. Have participants perform the skill several times and then change places with their partners and repeat the practice. Have participants practice the skill until they feel comfortable performing it. Check off the participants' skills as you watch them practice.

Multiple-Victim Rescue (20 minutes)

A rescue situation may involve two or more victims. Often a victim will clutch a nearby person in an effort to stay at the surface.

If you are the only lifeguard in a situation where two victims are clutching each other, use the multiple-victim rescue.

Explain and demonstrate the multiple-victim rescue. Assign or ask participants to work in groups of three (two victims, one lifeguard). Guide participants through the following steps:
1. Approach one victim from the rear and slow your approach before you make contact.
2. Grasp the victim by reaching under the victim's armpits and grasping the shoulders (Fig. 6–11, A). Squeeze the rescue tube between your chest and the victim's back.

Primary Points:

Lifeguarding Today
page 120

Activity:

Figure 6–11, A

3. Begin kicking and lean back. This helps bring the faces of both victims out of the water (Fig. 6–11, B). Remember to talk to the victims to calm them.

Figure 6–11, B

4. Move the victims to safety.
5. Have participants rotate so that each participant performs the skill as the rescuer. Have participants practice the skill until they feel comfortable performing it. Check off the participants' skills as you watch them practice.

Passive Victim Rear Rescue (20 minutes)

Primary Points:

Lifeguarding Today
page 116

You use the passive victim rear rescue when the victim seems unconscious and you do not suspect a spinal injury.

Because of differences in buoyancy, the victim's position may vary from nearly vertical to nearly horizontal.

Activity:

Explain and demonstrate the passive victim rear rescue. Assign partners or ask participants to find a partner. Guide participants through the following steps:
1. Approach the victim from the rear.
2. Reach under the victim's armpits and grasp the shoulders. Squeeze the rescue tube between your chest and the victim's back (Fig. 6–12, A).
3. Roll the victim over so that he or she is face up on top of the rescue tube (Fig. 6–12, B).
4. Move the victim to safety; use one hand to stroke if you prefer. To do this, reach your right arm over the victim's right shoulder and grasp the rescue tube. Then use your left hand to stroke

(Fig. 6–12, C). You can also reach with your left arm and stroke with your right hand.

Figure 6–12, A

Figure 6–12, B

Figure 6–12, C

5. Have participants perform the skill several times and then change places with their partners and repeat the practice. Have participants practice the skill until they feel comfortable performing it. Check off the participants' skills as you watch them practice.

CLOSING

Time: 5 minutes

Activity:

- Summarize the rescue skills covered in this lesson:
  - Entries
  - Approaches
  - Extension Assist From the Deck
  - Swimming Extension Rescue
  - Active Victim Rear Rescue
  - Multiple Victim Rescue
  - Passive Victim Rear Rescue
- Answer any questions.

Assignment:

Review Chapter 8 of *Lifeguarding Today*.

Lesson 7 Rescue Skills Part II

Class Assignment prior to this lesson: Review Chapter 8 of *Lifeguarding Today*.

Length: 3 hours

Equipment/Supplies: Video—*Lifeguarding Today;* VCR and monitor; rescue tubes (one rescue tube per two or three participants); Lifeguarding Skills Checklist (Appendix M)

Goal: Participants will be able to perform the following rescue skills: submerged victim rescue, removal from the water, and emergency care.

Objectives

After completing this lesson, participants should be able to—

1. Demonstrate the feet-first surface dive.
2. Demonstrate the submerged victim rescue.
3. Explain the factors involved in deciding whether to move a victim from the water.
4. Demonstrate how to remove a victim from the water using the two-lifeguard lift.
5. Explain the importance of follow-up care.

REVIEW OF PREVIOUS MATERIAL

Time: 5 minutes

Primary Points:

Review

- The seven steps of a rescue include—
  - Activating the facility's emergency action plan.
  - Entering the water.
  - Approaching the victim.
  - Performing an appropriate rescue.
  - Moving the victim to safety.
  - Removing the victim from the water.
  - Providing emergency care as needed.
- The rescue tube is the primary piece of rescue equipment a lifeguard uses when performing a rescue.

RESCUE SKILLS

Time: 10 minutes

Video:

Show the video segment: "Rescues—Part 2." (approx. 8 minutes)

Primary Points:

Review the following primary points of the video:
- A feet-first surface dive enables you to submerge quickly in order to perform a rescue below the surface of the water.
- To rescue a person who is below the surface and beyond your reach, you can use the submerged victim rescue.
- To remove a victim from the water, use either a two-lifeguard lift or a one-lifeguard lift, depending on the availability of assistance.
- Depending on the victim's condition you may have to provide emergency care until EMS personnel arrive. Emergency care may include—
  - Rescue breathing.
  - CPR.
  - First aid.
- Remember that the life of every swimmer depends on your ability to act quickly and effectively in an emergency.

BREAK

Time: 10 minutes

Participants should change into swimsuits and prepare for the in-water skills practice.

SKILL PRACTICE: RESCUE SKILLS

Time: 75 minutes

Feet-First Surface Dive (15 minutes)

Primary Point:

By surface diving, you can submerge to rescue or search for a submerged victim.

Activity:

Lifeguarding Today
page 117

Rescue Tubes

Explain and demonstrate how to perform a feet-first surface dive. Have participants perform this skill first without the use of a rescue tube. Once participants feel comfortable with this skill, have them try it with the rescue tube attached. Guide them through the following steps:

1. When you are over the victim, let go of the rescue tube but keep hold of the strap. From a vertical position, press downward with your hands and give a strong kick to rise in the water (Fig. 7–1, A). Take a breath and let your body sink. Keep your legs straight and together with the toes pointed (Fig. 7–1, B).

Figure 7–1, A

Figure 7–1, B

2. When your downward momentum slows, turn your palms outward and sweep your hands and arms upward. Repeat this arm movement until you reach the desired depth (Fig. 7–1, C).

Figure 7–1, C

3. Have participants practice the skill until they feel comfortable. Check off the participants' skills on the Lifeguarding Skills Checklist (Appendix M) as you watch them practice.

Submerged Victim Rescue (35 minutes)

Primary Point:

A submerged victim may either be passive or active, but you use the same rescue skill in both cases.

Activity:

Explain and demonstrate how to perform a submerged victim rescue.

Lifeguarding Today pages 118 & 119

TEACHING TIP:

Demonstrate this skill on deck near a 1-meter diving board or another structure that is high enough and safe to stand on. Have a co-instructor, instructor aide, or participant stand on the board and hold the rescue tube up high vertically. The strap of the rescue tube is attached to you when demonstrating this skill (Fig. 7–2). By doing this, you can show participants both how to secure the victim and the interchange when pulling the towline down and placing it in the other hand.

Figure 7–2

Assign partners or ask participants to find a partner. Guide the participants through the following steps:

SAFETY TIP:

Do not use swim goggles when performing this skill because serious injury may result. Swim goggles, unlike a scuba mask, do not allow you to relieve the pressure when diving or swimming to a depth.

---

1. Do a feet-first surface dive and position yourself behind the victim.
2. Reach one arm under the victim's arm (right arm to right side or left arm to left side) and across the victim's chest. Hold firmly on to the victim's opposite side (Fig. 7–3, A).
3. When you have secured the victim, reach up with the other hand and grasp the towline, then pull it down and place it in the hand holding the victim (Fig. 7–3, B). Keep pulling it until you reach the surface. If possible, push off the bottom and kick to help you reach the surface.
4. As you near the surface, position the rescue tube so that it is squeezed between your chest and the victim's back (7–3, C).

5. Reach your free arm under the victim's armpit and grasp his or her shoulder (right arm to right shoulder or left arm to left shoulder) (Fig. 7–3, D).
6. Move the other arm from across the victim's chest and grasp his or her shoulder.
7. Support the victim in a face-up position on the rescue tube as in the active or passive victim rear rescue (Fig. 7–3, E).
8. Move the victim to safety.
9. Have participants perform the skill several times and then change places with their partners and repeat the practice. Have participants practice the skill until they feel comfortable performing it. Check off the participants' skills as you watch them practice.

Figure 7–3, A

Figure 7–3, B

Figure 7–3, C

Figure 7–3, D

Figure 7–3, E

Removal From the Water (25 minutes)

Primary Points:

Lifeguarding Today
page 121

Explain to the participants that their decision whether to remove the victim from the water depends on—
- The victim's condition.
- The length of time before you expect help to arrive.
- The size of the victim.
- Others available to help you.

If a victim needs rescue breathing or CPR, remove him or her from the water as soon as possible.

Remind participants that they would not perform the following two removal skills if they suspect spinal injury and the person is breathing.

Note: Care for suspected spinal injury is covered in Lesson 9.

Two-Lifeguard Lift

Primary Point:

Emphasize that two lifeguards are needed to remove a victim safely from the water.

Activity:

Lifeguarding Today
pages 121–123

Explain and demonstrate the two-lifeguard lift. Assign or ask participants to work in groups of three (two lifeguards, one victim). Guide participants through the following steps:

> **SAFETY TIP:**
>
> Make sure participants lift with their legs and not with their backs when practicing this skill. Improper lifting can cause injury.

1. Bring the victim to the side of the pool and rotate the victim to face the deck (Fig. 7–4, A).

Figure 7–4, A

2. Support the victim with your knee (7–4, B). Reach under the victim's armpits and grasp the edge of the deck.

Figure 7–4, B

3. Place the victim's hands one on top of the other on the deck or overflow trough. The second lifeguard then takes the hands and pulls the victim up slightly to keep the head above water. **Be sure to support the victim's head so that it does not fall forward and strike the deck** (7–4, C).

Figure 7–4, C

4. Remove rescue tube and climb out of the water to help the second lifeguard.
5. Each lifeguard grasps one of the victim's wrists and upper arm (Fig. 7–4, D). Lift together until the victim's hips or thighs are at deck level (7–4, E).

Figure 7–4, D

Figure 7–4, E

6. Step backward and lower the victim to the deck. **Be sure to protect the victim's head from striking the deck** (7–4, F).

Figure 7–4, F

7. If necessary, pull the victim's legs out of the water, taking care not to twist the victim's back. Roll the victim as a unit onto his or her back (7–4, G).

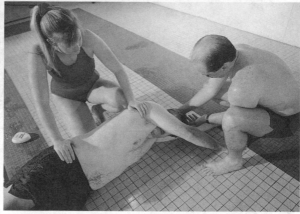

Figure 7–4, G

SAFETY TIP:

Make sure that participants support the victim's head while practicing this skill. To provide extra protection for the participants' safety, place several towels on the overflow trough or deck for padding.

---

8. Have participants rotate so that each participant performs the skill as the rescuer. Have participants practice the skill until they feel comfortable performing it. Check off the participants' skills as you watch them practice.

One-Lifeguard Lift

Primary Point:

If no other lifeguard or bystander is available to help you remove a victim from the water, send someone to get help. If necessary, try to remove the victim by yourself.

Activity:

Lifeguarding Today
page 123

Explain and demonstrate how to perform a one-lifeguard lift. Assign partners or ask participants to find a partner. Guide participants through the following steps:

1. Bring the victim to the side of the pool and rotate him or her to face the deck.

2. Support the victim with your knee. Reach under the victim's armpits and grasp the edge of the deck or overflow trough.
3. Place the victim's hands, one on top of the other, on the deck or overflow trough.
4. Hold the victim's hands on the deck or overflow trough with one hand. Remove the rescue tube and climb out of the water (Fig. 7–5, A).

Figure 7–5, A

5. Grasp both of the victim's wrists and, using your legs, lift the victim until his or her hips or thighs are at deck level (7–5, B).

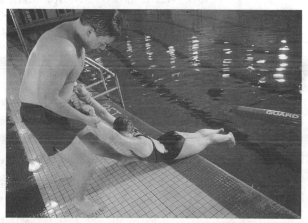

Figure 7–5, B

6. Step back and lower the victim to the deck. **Be sure to protect the victim's head from striking the deck** (7–5, C).

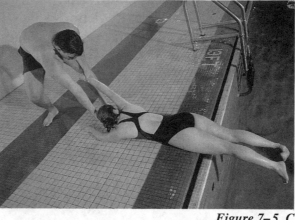

Figure 7–5, C

7. If necessary, pull the victim's legs out of the water, being careful not to twist the victim's back. Roll the victim as a unit onto his or her back being careful to protect the head.
8. Have participants perform the skill several times and then change places with their partners and repeat the practice. Have participants practice the skill until they feel comfortable performing it. Check off the participants' skills as you watch them practice.

Remind the participants that if the victim is too large or heavy for them to remove from the water by themselves, they should support the victim in the water until help arrives.

SKILLS REVIEW

Time: 75 minutes

Activity:

Review of Skills (25 minutes)

1. Ask participants if they have questions about any of the skills they have practiced. Answer any questions.
2. Have participants practice rescue skills. These include: entries, approaches, extension assist from the deck, swimming extension rescue, active victim rear rescue, multiple-victim rescue, passive victim rescue, surface dives, submerged victim rescue, and removal from the water.

Note: If there are participants who did not have some skills checked off previously, this would be an opportune time to recheck these skills.

Putting it All Together (50 minutes)

This activity enables the participants to apply previously learned skills and knowledge. The goal of this activity is to help participants retain skills and knowledge so that they can apply them in real emergencies.

Divide the participants into groups of three.

Situation 1 — Active Victim Rescue

Have participants perform an active victim rescue using the seven steps of a rescue. These include the following:

1. Activate your facility's emergency action plan.
2. Enter the water.
3. Approach the victim.
4. Perform an appropriate rescue.
5. Move the victim to safety.
6. Remove the victim from the water.
7. Provide emergency care as needed.

The victim is exhausted and needs help getting out of the water. The victim does not need emergency care.

Have participants rotate so that each participant performs this rescue. When everyone has performed the rescue, move on to Situation 2.

Situation 2 — Submerged Victim Rescue

Have participants perform a submerged victim rescue using the seven steps of a rescue. The submerged victim is passive.

After the participants have removed their partners (victims) from the water, have them perform the steps for CPR. Participants should simulate CPR until they have completed the second pulse check at the end of the first cycle.

SAFETY TIP:

Emphasize that participants are to simulate CPR upon removing their partners (victims) from the water. Participants should not perform actual chest compressions, should not make mouth-to-mouth contact, and should not give actual breaths.

CLOSING

Time: 5 minutes

Activity:

- Summarize the rescue skills covered in this lesson.
  - Feet-first surface dive
  - Submerged victim rescue
  - Removal from the water
    - Two-lifeguard lift
    - One-lifeguard lift
  - Emergency Care
- Respond to any questions.

Assignment:

Read Chapters 9 and 10 of *Lifeguarding Today*. Complete the study questions at the end of each chapter.

Lesson 8

First Aid

Class Assignment prior to this lesson: Read Chapters 9 and 10 in *Lifeguarding Today*.

Length: 3 hours

Equipment/Supplies: Video—*Community First Aid;* VCR and monitor; Skill Summaries: "Controlling Bleeding," "Applying an Anatomic Splint," "Applying a Soft Splint," "Applying a Sling," "Applying a Rigid Splint"; blankets; triangular bandages; gauze dressings; roller gauze; rigid splinting material; and latex gloves.

Goal: After completing this lesson, participants will be familiar with how to recognize and care for victims of injuries and sudden illness.

Objectives

After completing this lesson, participants should be able to—

1. Describe four types of open wounds.
2. Explain the uses of dressings and bandages.
3. Describe the care for closed wounds.
4. Describe the care for major and minor open wounds.
5. Demonstrate how to control bleeding.
6. Describe the signs and symptoms of shock.
7. Describe how to care for an impaled object and a severed body part.
8. List the general care steps for burns.
9. Describe the burn injuries for which you would call EMS.
10. Describe the care for chemical and electrical burns.
11. List five common signs and symptoms of musculoskeletal injuries.
12. List three signs and symptoms that would cause you to suspect a serious musculoskeletal injury.
13. Describe the general care for musculoskeletal injuries.
14. Demonstrate how to effectively immobilize an injured body part.
15. Explain when to immobilize an injured body part.
16. List six signs and symptoms of head injury.
17. Identify at least eight general signs and symptoms of sudden illness.
18. List at least six basic principles of care for any sudden illness.
19. Describe the care for a person who you suspect is having a diabetic emergency.
20. List at least seven instances when you should call EMS personnel for a person having a seizure.
21. Describe the care for a seizure victim.
22. Describe the care for a stroke victim.
23. Describe the general care for a suspected poisoning emergency.

24.	List four signs and symptoms that would lead you to suspect a heat-related illness.	**26.**	Describe how to care for a person you suspect is suffering from hypothermia.
25.	List three signs and symptoms that would lead you to suspect hypothermia.		

INJURIES

Time: 5 minutes

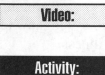

Video:

Tell participants that they are going to see a short video segment on injuries. Show the video segment: "Injuries." (approx. 4 minutes)

Activity:

Ask participants to recall a time when they were injured and how it might have been prevented.

SOFT TISSUE INJURIES

Time: 10 minutes

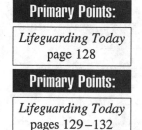

Primary Points:

Lifeguarding Today
page 128

Primary Points:

Lifeguarding Today
pages 129–132

- Soft tissues include the layers of the skin, fat, and muscles of the human body.

Soft Tissue Injuries

- Injury to soft tissue is called a wound.
- These injuries are classified as either closed wounds or open wounds.
- A closed wound is an injury that occurs under the skin's surface. This is commonly called a bruise. A bruise is an indication of internal bleeding (bleeding beneath the skin).
- Some signs of internal bleeding include—
  - Tender, swollen, bruised, or hard areas of the body, such as the abdomen.
  - Rapid, weak pulse.
  - Cool, moist, pale skin color.
  - Vomiting or coughing blood.
  - Dizziness or loss of consciousness.
  - Excessive thirst.
- Open wounds are those injuries in which there is a break in the skin surface.

- The four main types of open wounds are—
  - **Abrasions**—Rubbing or scraping away of skin.
  - **Lacerations**—Cutting the skin surface. These wounds bleed freely and sometimes heavily.
  - **Avulsion**—Partial or complete tearing away of skin or soft tissue. They often bleed heavily.
  - **Punctures**—Piercing of skin. Generally, puncture wounds do not bleed heavily externally, but there is a high risk of infection. In some cases the object may remain stuck in the wound. This is called an impaled object.

Activity:

Ask participants to identify possible ways in which closed and open wounds occur in an aquatic environment (Examples may include: slipping on ladders or diving boards, falling on deck or locker room floor, wooden benches, and horseplay, etc.).

CARING FOR WOUNDS

Time: 10 minutes

Dressings and Bandages

Primary Points:

Lifeguarding Today
pages 133–134

- A dressing is a covering placed directly on an open wound. To minimize the chance of infection, the dressing should be sterile.
- A bandage is any material used to wrap or cover the body. It is often used to hold a dressing in place, provide pressure to control bleeding, protect a wound from dirt and infection, and provide support to an injured body part.

Closed Wounds

Primary Points:

Lifeguarding Today
page 134

- To decrease bleeding associated with closed wounds, pressure may be used.
- Elevating the injured part and applying ice or cold packs may reduce swelling to the area.
- If an injured person complains of severe pain or cannot move the body part without pain, call EMS personnel immediately.

Video:

Show the video segment, "Controlling Bleeding." (approx. 7 minutes)

Minor Open Wounds

Primary Points:

Lifeguarding Today
page 137

- When caring for a major wound with heavy bleeding—
  - Have someone call EMS.
  - Put on latex gloves.
  - Control bleeding with direct pressure and elevation.
  - Apply bandages over dressing to maintain pressure on the wound.
  - If bleeding cannot be controlled, use a pressure point.
  - Wash your hands after completing care.

Major Open Wounds

Primary Points:

Lifeguarding Today
page 137

- When caring for a minor wound—
  - Wear latex gloves.
  - Wash the wound thoroughly with soap and water.
  - Place a sterile dressing over the wound.
  - Apply direct pressure to control any bleeding.
  - Once bleeding is controlled, remove the dressing and apply an antibiotic ointment.
  - Apply a new sterile dressing.
  - Hold the dressing in place with a bandage or tape.
  - Wash your hands after completing care.

SKILL PRACTICE: CONTROLLING BLEEDING

Time: 20 minutes

Activity:

Lifeguarding Today
pages 166 & 167

Gauze Dressings
Roller Gauze
Latex Gloves

1. Ask the participants to take their skill summaries with them to the practice area.
2. Assign partners or ask participants to find a partner.
3. Explain that one partner in each pair acts as rescuer, the other acts as the victim. Each pair should have four gauze dressings, two 3-inch roller gauze, and two pairs of latex gloves.
4. Have participants put the latex gloves on their hands.
5. Guide participants through the skill.
6. Have participants perform the skill several times and then change places with their partners and repeat the practice. Have participants practice the skill until they feel comfortable with performing it. Check off participants' skills on the Lifeguarding Skills Check List (Appendix M) as you watch them practice.
7. Answer any questions.

SHOCK

Time: 5 minutes

Primary Points:

Lifeguarding Today
pages 137 & 138

- Shock is likely to develop as a result of any serious injury or illness.
- Shock is the body's natural defense mechanism to protect vital organs by supplying them with oxygen-rich blood.
- Signs and symptoms of shock include—
  - Restlessness or irritability.
  - Altered consciousness.
  - Pale, cool, moist skin.
  - Rapid breathing.
  - Rapid pulse.
- To care for shock—
  - Have victim lie down.
  - Control any external bleeding.
  - Help victim maintain normal body temperature.
  - Try to reassure the victim.
  - Elevate the legs about 12 inches (unless you suspect neck or back injuries, or serious injury of hips or legs).
  - Do not give anything to eat or drink.
  - Call EMS personnel.

SPECIAL SITUATIONS

Time: 5 minutes

Severed Body Part

Primary Points:

Lifeguarding Today
page 138

- If a victim has a body part that is completely severed—
  - Retrieve the severed part.
  - Wrap the part in sterile gauze.
  - Place the wrapped part in a plastic bag.
  - Keep the part cool by placing the bag on ice.
  - Transport the part with the victim to a medical facility.

Impaled Object

Primary Points:

Lifeguarding Today
page 138

- To care for an impaled object—
  - Do not remove the object.
  - Use bulky dressings to stabilize the object.
  - Control bleeding by bandaging the dressings in place around the object.

Head and Face Injuries

Primary Points:

Lifeguarding Today
pages 139–141

- Do not put pressure directly over any area of scalp that is depressed or spongy. Call EMS personnel.
    - Attempt to control bleeding with pressure on the area around the wound.
- Control a nosebleed by having the victim sit with the head slightly forward and pinch the nostrils.
- Eye injuries, such as a chemical (granular chlorine) that gets in the eye, should be flushed with water.
- If a tooth is knocked out, control any bleeding by placing a rolled sterile dressing in the place left by the tooth, and have the victim bite down.
    - Save any knocked out whole teeth, so they can be replanted by a dentist. If possible, place the tooth back in its socket in the normal position. If this is not possible, save the tooth in cool milk or water.

BURNS

Time: 10 minutes

Primary Points:

Lifeguarding Today
pages 141 & 142

- Burns are caused by—
    - Heat.
    - Chemicals.
    - Electricity.
    - Radiation.
- The severity of a burn depends on—
    - Temperature or strength of whatever caused the burn.
    - Length of exposure to the burn source.
    - Location of the burn.
    - Size of the area burned.
    - Age and medical condition of the victim.

Types of Burns

Primary Points:

Lifeguarding Today
pages 142–145

- Superficial burns—First degree
    - Only damage first layer of skin.
    - Appear red or darker and dry.
    - Burned area is painful.
- Partial Thickness burns—Second degree
    - Involve both layers of skin.
    - Appear red and blistered.
    - Burned area is painful and often swells.

- Full Thickness burns—Third degree
  - Burn destroys both layers of skin as well as fat, muscle, and blood vessels beneath.
  - Appear brown or blackish, and tissue underneath may appear white.
  - Burned area may be either extremely painful or pain free (nerve damage).
- General care for burns includes the following four steps:
  1. Cool the burned area (unless burn was caused by electricity).
  2. Cover the burned area.
  3. Prevent infection.
  4. Minimize shock.
- Call EMS personnel immediately if—
  - The person is having trouble breathing or has burns on more than one part of the body.
  - The victim has burns on the head, chest, neck, back, both hands, both feet, or genitals.
  - The burns are caused by chemicals, explosion, or electricity.
  - A child or elderly person has any burn other than a very minor one.

Chemical Burns

Primary Points:

Lifeguarding Today pages 145 & 146

- Chemical burns should be cared for by—
  - Flushing the burned area until EMS personnel arrive.
  - Removing clothing with the chemical on it.
  - Taking steps to minimize shock.

Electrical Burns

Primary Points:

Lifeguarding Today pages 146 & 147

- Contact with an electrical source can conduct electricity through the body.
- Severity of an electrical burn depends on—
  - The type and amount of contact.
  - The current's path through the body.
  - Length of the contact time.
- Signs of electrical burns include—
  - Unconsciousness.
  - Dazed, confused behavior.
  - Obvious burns on the skin's surface.
  - Breathing difficult.
  - Weak irregular and absent pulse.
  - Entrance and exit burns on body surface.

- Never approach a victim of an electrical burn until you are sure the power is turned off.
- To care for a victim of an electrical emergency—
  - Call EMS personnel immediately.
  - Care for any life-threatening conditions, such as cardiac arrest.
  - Do not cool the burn(s). Cover with a dry, sterile dressing, and care for shock.

MUSCULOSKELETAL INJURIES

Time: 20 minutes

Video:

Show the video segment: "Immobilizing Muscle, Bone, and Joint Injuries." (approx. 11 minutes)

Lifeguarding Today
pages 149–156

- The musculoskeletal system is composed of—
  - Muscles.
  - Bones.
  - Tendons.
  - Ligaments.
- The four types of musculoskeletal injuries are—
  - **Fracture**—A chip, crack, or break of a bone.
  - **Dislocation**—Displacement or separation of a bone from its normal position at a joint.
  - **Sprain**—Tearing of ligaments and other tissues at a joint.
  - **Strain**—Stretching or tearing of muscles or tendons.
- Five common signs and symptoms of musculoskeletal injuries are—
  - Pain.
  - Swelling.
  - Deformity.
  - Discolored skin.
  - Inability to move or use the injured part.
- Signs and symptoms of serious musculoskeletal injuries include—
  - The victim felt bones grating or heard a snap or pop at the time of injury.
  - Numbness, tingling, or change in color in hand, foot, fingers, or toes, indicating loss of circulation.
  - Cause of injury suggests the injury might be severe.
- Care for musculoskeletal injuries includes—
  - Making the victim more comfortable.
  - Applying ice to reduce pain and swelling.
  - Elevating the injured part if not painful to do so.

- If the injury is serious, call EMS personnel.
- Immobilizing the injured part.
- Immobilize the injured part and contact EMS personnel if—
  - The injury involves the head, neck or back.
  - You suspect a fracture or dislocation.
  - The victim has difficulty breathing.
  - The victim is unable to move or use the injured part.
  - You suspect or see more than one injured body part.

SKILL PRACTICE: IMMOBILIZING MUSCLE, BONE, AND JOINT INJURIES

Time: 35 minutes

Activity:

Lifeguarding Today
pages 168–175

Triangular Bandages
Blankets
Rigid Splints

1. Ask the participants to take their skills summaries with them to the practice area.
2. Assign partners or ask participants to find a partner.
3. Give each pair four triangular bandages, a folded blanket, and a rigid splint.
4. Assign or allow the participants to select two of the four skills from the skill summaries to perform.
5. Guide participants through the skills.
6. Have participants perform the first skill several times and then change places with their partners and repeat the practice. Have participants practice the skill until they feel comfortable with it. Check off participants' skills as you watch them practice.
7. Repeat for the second skill.

SPECIAL SITUATIONS

Time: 10 minutes

Primary Points:

Lifeguarding Today
pages 156 & 157

Head Injuries

- Signs and symptoms of a head injury include—
  - Change in the level of consciousness.
  - Severe pain or pressure in the head.
  - Tingling or loss of sensation in the hands or feet.
  - Partial or complete loss of movement of any body part.
  - Unusual bumps or depressions on the head.
  - Blood or other fluids in the ears or nose.
  - Heavy external bleeding of the head.
  - Seizures.
  - Impaired breathing.

- Impaired vision.
- Nausea or vomiting.
- Persistent headache.
- Loss of balance.
- Bruising of the head, especially around the eyes and behind the ears.
- General guidelines for the care of a head injury include—
  - Contacting EMS personnel.
  - Minimizing movement of the victims head and body.
  - Maintaining an open airway.
  - Monitoring consciousness and breathing.
  - Controlling any external bleeding.
  - Maintaining normal body temperature.

Note: Participants will receive additional information on caring for head injuries in the water in Lesson 9 "Spinal Injury Management."

Injuries to the Chest Abdomen and Pelvis

Primary Points:

Lifeguarding Today pages 157–160

- General care for injuries to the chest, abdomen, and pelvis includes—
  - Calling EMS personnel immediately.
  - Monitoring breathing and pulse.
  - Controlling bleeding.
  - Minimizing shock.
  - Limiting movement.
- Signs and symptoms of chest injuries include—
  - Difficulty breathing.
  - Severe pain at the sight of injury.
  - Flushed, pale, or bluish discoloration of the skin.
  - Obvious deformity, such as caused by a fracture.
  - Coughing up blood.
- Signs and symptoms of serious abdominal injury include—
  - Severe pain.
  - Bruising.
  - External bleeding.
  - Nausea.
  - Vomiting (sometimes vomit contains blood).
  - Weakness.
  - Thirst.
  - Pain, tenderness, or a tight feeling in the abdomen.
  - Organs possibly protruding from the abdomen.

SUDDEN ILLNESS

Time: 30 minutes

Video:

Primary Points:

Lifeguarding Today
page 178

Show the video segment: "Sudden Illness." (approx. 8 minutes)

- Often you will not know the cause of a sudden illness, but you will be able to recognize some of the signs and symptoms of sudden illness—
  - Feeling light-headed, dizzy, confused, or weak.
  - Changes in skin color.
  - Sweating.
  - Slurred speech.
  - Nausea or vomiting.
  - Diarrhea.
  - Difficulty seeing.
  - Severe headache.
  - Persistent pressure or pain.
  - Difficulty breathing.
  - Seizures.
  - Paralysis.
  - Changes in consciousness.
- Just because you don't know exactly what may have caused a sudden illness does not mean you cannot provide appropriate care. Care for what you find. The basic principles of care include—
  - Care for any life-threatening conditions first.
  - Call EMS personnel if victim has any life-threatening conditions or you have any doubts about the seriousness of the victim's condition.
  - Help the victim to rest comfortably.
  - Maintain body temperature.
  - Reassure the victim.
  - Watch for changes in consciousness and breathing.
  - Do not give the victim anything to eat or drink unless the victim is fully conscious.
  - If the victim vomits, place the victim on one side.

Diabetic Emergencies

Primary Points:

Lifeguarding Today
pages 179 & 180

- Signs and symptoms of diabetic emergencies include—
  - Changes in the level of consciousness including dizziness, drowsiness, and confusion.
  - Rapid breathing.
  - Rapid pulse.
  - Feeling or looking ill.
- Care for a diabetic emergency by—
  - If the victim is conscious give him or her sugar.
  - If the victim is unconscious do not give him or her anything by mouth, call EMS personnel, monitor breathing.

Seizures

Primary Points:

Lifeguarding Today
pages 181 & 182

- Seizures are a loss of body control as a result of disruption of the electrical activity of the brain.
- Care for seizures includes the following:
  - Do not attempt to stop the seizure.
  - Do not hold or restrain the person, unless in the water. If seizure occurs in the water, support the victim to prevent water from entering mouth and nose.
- EMS personnel should be called if—
  - The seizure lasts more than a few minutes.
  - The person has repeated seizures.
  - The person appears to be injured.
  - You are uncertain of the cause of the seizure.
  - The person is pregnant.
  - The person is a known diabetic.
  - The person is an infant or child.
  - The seizure takes place in the water.
  - The person fails to regain consciousness after the seizure.

Stroke

Primary Points:

Lifeguarding Today
page 182

- A stroke is a disruption of blood flow to a part of the brain that is serious enough to damage brain tissue.
- Signs and symptoms of a stroke include—
  - Sudden weakness of muscles.
  - Numbness in the face, arm, or leg (usually on one side of the body).
  - Victim may have difficulty speaking or understanding speech.
  - Blurred or dimmed vision.
  - Unequal pupils.
  - Sudden and severe headache.

- Dizziness and confusion.
- Changes in mood.
- Ringing in ears.
- Loss of bowel or bladder control.
■ Control for the victim of a stroke by—
  - Maintaining the airway.
  - Caring for life-threatening conditions.
  - Having someone call EMS personnel immediately.
  - Positioning victim on side if fluid or vomit is in the victim's mouth.
  - Comforting and reassuring the victim.
  - Having the victim rest in a comfortable position.

Poisoning

Primary Points:

Lifeguarding Today
page 184

■ Signs and symptoms of poisoning are—
  - Nausea.
  - Vomiting.
  - Diarrhea.
  - Chest and abdominal pain.
  - Breathing difficulty.
  - Sweating.
  - Loss of consciousness.
  - Seizures.
■ These general principles should be followed during a poisoning emergency:
  - Make sure it is safe to approach and to gather clues about what happened.
  - Remove the victim from the source of poison, if necessary.
  - Assess the victim's airway, breathing, and circulation.
  - Care for any life-threatening conditions.
  - If the victim is conscious, gather additional information.
  - Look for any containers and take them to the telephone.
  - Call your local poison control center (PCC).
  - Follow directions given to you by PCC or EMS dispatcher.
  - Do not give the victim anything to eat or drink unless directed by medical professionals.

Heat and Cold Exposure

Primary Points:

Lifeguarding Today
pages 192–195

■ Heat cramps are painful muscle spasms. Heat exhaustion is a more severe condition than heat cramps.
■ Signs and symptoms of heat exhaustion include—
  - Normal or below normal body temperatures.

- Cool, moist, pale, or red skin.
- Headache.
- Nausea.
- Dizziness and weakness.
- Exhaustion.

■ Heat stroke is the most severe heat emergency. Heat stroke develops when the body systems are overwhelmed by heat and stop functioning.

■ Care for heat stroke and heat exhaustion includes—
- Immediately getting the victim out of the heat.
- Cooling the body with cool wet cloths.
- If the victim is conscious, giving him or her cool water to drink.
- Minimizing shock.
- Calling EMS personnel immediately.

■ Hypothermia is a general body cooling that develops when the body can no longer generate sufficient heat to maintain normal body temperature.

■ Signs and symptoms of hypothermia include—
- Shivering.
- Low, irregular pulse.
- Numbness.
- Glassy stare.
- Apathy.
- Decreased levels of consciousness.

■ Care for hypothermia includes—
- Calling EMS personnel.
- Removing wet clothing.
- Drying the victim.
- Warming the body gradually by wrapping the victim in blankets.
- Putting the victim in a warm environment.

Activity:

Ask participants to identify activities that could result in hypothermia. Examples may include—

■ Swimming early or late in the summer season when water temperatures are colder.

■ Swimming and lounging on a cool, windy day.

■ Remaining in the water for an extended time.

CARING FOR CHILDREN

Time: 5 minutes

Primary Points:

Lifeguarding Today
pages 195 & 196

- Children have unique needs that require special care.
- Caring for an injured or ill child requires that a rescuer recognize a child's fear and anxiety.
- Following these five guidelines can help make it easier for you to check and care for a child:
  - Observe the child. Don't just rush up and touch the child.
  - Remain calm. Children will be more upset if you are excited.
  - Talk clearly and simply.
  - Do not separate child from loved ones, such as parents.
  - Gain trust through your actions.

CARING FOR THE ELDERLY

Time: 5 minutes

Primary Points:

Lifeguarding Today
page 196

- Care for the elderly requires that you keep in mind special problems and concerns.
- Often the problem seems unimportant to the elderly victim.
- Often fear of loss of independence will cause an elderly victim to avoid treatment.
- Do not talk down to an elderly victim.
- Falls are a common source of injury for the elderly.
- The most important action you can take is to see that if appropriate, the victim is taken to a medical facility.

PUTTING IT ALL TOGETHER

Time: 5 minutes

Activity:

1. Present the following scenario to the participants:

   "You respond to an injury caused by a fall on the pool deck. The victim is an 8-year-old girl. You arrive to find her lying on her side, crying. You notice there is some blood on her head and that she is holding her arm."

2. Ask the participants to explain the care they would provide in this situation. They should also be able to respond to questions you may pose.

3. Check to see that the participants followed some basic principles that include—
   - Activating the emergency action plan.
   - Checking and correcting any immediately life-threatening problems (airway, breathing, circulation).
   - Summoning EMS personnel.
   - Providing proper care for the victim.
   - Using proper barrier protection to avoid disease transmission.
   - Using available bystanders to help.

Note: Participants should determine that the scene is safe, then check for and correct life-threatening conditions. This check reveals that the victim is conscious and breathing. The victim should not be moved. Bleeding should be controlled and her arm splinted. EMS personnel should be summoned.

CLOSING

Time: 5 minutes

Activity: Respond to any questions from the participants.

Assignment: Read Chapter 11 of *Lifeguarding Today*. Complete the study questions at the end of the chapter.

Lesson 9

Spinal Injury Management

Class Assignment prior to this lesson: Read Chapter 11 of *Lifeguarding Today.*

Length: 3 hours

Equipment/Supplies: Video—*Lifeguarding Today;* backboards with a minimum of three straps and a commercial head immobilizer attached (one backboard per five participants); Lifeguarding Skills Checklist (Appendix M).

Goal: Participants will become familiar with the common causes of aquatic spinal injuries, the signs and symptoms of possible spinal injuries, and how to provide care for victims with spinal injuries.

Objectives

After completing this lesson, participants should be able to—

1. List three situations in which aquatic-related spinal injury is possible.
2. List at least five physical indications of a possible spinal injury.
3. List the seven general guidelines for caring for a possible spinal injury.
4. Demonstrate two ways to stabilize a victim's head and neck.
5. Demonstrate how to immobilize a victim on a backboard.

OVERVIEW

Time: 5 minutes

Primary Points:

Lifeguarding Today
page 200

- Although injuries to the spine account for only a small percentage of all injuries, when they occur, they can result in death or permanent paralysis.
- Sports and recreational activities account for approximately 13 percent of all head and spinal injuries each year (about 250,000).
- Most aquatic spinal injuries occur as a result of unsupervised activity.
- In pools, spinal injuries occur in shallow areas, corners, and areas where the pool slopes from shallow to deep water.
- In open-water areas, spinal injuries result from swimmers running and plunging headfirst into shallow water or into breaking waves,

causing them to strike their head on the bottom, or from striking underwater hazards, such as rocks, sandbars, or tree stumps.

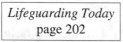

1. Ask participants if they know about any situations (land or water) in which someone suffered a serious head or spinal injury. Ask participants to discuss what they remember about the incident, such as how the injury happened or what care was given.

ANATOMY AND FUNCTION OF THE SPINE

Time: 5 minutes

Primary Points:

Lifeguarding Today
page 202

- The spine is a flexible column of bones (vertebrae) with circular openings that extends from the skull to the tailbone. This column protects the bundle of nerves (spinal cord) that runs through the hollow part of the vertebrae.
- The spine has five regions—cervical (neck), thoracic (mid back), lumbar (lower back), sacrum, and coccyx (tail bone).
- Nerve branches extend to various parts of the body through openings on the sides of the vertebrae.
- The higher on the spine an injury occurs, the more damage and paralysis it is likely to cause.

RECOGNIZING SPINAL INJURY

Time: 10 minutes

Primary Points:

Lifeguarding Today
page 202

- When determining whether someone may have suffered a spinal injury, consider the cause of the injury, as well as physical signs and symptoms.
- Situations that could cause a spinal injury include injury involving a diving board, a water slide, or an entry from a height; a headfirst entry into shallow water; or a fall from a height greater than the height of the victim.

Activity:

1. There are many physical signs and symptoms that indicate a possible spinal injury. Ask participants to identify some of these signs and symptoms. Answers will vary but should include the following:
   - Neck or back pain
   - Loss of body movement below the injury site
   - Tingling or loss of sensation in the arms or legs

- Bumps or depressions on the head, neck, or back
- Altered consciousness
- Bruising of the head, neck, or back
- Impaired breathing
- Loss of balance
- Fluid or blood in the ears
- Seizures

2. Explain to participants that when injuries occur in the water, you may not be able to recognize some of these signs and symptoms; therefore, your decision to provide care for a possible spinal injury may have to be based primarily on what you witness or are told.
    - Consider all suspected spinal injuries as serious injuries, and care for them accordingly.

CARING FOR SPINAL INJURY

Time: 30 minutes

Video:

Show the video segment: "Spinal Injury Management." (approx. 23 minutes)

Primary Points:

Lifeguarding Today pages 202–204

Review the following primary points of the video:
- Caring for spinal injuries involves first stabilizing the head and neck and then immobilizing the victim's entire body on a backboard.
- To care for a victim with a possible spinal injury on land, you first stabilize the victim's head and neck by holding the head in line with the body. Maintain this position until EMS personnel arrive and take over.

TEACHING TIP:

You may want to demonstrate stabilizing a victim's head and neck. Have a co-instructor, instructor aide, or participant stand or sit in a chair as you demonstrate.

Note: EMS personnel will secure the victim to a backboard (or scoop stretcher) while the victim is standing. There is no need to have the victim sit or lie down, unless he or she is dizzy and unable to stay standing. EMS personnel are specially trained to perform the maneuver required to place a standing or seated person on a backboard.

■ There are several general guidelines to follow when providing care for a victim with a possible spinal injury in the water. These include the following:
  ■ Always activate your emergency action plan before entering the water.
  ■ Minimize movement of the victim's head and spine. This is done by applying in-line stabilization. There are two techniques used for in-line stabilization: the head and chin support and the head splint.
  ■ Position the victim face up.
  ■ Check for consciousness and breathing. Talk to the victim. If he or she does not respond, look, listen, and feel for breathing. If the victim is not breathing, remove him or her from the water to provide proper care. In this case, do not take time to secure the victim to the backboard. If possible, slide the backboard under the victim, and with help, move the victim on the backboard onto the deck. If a backboard is not readily available, remove the victim from the water and provide care.
  ■ Move the victim to shallow water whenever possible. If you enter deep water to assist the victim, always take your rescue tube. It will help support both you and the victim.
  ■ Immobilize the victim on a backboard. First secure the victim's body to the backboard, then his or her head. These backboarding techniques vary around the country and are based on the number of lifeguards available and the type of equipment used. The video segment you just saw shows one way to secure a victim on a backboard, but there are others.
  ■ Remove the victim from the water and provide additional care.

Activity: Ask participants if they have any questions. Answer them.

BREAK

Time: 10 minutes

Participants should change into swimsuits and prepare for the in-water skills practice.

SKILL PRACTICE: IN-LINE STABILIZATION TECHNIQUES

Time: 50 minutes

Primary Point:

Lifeguarding Today
page 206

The two specific rescue techniques used in the water to minimize movement of a victim's head and neck are the head splint and the head and chin support.

> ### TEACHING TIP:
>
> You may want to demonstrate the in-line stabilization techniques on land first. Have a co-instructor, instructor aide, or participant stand on the deck as you demonstrate these skills. By doing this, you can show the placement of the hands and arms when performing these skills.

Head Splint Technique

Primary Point:

Lifeguarding Today
page 206

The head splint technique is used for victims found facedown at or near the surface. It can be used in both shallow and deep water.

Standing in shallow water, explain and demonstrate the head splint technique. Assign partners or ask participants to find a partner. Guide participants through the following steps:
1. Approach the victim from the side.
2. Position the victim's arms against his or her head. Do this by grasping the victim's arms midway between the shoulder and the elbow. Grasp the victim's right arm with your right hand and the victim's left arm with your left hand.
3. Squeeze the arms against the victim's head in an effort to immobilize the head and neck (Fig. 9–1, A).

Figure 9–1, A

4. With your body at about shoulder depth in the water, glide the victim slowly forward.

5. While moving, rotate the victim toward you so that he or she turns faceup in the water. This is done by pushing the victim's arm that is closer to you under water while pulling the victim's other arm across the surface (Fig. 9–1, B).

Figure 9–1, B

6. Position the victim's head in the crook of your arm, with the head in line with the body (Fig. 9–1, C).

Figure 9–1, C

7. Maintain this position until help arrives.

8. Have participants perform the skill several times and then change places with their partners and repeat the practice. Have participants practice the skill until they feel comfortable performing it. Check off the participants' skills on the Lifeguarding Skills Checklist (Appendix M) as you watch them practice.

Head and Chin Support Technique

The head and chin support can be used for a victim who is face up or face down. It can be used in deep water and in shallow water more than 3 feet deep.

Standing in shallow water, explain and demonstrate the head and chin support technique for both a face-up and face-down victim. Guide participants through the following steps:

1. Approach the victim from the side.
2. With your body at about shoulder depth in the water, place one forearm along the length of the victim's breastbone and the other forearm along the victim's spine.
3. Use your hands to gently position the victim's head in line with the body. Hold the victim's lower jaw with one hand and the back of the head with the other hand (Fig. 9–2, A and B).

Primary Point:

Lifeguarding Today
pages 206 & 207

Figure 9–2, A

Figure 9–2, B

4. Squeeze your forearms together, clamping the victim's chest and back. Continue to support the victim's head.

5. If the victim is face down, you must turn him or her face up. Using the head and chin support to stabilize the spine, begin moving the victim forward. Rotate the victim toward you while you start to submerge (Fig. 9–2, C). Roll under the victim while turning the victim over in the water (Fig. 9–2, D). Do this slowly to avoid twisting the victim's body. The victim will be face up when you surface on the other side (Fig. 9–2, E).

Figure 9–2, C

Figure 9–2, D

Figure 9–2, E

6. Support the victim faceup in the water until help arrives.
7. Have participants perform the skill several times and then change places with their partners and repeat the practice. Have participants practice the skill until they feel comfortable performing it. Check off the participants' skills as you watch them practice.

SKILL PRACTICE: USING A BACKBOARD (SHALLOW WATER)

Time: 65 minutes

Primary Point:

Lifeguarding Today
pages 208–212

Activity:

Backboards
Straps
Head Immobilizers

Once you have stabilized the victim's head and neck with either the head splint or the head and chin support technique, immobilize the victim on a backboard and remove him or her from the water.

In shallow water, explain and demonstrate how to immobilize a victim on a backboard. Assign or ask participants to work in groups of five (one victim, two lifeguards, two bystanders).

Note: If you have extra backboards, you can form groups with fewer than five participants.

Have participants rotate, so that each participant plays the role of the primary rescuer, second lifeguard, and victim. Each participant will have 10 minutes to immobilize a victim on a backboard and remove the victim from the water. Guide participants through the following steps:

1. As you bring the victim toward the side of the pool, a second lifeguard enters the water, submerges the backboard, and slides it

under the victim (Fig. 9–3, A). The backboard must be positioned so that it extends beyond the victim's head when the backboard is raised (Fig. 9–3, B).

Figure 9–3, A

Figure 9–3, B

2. While the second lifeguard raises the backboard into place, carefully withdraw your arm from beneath the victim. If you are using the head and chin support, keep your hand on the chin and place your other hand under the backboard. If you are using the head splint technique, move your arm that is under the victim toward the top of the victim's head while the second lifeguard holds the victim using the head and chin support (one hand on the chin and one hand on the board).

3. When the backboard is raised, the second lifeguard holds the backboard in place. This is done by supporting the backboard

against the chest and shoulders and squeezing the sides of the backboard with the arms. The victim's head is supported by the second lifeguard placing both hands on the sides of the head (Fig. 9–3, C). If other rescuers are available, they can help support the backboard at the sides.

Figure 9–3, C

4. Secure the victim to the backboard. Straps should be placed across the victim's chest, hips, and thighs. The strap used on the chest should be placed across the chest and under the arms. Securing this strap tightly under the armpits helps prevent the victim from sliding on the backboard during removal from the water (Fig. 9–3, D). Using the hip strap, secure the victim's hands along his or her sides (Fig. 9–3, E) or in front of the body (Fig. 9–3, F). The third strap is placed across the victim's thighs (Fig. 9–3, G).

Figure 9–3, D

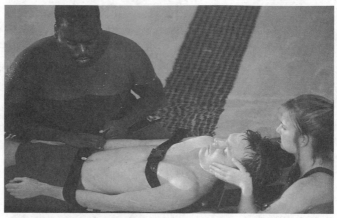

Figure 9–3, E

Figure 9–3, F

Figure 9–3, G

5. Using a head immobilizing device, secure the victim's head to the board. To do this, place pads on each side of the victim's head. Then secure a strap across the victim's forehead (Fig. 9–3, H).

Figure 9–3, H

6. Once the victim is secured on the backboard, remove him or her from the water. To do this, position the backboard with the head end by the side of the pool and the foot end straight out into the pool.

SAFETY TIP:

Make sure participants lift with their legs and not with their backs when practicing this skill. Improper lifting can cause injury.

---

7. With one lifeguard on each side, lift the head of the backboard slightly and place it on the edge of the overflow trough if possible (Fig. 9–4, A).

Figure 9–4, A

8. One lifeguard gets out of the pool and grasps the head of the backboard. The other lifeguard moves to the foot end of the backboard (Fig. 9–4, B). As the lifeguard on deck stands up, steps backward, and pulls the backboard, the lifeguard at the foot end pushes on the backboard (Fig. 9–4, C). Together they slide the backboard up over the edge of the deck, out of and away from the water (Fig. 9–4, D). If others are there to assist, they should position themselves in the water at the sides of the backboard and help lift the backboard onto the deck.

Figure 9–4, B

Figure 9–4, C

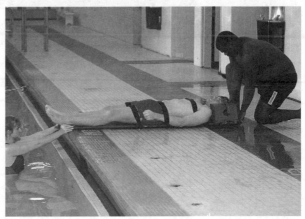

Figure 9–4, D

9. Have participants practice the skill until they feel comfortable. Check off participants' skills when they assume the position of the primary rescuer and perform the skill correctly.

Note: The skills for deep water backboarding are taught in Lesson 10 of this instructor's manual.

CLOSING:

Time: 5 minutes

Primary Points:

■ Briefly reinforce that caring for a spinal injury requires the lifeguard to minimize movement to the victim's head and body.

■ The two techniques practiced will enable the lifeguard to keep the head in-line with the body and minimize movement.

Activity:

Respond to any questions from participants.

Assignment:

Review Chapter 11 of *Lifeguarding Today,* and read Chapter 12 of *Lifeguarding Today.*

Lesson 10 After an Emergency

Class Assignment prior to this lesson: Review Chapter 11, the section—"Caring for a Victim in Deep Water" and read Chapter 12 of *Lifeguarding Today*.

Length: 3 hours

Equipment/Supplies: Incident Report Form, one blank form for each participant (Appendix O); backboards with a minimum of three straps and a commercial head immobilizer attached (one backboard per five participants); rescue tubes; Lifeguarding Skills Checklist (Appendix M)

Goal: Participants will understand their responsibilities following an incident and the procedures to cope with reactions to stress. Participants will also become familiar with how to provide care for victims with spinal injury in deep water.

Objectives

After completing this lesson, participants should be able to—

1. Name six facility-related responsibilities of a lifeguard after an emergency.
2. Describe how to control a crowd that gathers around the victim of an emergency.
3. Explain how an incident or injury report may help prevent similar incidents in the future.
4. Explain how a lifeguard should respond to questions from the media and others not affiliated with the facility after an emergency.
5. List three purposes of a staff debriefing.
6. Explain what stress is and list six negative effects of stress.
7. Describe six ways of coping with stress.
8. Explain the purpose of a critical stress debriefing.
9. Make appropriate decisions about care when given an example of an emergency involving a possible injury to the spine.
10. Demonstrate how to immobilize a victim on a backboard in deep water.

REVIEW OF PREVIOUS MATERIAL

Time: 5 minutes

Primary Points:

Review

- Injuries to the spine account for a small percentage of all injuries, but when they occur, they can result in death or paralysis.
- To determine whether someone has a spinal injury, consider the cause and signs and symptoms.
- If you suspect spinal injury in the water, activate your emergency action plan.
- Care for a spinal injury first by stabilizing the head and neck and then immobilizing the victim's body on a backboard.

RESPONSIBILITIES RELATED TO THE FACILITY

Time: 30 minutes

Primary Points:

Lifeguarding Today
page 220

- A lifeguard has the following responsibilities after an emergency:
  - Facility responsibilities, such as—
    - Controlling bystanders.
    - Filing a report.
    - Checking equipment.
  - The responsibility of the lifeguard to take care of himself or herself by dealing with the emotional effects of an emergency.

Controlling Bystanders

Primary Points:

Lifeguarding Today
page 220

- When an emergency occurs, one responsibility of a lifeguard may be to control bystanders.
  - If you are providing care to a victim, controlling bystanders may be the responsibility of support staff, such as cashiers, maintenance personnel, or swimming instructors.
  - Bystanders can also help with crowd control.
- Depending on time and available help, you may rope off the emergency area to keep patrons at a distance.
- When controlling a crowd, try to move the crowd away from the victim and the pool. Give the victim as much privacy and comfort as possible.
- Use a public address (PA) system, to instruct the crowd to keep back.
  - If you do not have a PA system, use verbal commands and hand movements.
- Make sure EMS personnel have been called, if necessary, and have access to the victim.

Closing the Pool

Primary Points:

Lifeguarding Today
pages 220 & 221

- The decision to close or reopen a facility usually is made by the head lifeguard or the facility manager. This decision may depend on several factors:
  - Whether all required equipment is in place
  - Whether enough lifeguards are available and are not too upset or distracted to do effective surveillance
  - The number of patrons remaining in the facility
  - The amount of time the facility would otherwise remain open
- If the facility is reopened—
  - Lifeguards should be at their stations.
  - Patrons should return to the pool in an orderly way.

Filing a Report

Primary Points:

Lifeguarding Today
pages 221 & 222

- An incident report must be filed as soon as possible after an incident. This report contains information on the victim(s), the incident, care provided, witness statements, and other information required by the facility.
- An incident report—
  - Serves as a legal document in case of legal action.
  - Can be used to identify hazards.
  - Should contain no opinion or hearsay, only factual information.
  - Should not attribute fault or blame anyone.

Activity:

**Incident Report Form,
Appendix O**

Give each participant a blank incident report form. Ask participants to take 5 minutes to fill out the report using a simulated injury, such as a fall on the deck resulting in a head injury, as the incident. Take 5 minutes to discuss the form, emphasizing their description of the incident, type of injury sustained, and the care given prior to EMS arrival.

Dealing With Questions

Primary Points:

Lifeguarding Today
page 222

- After an emergency, people such as attorneys, TV or newspaper reporters, and insurance company representatives may ask you questions.
- Do not give anyone any information about the emergency.
- If people ask you questions, refer them to the facility's spokesperson identified in your facility's policies and procedures manual or emergency action plan.
  - Only the facility's spokesperson should speak to the public and others about the emergency.

Checking Equipment

Primary Points:

Lifeguarding Today
pages 222–225

- Lifeguards must check equipment and supplies after an incident and ensure that any used or moved during the emergency are replaced.
- Lifeguards should report any equipment that malfunctioned to the head lifeguard or facility management.

Staff Debriefing

Primary Points:

Lifeguarding Today
page 225

- The purpose of staff debriefing is to examine what happened and how to prevent similar incidents in the future.
- The purpose is **not** to assign blame or criticize.
- The debriefing should take place as soon as possible after the incident.

RESPONSIBILITY TO YOURSELF

Time: 15 minutes

Primary Point:

Lifeguarding Today
page 225

- You have a responsibility to yourself to understand the physical and emotional effects an emergency can have on you and to cope with them.

Stress

Primary Points:

Lifeguarding Today
pages 225 & 226

- Stress is a natural response to an emergency. It is a physical, mental, or emotional state that causes distress or disruption in a person's mental or emotional balance.
- Too much stress can have negative effects on a person. Some of these effects include—
    - Sleeplessness.
    - Anxiety.
    - Depression.
    - Exhaustion.
    - Nausea.
    - Nightmares.
- Stress needs to be recognized and dealt with in a positive way. Six ways of coping with stress are—
    - Alternating physical exercise, such as swimming 1/4 mile with periods of relaxation in the first 24 hours after the incident.
    - Keeping busy.
    - Not withdrawing from contact and communication with other people.
    - Not suppressing or hiding your feelings if you feel miserable.

- Reminding yourself that your reaction is normal and you are not going crazy.
- Watching your diet. Cut down on sugar, fats, and caffeine while feeling effects of stress.
- Avoiding alcohol and drugs.
- Keeping your life as normal as possible, sticking to your regular schedule, and eating regular meals.
■ Rescues can be stressful for any lifeguard, especially if they involve severe injury or death. In such cases, coping with stress may require outside intervention.
■ Critical incident stress debriefing is designed to help people who have been through very stressful incidents deal with the effects of that stress.
- The debriefing is conducted by a trained person, often a mental health professional.
- That person's job is to help everyone involved express their feelings and reactions, recognize them as normal, and learn ways to cope with them.
■ Taking part in this process does **not** in any way mean you are weak.

BREAK

Time: 10 minutes

Participants should change into swimsuits and prepare for the in-water skills practice.

PUTTING IT ALL TOGETHER — SHALLOW WATER SPINAL INJURY MANAGEMENT SKILLS REVIEW

Time: 20 minutes

Activity:

This activity enables the participants to review and apply previously learned spinal injury management skills and knowledge.

1. Divide the participants into two groups.
2. Select one participant in each group to play the role of the primary lifeguard. Select another participant to play the role of the secondary lifeguard. The remaining participants play the roles of bystanders, providing help as needed.
3. From the following two situations, assign one group situation #1 and the other group situation #2:

Situation #1—Victim is face up in shallow water.
Situation #2—Victim is face down in shallow water.

4. Have the first group give care to a victim of suspected spinal injury based on the situation given them. Care for spinal injury includes—
   - Activating the emergency action plan.
   - Providing in-line stabilization.
   - Positioning the victim face up.
   - Immobilizing the victim on a backboard.
   - Removing the victim from the water.

   The participants from the second group can observe and provide feedback.
5. Have the second group provide care for the situation given them while the first group observes and provides feedback.

CARING FOR SPINAL INJURY IN DEEP WATER

Time: 5 minutes

Primary Points:

Lifeguarding Today
page 214

- It is rare for a spinal injury to occur in deep water. If one does occur, however, you will want to try to move the victim to shallow water.
- Enter the deep water with a rescue tube. If the victim is at the surface and face down, use the head splint technique with a rescue tube. If the victim is face up, use the head and chin support technique. If the victim is submerged, use the head and chin support technique. This requires you to release your rescue tube, submerge, perform the technique, and bring the victim to the surface. A second lifeguard can retrieve and position your rescue tube under your arms once you surface.
- Secure the victim to the backboard in the same manner as was done in shallow water. Use additional rescuers whenever available to help support the board, secure the straps, and remove the victim from the water.

Note: Additional rescuers can use a platform attached to the deck, more rescue tubes, or lifejackets to help support themselves when assisting in deep water backboarding.

SKILL PRACTICE: IN-LINE STABILIZATION TECHNIQUES (DEEP WATER)

Time: 30 minutes

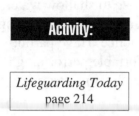

Activity:

Lifeguarding Today
page 214

Rescue Tubes

Head Splint Technique

In deep water, explain and demonstrate the head splint technique with the use of a rescue tube. Tell the participants that this is the same skill that they learned in shallow water, but with the use of a rescue tube for support. Assign partners or ask participants to find a partner. Guide participants through the following steps:

1. Approach the victim from the side.
2. While using the rescue tube to support yourself above water, position the victim's arms against his or her head. Do this by grasping the victim's arms midway between the shoulder and the elbow. Grasp the victim's right arm with your right hand and the victim's left arm with your left hand.
3. Squeeze the arms against the victim's head in an effort to immobilize the head and neck.
4. Glide the victim slowly forward.
5. While moving, rotate the victim toward you so that he or she turns faceup in the water. This is done by pushing the victim's arm that is closer to you under water while pulling the victim's other arm across the surface.
6. Position the victim's head in the crook of your arm, with the head in line with the body.
7. Maintain this position until help arrives.
8. Have participants perform the skill several times and then change places with their partners and repeat the practice. Have participants practice the skill until they feel comfortable performing it. Check off the participants' skills on the Lifeguarding Skills Checklist (Appendix M) as you watch them practice.

Head and Chin Support Technique

Activity:

Lifeguarding Today
pages 214 & 215

In deep water, explain and demonstrate the head and chin support technique for a face-up victim. Assign or ask participants to work in groups of three (one primary rescuer, one secondary rescuer, and one victim). Guide participants through the following steps:

1. Approach the victim from the side.
2. While using the rescue tube to support yourself above water, place one forearm along the length of the victim's breastbone and the other forearm along the victim's spine.

3. Use your hands to gently position the victim's head in line with the body. Hold the victim's lower jaw with one hand and the back of the head with the other hand.
4. Squeeze your forearms together, clamping the victim's chest and back. Continue to support the victim's head.
5. Support the victim face up in the water. Move to shallow water.
6. Have participants perform the skill several times and then change places with their partners and repeat the practice. Have participants practice the skill until they feel comfortable performing it. Check off the participants' skills as you watch them practice.

Submerged Spinal Injury Victim

Activity:

Lifeguarding Today
page 208

In deep water, explain and demonstrate the procedure for rescuing a submerged spinal injury victim. Assign or ask participants to work in groups of three (one primary rescuer, one secondary rescuer, and one victim). Guide participants through the following steps:
1. Release your rescue tube and submerge and position yourself to the victim's side.
2. Place one forearm along the length of the victim's breastbone and the other forearm along the victim's spine.
3. Use your hands to gently position the victim's head in line with the body. Hold the victim's lower jaw with one hand and the back of the head with the other hand.
4. Squeeze your forearms together, clamping the victim's chest and back. Continue to support the victim's head.
5. Move the victim up and forward to bring him or her to the surface. If the victim was found face down, you must turn him or her face up as you surface. Roll under the victim while turning the victim over in the water. Do this slowly to avoid twisting the victim's body. The victim will be face up when you surface on the other side.
6. To provide support above water, a second rescuer replaces the rescue tube by placing it under your arms (Fig. 10–1).
   ■ The second rescuer submerges one end of the rescue tube under your arms and positions it, without hitting the victim, so that it is under both arms.
7. Support the victim face up in the water until help arrives.
8. Have participants perform the skill several times and then change places with their partners and repeat the practice. Have participants practice the skill until they feel comfortable performing it. Check off the participants' skills as you watch them practice.

Figure 10–1

SKILL PRACTICE: USING A BACKBOARD (DEEP WATER)

Time: 60 minutes

Primary Point:

Lifeguarding Today
pages 214–215

Activity:

**Backboards
Straps
Head Immobilizers**

Once you have stabilized the victim's head and neck with either the head splint or the head and chin support technique, immobilize the victim on a backboard and remove him or her from the water.

In deep water, explain and demonstrate how to immobilize a victim on a backboard. Assign or ask participants to work in groups of five (one victim, two lifeguards, two bystanders).

Note: If you have extra backboards, you can form groups with fewer than five participants.

Have participants rotate, so that each participant plays the role of the primary rescuer, second lifeguard, and victim. Each participant will have 10 minutes to immobilize a victim on a backboard and remove the victim from the water. Guide participants through the following steps:

1. As you bring the victim toward the corner of the pool, a second lifeguard enters the water, submerges the backboard, and slides it under the victim. The backboard must be positioned so that it extends beyond the victim's head when the backboard is raised.

2. While the second lifeguard raises the backboard into place, carefully withdraw your arm from beneath the victim. If you are using the head and chin support, keep your hand on the chin and place your other hand under the backboard. If you are using the

head splint technique, move your arm that is under the victim toward the top of the victim's head while the second lifeguard holds the victim using the head and chin support (one hand on the chin and one hand on the board).

3. When the backboard is raised, the second lifeguard holds the backboard in place. This is done by resting the backboard on the rescue tube (Fig. 10–2). The victim's head is supported by the second lifeguard placing both hands on the sides of the head. If other rescuers are available, they can help support the backboard at the sides.

Figure 10–2

4. Secure the victim to the backboard. Straps should be placed across the victim's chest, hips, and thighs. The strap used on the chest should be placed across the chest and under the arms. Securing this strap tightly under the armpits helps prevent the victim from sliding on the backboard during removal from the water. Using the hip strap, secure the victim's hands along his or her sides or in front of the body. The third strap is placed across the victim's thighs.

5. Using a head immobilizing device, secure the victim's head to the board. To do this, place pads on each side of the victim's head. Then secure a strap across the victim's forehead.

6. Once the victim is secured on the backboard, remove him or her from the water. To do this, position the backboard with the head end by the side of the pool and the foot end straight out into the pool.

Note: Whenever possible, move the victim to shallow water to remove.

7. With one lifeguard on each side, lift the head of the backboard slightly and place it on the edge of the overflow trough if possible.
8. One lifeguard gets out of the pool and grasps the head of the backboard. The other lifeguard moves to the foot end of the backboard. As the lifeguard on deck stands up, steps backward, and pulls the backboard, the lifeguard at the foot end pushes on the backboard. Together they slide the backboard up over the edge of the deck, out of and away from the water. If others are there to assist, they should position themselves in the water at the sides of the backboard and help lift the backboard onto the deck.
9. Have participants practice the skill until they feel comfortable. Check off participants' skills when they assume the position of the primary rescuer and perform the skill correctly.

CLOSING

Time: 5 minutes

Primary Points:

- Use a rescue tube to help keep you and the victim above water when you perform in-line stabilization in deep water.
- When possible, move a victim of suspected spinal injury from deep water to shallow water.
- If you are unable to move to shallow water, move to a corner of the pool and immobilize the victim on a backboard.
  - Additional rescuers can provide more support.

Activity:

1. Respond to any questions from the participants.
2. Remind participants that they will be taking the final written exam and skills test in the next class session.

Assignment:

Review Chapters 1–12 of *Lifeguarding Today,* review study questions, and bring questions about the course material and skills to the next class session.

Lesson 11

Written Exam and Final Skills Scenarios

Class Assignment prior to this lesson:	Review Chapters 1–12 of *Lifeguarding Today* and review study questions.
Length:	3 hours
Equipment/Supplies:	Copies of Lifeguard Training exams A and B and answer sheets for each participant (Appendix S); pencils, rescue tubes (one rescue tube per two or three participants); Lifeguarding Skills Checklist (Appendix M); envelope or box
Goal:	Participants will indicate whether they have acquired the knowledge and skills required to successfully complete the American Red Cross Lifeguard Training course by making appropriate decisions for care when given two scenarios involving emergency situations and by passing a written exam.

REVIEW OF COURSE MATERIAL

Time: 15 minutes

Activity:

Ask participants if they have any questions regarding the course material before taking the written exam and final skills scenarios. Respond to any questions the participants may have.

FINAL WRITTEN EXAM

Time: 45 minutes

Activity:

Written Exams
Answer Sheets
Pencils

1. Tell participants that they will now take a 50-question examination. They will have 45 minutes to complete the exam and must answer at least 40 questions correctly to pass. They may not use their participant's manuals to find the answers.
2. Hand out an examination and answer sheet to each participant.
3. Tell participants to write only on the answer sheet, mark answers clearly, and use pencil only (in case they want to erase or change an answer).
4. Tell them to check their answers before handing them in.
5. Tell them to come to you or raise one hand when they have finished the exam or have any questions.
6. Score the exams. The answer keys for both exams are at the end of this instructor's manual.

Note: As participants hand in their answer sheets and exams, quickly grade each exam and return it so that the participant can review any missed questions. If time allows, discuss with the class any exam items that were a problem. Collect all answer sheets and exams. If a participant fails the exam, ask him or her to see you after class to schedule a retest.

BREAK

Time: 10 minutes

Participants should change into swimsuits and prepare for the final skills scenarios.

FINAL SKILLS SCENARIOS

Time: 90 minutes

Activity:

Rescue Tubes

Explain the following procedures:

- Each participant will have the opportunity to participate in two skills scenarios.
- Each skills scenario consists of a rescue using a rescue tube.
- Decide the order in which the participants will go. Participants may volunteer, or you may select them alphabetically or randomly.
- After all the participants have performed and completed skills scenario 1, they will perform and complete skills scenario 2.

Note: If you have a co-instructor, you can divide the participants into two groups. One group can perform skills scenario 1 while the other group performs skills scenario 2. When each group has completed their respective scenario, have them perform the other skills scenario.

- Each participant must perform the two skills scenarios satisfactorily to pass the course and receive certification in American Red Cross Lifeguard Training.
- Participants have only one opportunity to reattempt a skills scenario if they do not successfully perform it the first time. If a participant does not successfully perform one or both skills scenarios, ask him or her to see you after class to schedule a retest, if time does not allow you to retest immediately.

Scenario 1:

You are in the lifeguard chair (or lifeguard station) when you notice an active drowning victim in the deep water. The victim is facing away from you.

Participants must —
- Enter the water with a rescue tube.
- Approach an active drowning victim on the surface of the water.
- Make contact with the victim and perform an appropriate rescue.
- Bring the victim to safety.

Scenario 2:

You are in the lifeguard chair (or lifeguard station) when you notice a passive drowning victim sinking to the bottom of the pool.

Participants must—
- Enter the water with a rescue tube.
- Approach the submerged, unconscious victim.
- Make contact with the victim and perform an appropriate rescue.
- Bring the victim to safety.
- Remove the victim from the water with the assistance of a second rescuer.
- Explain how to provide care for a nonbreathing victim who has a pulse.

Note: When you are evaluating the participants' performance of these skills scenarios, remember to evaluate them on their ability to meet the objective of each critical skill in the scenarios, not on whether they performed the skill "perfectly." Refer to the Lifeguarding Critical Skills Chart (Appendix N) for the performance objectives of each critical skill.

Once each participant has successfully completed each skills scenario, check off the skills scenarios on the space provided under "Final Skills Scenarios" in the Lifeguarding Skills Checklist in Appendix M.

BREAK

Time: 10 minutes

Participants should change into dry clothes and meet in the classroom for the course closing.

CLOSING

Time: 10 minutes

Envelope or Box

1. Refer participants to the back of their *Lifeguarding Today* participant's manuals for a copy of the Participant Course Evaluation form. Ask participants to complete the form and leave it in the box or envelope you have provided near the door.

2. Issue (or explain you will mail later) an *American Red Cross Lifeguard Training Course Completion* certificate and a *CPR for the Professional Rescuer* certificate to participants who scored 80 percent or better on each written exam, who demonstrated competency in each critical skill and CPR skill taught, and who successfully performed the two skills scenarios.

3. Thank all participants for attending the course.

4. Make arrangements to retest any participants who did not successfully pass the written exam(s) or scenario(s).

Course Outline

Waterfront Lifeguarding Module

Activity	Approximate Time
Introduction to the Module	15 minutes
Introduction to Waterfront Lifeguarding	10 minutes
Injury Prevention	10 minutes
Facility Surveillance	20 minutes
Patron Surveillance	40 minutes
Preparing for Emergencies	10 minutes
Rescue Skills	40 minutes
Break	10 minutes
Skills Practice: Waterfront Rescue Skills	135 minutes
Entries and Approaches	(15 minutes)
The Rescue Board	(60 minutes)
Removal From the Water	(15 minutes)
Surface Diving	(10 minutes)
Using a Mask and Fins to Perform a Deep-water Line Search	(35 minutes)
Break	10 minutes
Final Written Exam and Closing	30 minutes
Waterfront Lifeguarding Module, Total Time	**5 hours, 30 minutes**

The purpose of the Waterfront Lifeguarding module is to teach lifeguards the skills and knowledge needed to prevent and respond to aquatic emergencies at a waterfront facility. The module content and activities prepare waterfront lifeguarding candidates to provide for the safety of patrons and to recognize and effectively respond to emergencies at a waterfront facility.

Administrative Notes

The following points apply to this module:

Prerequisites

To be eligible for the Waterfront Lifeguarding module, the candidate must have a current *American Red Cross Lifeguard Training* certificate and a current *American Red Cross CPR for the Professional Rescuer* certificate.

Module Length

This module is designed to be taught in a minimum of 5 hours, 30 minutes. This includes time for waterfront lifeguarding skills practice, class activities, and the showing of one video.

Since the times allotted in the lesson plans do not include relief breaks or a lunch break, you may have to build additional time into the module.

Class Size

It is recommended that there be one instructor for every 10 participants in the class. If the class has more than 10 participants, you should have a co-instructor or aide. Close supervision is necessary to ensure effective practice and the safety of participants. Furthermore, you can run a class more efficiently if you keep the class reasonably small, and you are less likely to exceed the allotted time periods for various activities.

Facilities

Classroom Space

The lessons in the Waterfront Lifeguarding module require classroom space suitable for discussion, video viewing, and taking the final written exam. The classroom should be conveniently located for participants. It should also be equipped with the necessary teaching aids and materials.

Swimming Area

The Waterfront Lifeguarding module may be conducted at either a waterfront or at a pool that is large enough to accommodate rescue boards.

An adequate number of lifeguards with no duties other than supervising the class should be present during all water sessions.

Equipment and Supplies

At the beginning of each lesson is a list of required equipment and supplies. A master list of equipment for the module is in Appendix G. Make sure all the equipment is ready and in working order before you teach the module.

All participants should have a copy of *Lifeguarding Today* (Stock No. 654110). The following video is required for this module: *Lifeguarding Today* (Stock No. 654114).

Testing and Certificates

On successful completion of the module, participants receive an *American Red Cross Course Completion* certificate (Cert. 3002) indicating *Waterfront Lifeguarding*. There is no validity period for the Waterfront Lifeguarding certificate.

To receive the course completion certificate for the American Red Cross Waterfront Lifeguarding module, the participant must—

■ Demonstrate competency in each critical skill taught in the module. (See the Lifeguarding Skills Checklist, Appendix M, and the Critical Skills Chart, Appendix N. For more information on critical skills, see Chapter 3.)

■ Correctly answer at least 80 percent of the written examination questions (20 out of a total of 25 questions).

For more information on awarding certificates, completing records, and conducting course evaluations, see Chapter 6.

The Waterfront Lifeguarding Module Lesson Plan

Class Assignment prior to this lesson: Read Chapter 13 of *Lifeguarding Today* and complete the study questions.

Length: 5 hours, 30 minutes

Equipment/Supplies: Name tags (optional); course roster; participant's manuals; video— *Lifeguarding Today;* VCR and monitor; chalkboard or newsprint (flip chart); chalk or markers; rescue tubes (one rescue tube per two participants); rescue boards (one rescue board per five participants); mask and fins (if the facility or local unit of the American Red Cross is unable to supply mask and fins for each participant, participants are responsible for providing them); Lifeguarding Skills Checklist (Appendix M); copies of Waterfront Lifeguarding Exams A and B, and answer sheets for each participant (Appendix S); pencils; envelope or box; Participant Course Evaluation forms

Goal: Participants will gain the knowledge and skills needed to lifeguard effectively at a waterfront facility.

Objectives

After completing this module, participants should be able to—

1. Describe different types, uses, and designs of waterfront facilities.
2. Describe two methods of zone coverage that may be used at a waterfront.
3. Describe environmental conditions that affect scanning at a waterfront.
4. List at least three potential hazards at a waterfront.
5. Describe how the buddy system and the buddy board are used to supervise swimmers at camp waterfronts.
6. Demonstrate the run-and-swim entry.
7. Demonstrate the walking assist and the beach drag.
8. Demonstrate the head-first surface dive.
9. Discuss how and when to use rescue boards and rescue craft at waterfront facilities.
10. Demonstrate how to use a rescue board to rescue a distressed swimmer.
11. Demonstrate how to use a rescue board to rescue someone who cannot get onto the rescue board.
12. Describe the appropriate rescue techniques and skills used in special rescue situations such as missing person procedures, search for a SCUBA diver, and cold water rescues.
13. Describe the sequence for a missing person procedure.
14. Demonstrate the proper use of mask and fins during a deep-water line search.

INTRODUCTION TO THE MODULE

Time: 15 Minutes

Activity:

Name Tags
Course Roster

Course Outline

1. **Instructor and Participant Introductions**
   - Introduce yourself and welcome participants to the American Red Cross Waterfront Lifeguarding module.
   - Have participants introduce themselves by sharing their names and their reasons for taking this module, and their expectations.
   - Give a brief description of your background and credentials. Identify yourself as an American Red Cross instructor, and explain that this module is one of many modules and courses offered by the American Red Cross. Ask the participants to write their full names and addresses on the course roster so that you can complete the American Red Cross *Course Record* (Form 6418 and 6418A).

2. **Orientation to the Facility**
   - Point out the locations of fire exits, telephones, rest rooms, and drinking fountains, and explain facility rules, if any.
   - Tell participants that they will need a swimsuit to participate in skill practice sessions.

3. **Course Schedule**
   - Distribute an outline that includes dates and times of class meetings, lesson content, and class assignments. Skill practice sessions and examinations should be clearly identified.

4. **Course Prerequisites**
   - To enroll in the Waterfront Lifeguarding module, participants must have a current American Red Cross *Lifeguard Training* certificate and a *CPR for the Professional Rescuer* certificate. If the participants' certificates were not checked at registration, check them at this time.

5. **Module Description**
   - Share the following goal statement with the class:
   The purpose of this module is to teach lifeguards the skills and knowledge needed to prevent and respond to aquatic emergencies at a waterfront facility.

6. **How Participants Will Learn**
   - Briefly explain that participants will learn through lectures, discussions, reading, group activities, and skill practice. This module is supported by video segments.

7. **Participant's Manual**
   - Identify the participant's manual for this module, American Red Cross *Lifeguarding Today,* and lead the participants through Chapter 13, "Waterfront Facilities." Instruct the participants in how best to use the manual to master the module content. Point out the following features of Chapter 13:
     - Objectives
     - Key Terms
     - Sidebars
     - Study Questions

   Lifeguarding Today, Chapter 13 "Waterfront Facilities" is required reading for this module.

8. **Module Completion Requirements**
   - Describe the American Red Cross requirements for successful module completion. To successfully complete this module, the participant must—
     - Correctly demonstrate the critical skills taught in the module.
     - Correctly answer at least 80 percent of the written examination questions (20 questions out of 25).

Note: If there are academic requirements or state or local requirements beyond the minimum completion requirements set by the American Red Cross, explain them to participants at this time.

INTRODUCTION TO WATERFRONT LIFEGUARDING

Time: 10 minutes

Video:

Tell participants they are going to see a video segment that will introduce them to the module. Show the introductory video segment: "Waterfront Lifeguarding." (approx. 6 minutes)

Primary Points:

Lifeguarding Today
page 230

- The term **open water** refers to lakes, rivers, bays, reservoirs, canals, the ocean—any body of water that is not enclosed as a swimming pool is.
- A waterfront facility is a nonsurf open-water area that may be found at a resort, park, summer camp, or campground.
- Lifeguarding at a waterfront facility is different from lifeguarding at a pool. You must be aware of the different hazards and environmental conditions, such as water quality, currents, and beach conditions that may exist at your facility. They present a variety of surveillance challenges.

- To lifeguard at a waterfront facility, you will use the rescue and lifeguarding skills you learned in your Lifeguard Training course and in Chapters 1–12 of *Lifeguarding Today,* along with the new ones you will learn in this module.
- Because each facility has unique conditions, this module will not cover every aspect of lifeguarding at every waterfront facility. When you begin lifeguarding at a waterfront facility, you should receive specific in-service training for that facility.

INJURY PREVENTION

Time: 10 minutes

Primary Points:

Lifeguarding Today page 230

- Review the three injury prevention strategies presented in Chapters 4, 5, and 6 of *Lifeguarding Today:*
  - **Communication** as an injury prevention strategy has three aspects:
    - Informing patrons about the potential for injury
    - Educating patrons about the consequences of inappropriate behavior
    - Enforcing rules and regulations that prevent injury
  - **Patron Surveillance** requires a lifeguard to maintain close watch over patrons using a facility.
  - Effective surveillance has four elements:
    - Recognizing how distressed swimmers and drowning persons behave
    - Using appropriate scanning techniques to identify patrons in trouble in the water
    - Proper stationing of lifeguards
    - Knowing your area of responsibility
  - **Facility Surveillance** is a method of preventing injuries caused by hazards in the facility environment.

Rules and Regulations

Primary Points:

Lifeguarding Today pages 230 & 231

- Rules and regulations that may be posted at a waterfront include—
  - Swim only when a lifeguard is on duty.
  - Swim only in designated areas.
  - Rough play is not allowed: no running, splashing, pushing, or dunking.
  - No playing or swimming under docks, rafts, or platforms.
  - No boats in the swimming area.
  - Dive only in designated areas.

- No glass containers allowed on the beach.
- No alcohol or other drugs allowed.
- Floats, air mattresses, and tubes not allowed.
- No fishing near the swimming area.
- Keep away from in front of the lifeguard stand areas.

Activity: Discuss with participants other rules and regulations that might be posted at a waterfront.

FACILITY SURVEILLANCE

Time: 20 minutes

Facility Characteristics

Primary Points:

Lifeguarding Today pages 231 & 232

- You need to know the potential changes in the environment that can affect your facility, such as changes caused by wind, erosion, tides, and weather.
- Water conditions, such as wave action, can affect surveillance techniques.
- All facilities should have a map or chart, called a contour map, showing the physical characteristics and structures in and around a waterfront. The chart should show—
  - Water depths.
  - Shape of the bottom.
  - Holes and drop-offs.
  - All structures, such as docks rafts, diving platforms, pilings, and lifeguard stands.

Activity: Review the different types of dock formations set up for specific needs of the facility. Refer participants to page 232, figures 13–3A to 13–3G in *Lifeguarding Today*.

The following is a listing of the dock formations on page 232 of *Lifeguarding Today:*

Figure	Dock Formation
13–3, A	"F" formation
13–3, B	"H" formation
13–3, C	"L" formation
13–3, D	"A" formation
13–3, E	Modified "H" formation
13–3, F	"T" formation
13–3, G	Large dock formation

Primary Points:

- Remind participants that as lifeguards at a waterfront, they should—
  - Be sure floating docks and rafts are anchored securely.
  - Check boundaries of diving area to ensure water depths are safe for diving.
  - Keep dock areas wet to protect patron's feet.
- Changing water conditions such as water depth and current may affect the safety of patrons.
  - Heavy rainfall and long dry periods can affect water depth.
  - When a dam releases water, water depths change above and below the dam.
  - Currents and wind can bring debris into the water. Plants, dirt, leaves, algae, and pollen can limit visibility.
  - Water is usually colder early in the season and after a rain. Colder areas can be present several feet below the surface. Cold water can lead to hypothermia.
- Safety checks should be done frequently because of the environmental changes that can occur at a waterfront facility.
- Inspect the area daily for sharp objects, broken glass, rocks, and litter. Check for objects around the lifeguard stands. Check docks for protruding nails, loose or rotting wood, and weak or frayed anchor lines.
- Make sure all safety equipment is in good working condition and placed in its proper location. Report any missing or damaged equipment. Clean off any suntan oils or lotion on equipment.

PATRON SURVEILLANCE

Time: 40 minutes

Video:

Show the Waterfront Lifeguarding video segment: "Patron Surveillance." (approx. 11 minutes)

Primary Points:

Lifeguarding Today
page 233

- A waterfront may have many activities, such as swimming, boating, sailing, canoeing, and SCUBA diving.
- A facility may have different zones for boating, swimming, fishing, and other activities.

Factors That Affect Zone Coverage

Primary Points:

Lifeguarding Today
page 233

- Factors that affect zone coverage include—
  - Size and shape of the waterfront.
  - Size and shape of docks and rafts.
  - Number of people using the waterfront.
  - Types of activities that may take place.

- Size of the lifeguarding staff.
- Environmental conditions, such as sun, wind, wave action, and water quality.
- History of injuries in the area.

■ Lifeguards should talk to the head lifeguard or facility manager if they feel their zone is so large that the response time in an emergency would be too long.

■ Location of lifeguard stations must enable a lifeguard to see the entire area of responsibility.

■ A lifeguard may have to move the stand to adjust for changes in sun, wind, and water conditions.

■ Swimming may have to be suspended if waves reduce visibility.

■ Some waterfronts have several swimming areas marked by buoyed lifelines for various skill levels.

■ Look for distressed swimmers clinging to a lifeline at the far end of the swimming area.

Supervision From Rescue Craft

Primary Points:

Lifeguarding Today
pages 234 & 235

■ Using rescue craft increases coverage of the swimming area.

■ Rescue craft can be used to patrol the outer edge of a swimming area.

■ It can be stationed opposite a lifeguard station on land.

■ Your facility will have the kind of rescue craft best suited for its conditions.

■ Rescue boat should have the following equipment:
  - Extra oars or paddles
  - Several life jackets
  - Rescue tube
  - Anchor and line
  - First aid kit
  - Bailer

■ Be sure you are well trained in operating your facility's rescue craft before you use it.

Patron Surveillance at Camps

Primary Points:

Lifeguarding Today
page 235

■ When working at a camp waterfront, pay special attention to the characteristics of the waterfront and the ages and abilities of the swimmers.

■ Screening of swimmers' abilities should be done at the beginning of the camp session to determine which activities individual campers may participate in.

Discuss with participants how to organize a screening session for a camp waterfront at the beginning of the camp session. Emphasize the need for ensuring the safety of swimmers during screening. Additional staff may be needed to help.

Supervision of Swimmers: The Buddy System

■ Using a buddy system at a camp helps with the supervision of swimmers. This system involves pairing campers with the same swimming abilities and keeping the paired swimmers in designated swimming areas.

■ Some camps use buddy boards as a way to help ensure buddies stay in their designated area. Buddy boards may also be used for boating.

- Each camper gets a colored tag with his or her name on it.
- Tags may be labeled with the camper's swimming ability.
- Tags are kept in the "out" section of board when campers are not in the swimming area.
- Before entering the swimming area, a camper puts his or her tag in the "in" section and pairs up with a buddy.
- A lifeguard stationed at the area checks to see that everything is done correctly.
- When the camper leaves, he or she places the tag in the "out" section.
- A tag found in the "in" section after the water has been cleared may indicate several possibilities:
  - The camper forgot to move the tag from the "in" side to the "out" side before leaving the area.
  - A tag was wrongly placed by another camper leaving the swim area.
  - A lifeguard or other person stationed at the buddy board did not make sure the tag was placed correctly when the camper left the area.
  - A tag has fallen off the buddy board and is not easily visible.
  - A camper may be playing a joke.
  - You may have a missing person.
  - You must perform the buddy check again. If you still do not know where the camper is, initiate your missing person procedure.

PREPARING FOR EMERGENCIES

Time: 10 minutes

Primary Points:

Lifeguarding Today
pages 237 & 238

Communication

- Communication systems used at waterfronts may include—
  - Whistles.
  - Two-way radios.
  - Telephones.
  - Flags.
  - Megaphones.
  - Signals with rescue equipment.
- Be sure you understand the methods of communication used at your facility.
- During your first daily safety check, ensure the telephones are working.

Emergency Action Plan

Primary Points:

Lifeguarding Today
page 238

- Emergency action plans at a waterfront and at camps may include additional steps because of the environment, the weather, the size of the waterfront and its surroundings, and possibly a longer response time of EMS personnel.
- Although other personnel, such as lookouts, rangers, and maintenance or security personnel, may be included in the emergency action plan, you and other lifeguards on duty still have primary responsibility for managing an emergency.
- In case of an emergency, lifeguards should be prepared to respond as follows:
  - Recognize that someone is in trouble in the water.
  - Activate the emergency action plan.
  - Determine the method of rescue needed.
  - If you are not the lifeguard making the rescue, make sure the rescuing lifeguard's zone is covered.
  - Once the situation is under control, complete an incident report form and file it.
  - Replace any rescue equipment used and return to duty.

RESCUE SKILLS

Time: 40 minutes

Primary Points:

Lifeguarding Today
page 239

You can use all the skills you learned in the American Red Cross Lifeguard Training course, as well as the new ones you will learn in this module. These include—
- Entries.
- Removal of the victim.
- Surface diving.
- Use of a rescue board.
- Missing person search procedures.
- Use of mask and fins.

Video:

Show the Waterfront Lifeguarding video segment: "Rescue Skills." (approx. 14 minutes)

Other Rescue Situations and Skills

Spinal Injury Management

Primary Points:

Lifeguarding Today
page 243

- At a waterfront, you may have to modify the techniques for spinal injury management presented in earlier chapters because of waves or currents. Your in-service training will teach you how to modify the techniques you have learned to your specific facility.
- In water with waves, move the victim to calmer water if possible.
- In a current, once the victim is face up, point the victim's head into the current. This will help align the body with the current and minimize the possibility of injury from the moving water.

Using Watercraft for a Rescue

Primary Points:

Lifeguarding Today
page 250

- If your facility uses rescue craft, be sure that you are given an orientation and practice in maneuvering these craft during in-service training. The following are basic guidelines for using watercraft to make a rescue:
  - If rescuing a distressed swimmer, extend an oar to the victim and pull him or her to the stern of the craft.
  - If the victim cannot grasp the stern, reach out and grasp the victim and pull him or her to the stern.
  - If the victim cannot hold onto the stern as you move to safety, you must bring the victim onto the craft. Help the victim over the stern. Be careful not to upset the craft.
  - If you are using a motorized watercraft, always approach the victim from downwind and downstream. Shut the engine off

when you are 3 boat-lengths away from the victim and paddle to him or her.

- Bring the victim on board before you restart the engine.

Sightings and Cross Bearings

Primary Points:

Lifeguarding Today
page 251

- Sightings and cross bearings are two techniques you can use to help you keep track of where a drowning person has submerged. You must make sure you are swimming in a straight line toward his or her last known position.
  - For a sighting, line up the spot where the victim submerged with an object on the far shore, such as a tree or building. Note the victim's distance to shore along this imaginary line.
  - For a cross bearing, two lifeguards each take a sighting on the spot where the victim was last seen. Spotters on shore can help direct the guards as they swim to the victim.

Missing Person Procedure

Primary Points:

Lifeguarding Today
pages 251 & 252

- All staff members should be thoroughly trained in missing person procedures.
- Time is critical.
- The missing person reported may be a child who has wandered off, but since you cannot know whether the person is in the water, you must take all reports seriously.
- To avoid confusion, one person must be in charge of the procedure. This person may be the head lifeguard or facility manager.
- A predetermined signal alerts all staff.
- Lifeguards clear all water areas then report to a designated location with other staff.
- The person who made the report gives a description of the missing person.
- The public address system can be used to broadcast the description and tell the missing person to report to the main lifeguard area.
- Lifeguards search the swimming area, starting where the person was last seen. You must look under docks and rafts and other dangerous locations.
- Ask volunteers to help search shallow areas. Trained lifeguards search the deeper areas. Other staff search bathrooms, locker rooms, and tents.
- Lifeguards concentrate on water areas. Other people, including volunteers, and park rangers, may check other camp sites, playgrounds, and wooded areas.

- The search continues until every person is accounted for.
- If the missing person is not found, other emergency personnel and agencies may be called in—police, fire department, and search and rescue.

Searching Shallow-Water Areas

Primary Points:

Lifeguarding Today
page 252

- To do a shallow-water line search, adults, volunteers, lifeguard staff, or other members of the safety team link arms or hold hands and form a line in the water. The tallest person should be in water no more than chest deep. Searchers move forward through the water, gently sweeping with their feet to try to locate the missing person.

Deep-Water Line Search

Primary Points:

Lifeguarding Today
pages 252 & 253

- A deep-water line search is done in water greater than chest deep. Lifeguards wearing mask and fins form a line to search for a submerged victim. Searchers dive and swim forward. If the water is murky, they sweep the bottom with their hands to try to locate the missing person. The process of diving and resurfacing continues until the victim is found or emergency personnel arrives to help.
- Lifeguards return to the surface as straight up as possible. The line backs up, the lead lifeguard checks to see that all searchers are accounted for, then they dive again.
- One lifeguard serves as an above-water lookout with rescue equipment in case the person is found or someone gets into trouble.

Searching for a Missing SCUBA Diver

Primary Points:

Lifeguarding Today
page 257

- Searches for missing SCUBA divers should be conducted only by trained search and rescue personnel.
- However, you may have one or more of the following responsibilities:
  - Find out where the diver was last seen, or look for bubbles.
  - Check all out-of-water areas, including the parking lot or equipment storage area.
  - Use a sighting or cross bearing to keep track of the spot where bubbles were seen or where the diver was last seen.

Cold Water Rescue

Primary Points:

Lifeguarding Today
pages 257 & 258

- Sudden entry into cold water (70° F or 21° C) can cause a person to become unconscious and drown.
- Sudden entry into cold water can cause the following reactions:
  - A gasp reflex, which can cause the person to inhale water.
  - Rapid breathing, which can lead to hyperventilation.

- Increase in heart rate and changes in blood pressure, which can lead to a heart attack.
- Hypothermia, if the person remains in the water, which can lead to unconsciousness.

■ Cold water can also have effects that are not negative and can increase a victim's chance of survival.
  - Body temperature begins to drop.
  - Body functions almost stop, so the person requires little oxygen. Any oxygen left in the blood goes to the heart and brain to maintain their minimal function.
  - Some people have been resuscitated with little or no brain damage after being submerged in cold water for an extended period.

■ Other factors that can increase the chance of survival include—
  - Victim's age: children survive more often than adults.
  - Laryngospasm—water taken in by the victim may go to the stomach rather than the lungs because a spasm of the vocal cord can close the airway.
  - Water temperature—the colder the water, the faster the protecting mechanism operates.
  - Rapid removal of the victim from the water.

■ To perform a rescue in cold water—
  - Remove the victim as quickly as possible.
  - Do not enter the water yourself, if possible.
  - If you must enter the water, get assistance and take your rescue tube with a tow line attached. Wear a wetsuit, if possible.
  - When the victim is out of the water, assess his or her condition. The victim may seem to be dead and have the following signs:
    - Decreased or undetectable pulse rate
    - No detectable breathing
    - Bluish, cold skin
    - Rigid muscles

■ Begin rescue breathing and CPR if appropriate. Give first aid for hypothermia. Call EMS immediately.

BREAK

Time: 10 minutes

Participants should change into swimsuits and prepare for the in-water skills practice.

SKILLS PRACTICE: WATERFRONT RESCUE SKILLS

Time: 135 minutes

Entries and Approaches (15 minutes)

Run-and-Swim Entry

Primary Point:

Activity:

Lifeguarding Today page 235

Rescue Tubes

Use the run-and-swim entry from a gradually sloping shoreline.

Explain and demonstrate how to perform the run-and-swim entry. Guide the participants through the following steps:

1. Hold the rescue tube in one hand and the strap over your shoulder. Run into the water, and lift your legs to avoid falling.
2. When you reach the point where you can no longer run, drop the tube to the side, lean forward, and start swimming.

> **SAFETY TIP:**
>
> Make sure that participants do not dive or plunge into the water because it can result in serious injury.

3. Have participants practice the skill until they feel comfortable performing it. Check off the participants' skills on the Lifeguarding Skills Checklist (Appendix M) as you watch them practice.

Swimming With the Rescue Tube

Activity:

Lifeguarding Today page 239

Explain to participants that after they have done a run-and-swim entry, they can approach the victim in one of two ways:

- For short distances, you can swim with the rescue tube under your armpits.
- If the distance is great, let the rescue tube trail behind as you swim to the victim.

The Rescue Board (60 minutes)

Primary Points:

Some waterfronts use rescue boards as standard equipment when rescuing victims. The rescue board comes in various sizes and is fast, stable, and easy to use.

Rescuing a Distressed Swimmer

Activity:

Explain and demonstrate how to launch a rescue board and then use it to rescue a distressed swimmer. Assign partners or ask participants to find a partner. Guide the participants through the following steps:

Lifeguarding Today
pages 245–247

Rescue Boards

1. When launching a rescue board, hold onto the sides.
2. When you are about knee-deep, lay the rescue board on the water and push it forward alongside you. Then climb on the board just behind the middle and lie down.
3. Paddle a few strokes and then raise yourself onto your knees. Continue paddling.
4. Point the front end of the board toward the victim and continue to paddle, keeping your head up and keeping the victim in sight.
5. Approach the victim from the side.
6. Grasp the victim's hand or wrist, and slide off the rescue board to the opposite side.
7. Help the victim extend his or her arms across the rescue board, and encourage him or her to relax and be calm.
8. Keep the rescue board as stable as possible, and assist the victim onto it.
9. Have the victim lie on his or her stomach with his or her head toward the bow.
10. Kick to turn the bow of the rescue board toward shore. Then carefully climb onto the rescue board from the back and lie down between the victim's legs. Be careful not to tip the rescue board; keep your legs in the water for stability.
11. Paddle the rescue board to shore.
12. Have participants practice the skill until they feel comfortable performing it. Have participants perform the skill several times and then change places with their partners and repeat the practice. Check off the participants' skills as you watch them practice.

Rescuing Someone Who Cannot Get on the Rescue Board

Activity:

Lifeguarding Today
pages 248 & 249

Explain and demonstrate how to rescue someone who cannot get on the rescue board. Assign partners or ask participants to find a partner. Guide the participants through the following steps:

1. Launch the rescue board and approach the victim from the side. Position the rescue board so that the victim is slightly forward of the middle of the board.
2. Grasp the victim's hand or wrist, then slide off the board to the opposite side and flip the rescue board toward you. At this point, you are holding the victim's arm across the rescue board, and the victim's chest is against the far edge of the rescue board.
3. Grasp the far edge of the rescue board with your other hand.
4. Kneel on the edge of the rescue board, and use your body weight to flip the board toward you. Protect the victim's head.

5. Rotate the victim so that he or she is lying lengthwise in the middle of the rescue board with his or her head toward the bow.

6. Kick to turn the bow of the rescue board toward shore. Then carefully climb onto the rescue board from the back, and lie between the victim's legs. Be careful not to flip the rescue board; keep your legs in the water for stability.

7. Have participants practice the skill until they feel comfortable performing it. Have participants perform the skill several times and then change places with their partners and repeat the practice. Check off the participants' skills as you watch them practice.

Removal From the Water (15 minutes)

In addition to the techniques you learned in Lifeguard Training, there are two other techniques that you can use when removing a victim from the water—

■ **The Walking Assist.** This assist is used to help a conscious victim walk out of the water.

■ **The Beach Drag.** This removal is used to help remove an unconscious person from the water. When possible, seek additional assistance from other staff to help you with this removal.

Walking Assist

Explain and demonstrate a walking assist. Assign partners or ask participants to find a partner. Guide the participants through the following steps:

1. Place one of the victim's arms around your neck and across your shoulder.

2. Grasp the wrist of the arm that is across your shoulder, and wrap your free arm around the victim's back or waist to provide support.

3. Maintain a firm grasp, and help the victim walk out of the water.

Beach Drag

Explain and demonstrate a beach drag. Assign partners or ask participants to find a partner. Guide the participants through the following steps:

1. Stand behind the victim and grasp him or her under the armpits, supporting the victim's head with your forearms.

2. While walking backward, drag the victim toward shore.

3. Remove the victim completely from the water or at least to a point where the head and shoulders are out of the water.

4. Have participants practice the skills until they feel comfortable performing them. Check off the participants' skills as you watch them practice.

Surface Diving (10 minutes)

Primary Points:

There are two types of surface dives that may be used when performing a deep-water line search:
- Feet-first surface dive
- Headfirst surface dive

Note: Participants have already learned how to perform the feet-first surface dive in their lifeguard training course.

Feet-First Surface Dive

Activity:

Lifeguarding Today page 242

Briefly review the steps of the feet-first surface dive. These include the following:
1. A feet-first surface dive is performed by pressing down with your hands to raise yourself up to gain momentum to sink.
2. Keep sweeping your hands and arms upward to help you sink. When you can no longer sink, tuck your body and roll horizontally and begin to swim under water.

Headfirst Surface Dive

Activity:

Lifeguarding Today page 243

Explain and demonstrate the headfirst surface dive. Guide the participants through the following steps:
1. A headfirst surface dive is performed by plunging one arm downward, bending at the hips, and tucking your chin, while bringing the other arm to meet the extended arm.
2. Lift your legs up toward the surface so the body is streamlined.
3. Swim down underwater toward the victim.
4. Have participants practice the skill until they feel comfortable performing it. Check off the participants' skills as you watch them practice.

Using a Mask and Fins to Perform a Deep-water Line Search (35 minutes)

Primary Point:

Mask and fins are tools used for underwater searches when locating a missing person.

Fitting a Mask

Explain and demonstrate how to properly fit a mask. Guide the participants through the following steps:

1. Place the mask against your face without using the strap.
2. Inhale slightly through your nose. The suction should keep the mask on your face without being held.
3. Adjust the strap so the mask is comfortable.
4. Try the mask in water. If it leaks, try adjusting the strap and if it still leaks, check it again with suction.
5. To prevent fogging, rub saliva or a commercial defogger on the inside of the face plate. Rinse the mask with water before you put it on.
6. Pressure from the water can cause pain in your ears as you go deeper. To equalize pressure in your ears when you descend, place your thumb and finger on the nosepiece of your mask, pinching your nose and trying to exhale. Repeat as needed. If the mask squeezes your face, exhale a small amount of air through your nose into the mask.
7. Have participants practice fitting their mask until they feel comfortable with it.

Fins

Explain and demonstrate how to put on fins and how to swim while wearing them. Guide the participants through the following steps:

1. Wet your feet and the fins. Push one foot into one fin and slide the heel or strap of the fin over your heel. Do the same for the other foot.
2. Lean forward and begin kicking, using a modified flutter kick. The modified flutter should be a deeper, slower kicking action with the knee bent slightly more than in a normal flutter kick.

Note: Have participants kick with the fins on underwater. Stress that they swim using their legs only, keeping their arms at their side.

3. Have participants practice kicking with the fins on until they feel comfortable.

Deep-Water Line Search

Explain and demonstrate, wearing a mask and fins, a deep-water line search. (Select several participants to assist you in the demonstration.) Guide participants through the following steps:

1. Have participants put on a mask and fins and form a straight line in deep water, no more than an arm's length apart.

Activity:

Lifeguarding Today page 254

Masks

Activity:

Lifeguarding Today page 256

Fins

Activity:

Lifeguarding Today pages 252 & 253

Note: Have participants put the mask and fins on in the water. For further information on how to enter the water wearing a mask and fins, see page 256 of Lifeguarding Today.

2. Select and place one participant on a raft or dock, with a rescue tube, to serve as lookout.
3. Appoint one participant to be the lead lifeguard, the person who gives the command to dive.
4. Tell participants that on command from the lead lifeguard, they are to do a headfirst surface dive, swim three strokes, and surface. Tell them to sweep with their hands while they are swimming forward.
5. When they return to the surface, have participants reform their line and dive again on command from the lead.
6. Have participants practice the skill until they are comfortable performing it. Check off participants' skills as you watch them practice.

BREAK

Time: 10 minutes

Participants should change into dry clothes and prepare for the final written exam.

FINAL WRITTEN EXAM AND CLOSING

Time: 30 minutes

Activity:

Written Exams
Answer Sheets
Pencils
Envelope or Box

1. Tell participants that they will now take a 25-question examination. They will have 20 minutes to complete the exam and must answer at least 20 questions correctly to pass. They may not use their participant's manuals to find the answers.
2. Hand out an examination and answer sheet to each participant.
3. Tell participants to write only on the answer sheet, mark answers clearly, and use pencil only (in case they want to erase or change an answer).
4. Tell them to check their answers before handing them in.
5. Tell them to come to you or raise one hand when they have finished the exam or have any questions.
6. Score the exams. The answer keys for both exams are at the end of this instructor's manual.

Note: As participants hand in their answer sheets and exams, quickly grade each exam and return it to the correct participant so that he or she can review any missed questions. If time allows, discuss with the class any exam items that were a problem. Collect all answer sheets and exams before the participants leave the class. If a participant fails the exam, ask him or her to see you after class to schedule a retest.

7. Give a copy of the Participant Course Evaluation form to each participant as he or she completes the written exam. Ask participants to leave the evaluations in a box or envelope you have provided near the door.

Note: Participants may have used the Participant Course Evaluation form at the back of their participant's manual when they took the Lifeguard Training course. You can obtain additional copies of these forms at your local American Red Cross unit.

8. Issue (or explain you will mail) an *American Red Cross Waterfront Lifeguarding Course Completion* certificate to participants who scored 80 percent or better on the written exam and who successfully performed the critical skills in this module.

9. Thank all participants for attending the module.

9

the waterpark
lifeguarding module

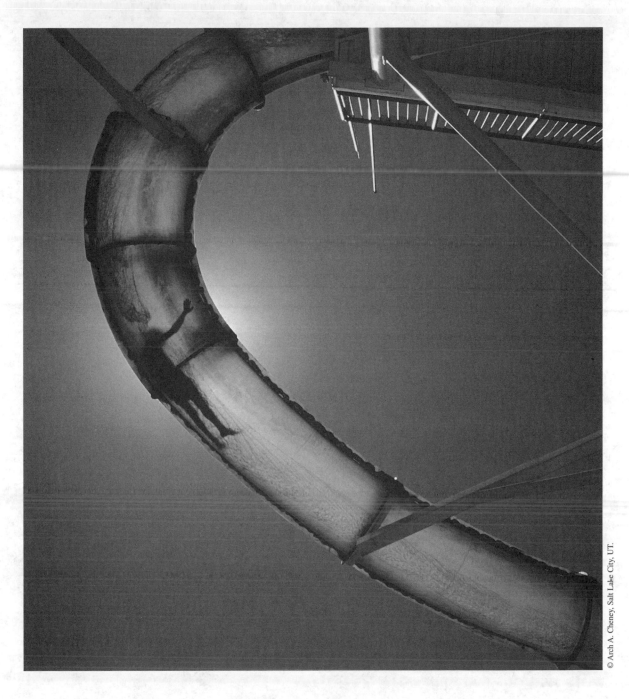

Course Outline

Waterpark Lifeguarding Module

Activity	Approximate Time
Introduction to the Module	15 minutes
Introduction to Waterpark Lifeguarding	10 minutes
Interacting with the Public	15 minutes
Injury Prevention	10 minutes
Surveillance	45 minutes
Preparing for Emergencies	15 minutes
Rescue Skills	20 minutes
Break	10 minutes
Skills Practice: Waterpark Rescue Skills	120 minutes
Entries	(20 minutes)
Assists	(10 minutes)
Removal From the Water	(30 minutes)
Spinal Injury Management	(60 minutes)
Break	10 minutes
Final Written Exam and Closing	30 minutes
Waterpark Lifeguarding Module, Total Time	**5 hours**

The purpose of the Waterpark Lifeguarding module is to teach lifeguards the skills and knowledge needed to prevent and respond to aquatic emergencies at a waterpark facility. The module content and activities prepare waterpark lifeguarding candidates to provide for the safety of patrons and to recognize and effectively respond to emergencies at a waterpark facility.

Administrative Notes

The following points apply to this module.

Prerequisites

To be eligible for the Waterpark Lifeguarding module, the candidate must have a current *American Red Cross Lifeguard Training* certificate and a current *American Red Cross CPR for the Professional Rescuer* certificate.

Module Length

This module is designed to be taught in a minimum of 5 hours. This includes time for waterpark lifeguarding skills practice, class activities, and showing one video.

Since the times allotted in the lesson plans do not include relief breaks or a lunch break, you may have to build additional time into the module.

Class Size

It is recommended that there be one instructor for every 10 participants in the class. If the class has more than 10 participants, you should have a co-instructor or aide. Close supervision is necessary to ensure effective practice and the safety of participants. Furthermore, you can run a class more efficiently if you keep the class reasonably small, and you are less likely to exceed the allotted time periods for various activities.

Facilities

Classroom Space

The lessons in the Waterpark Lifeguarding module require classroom space suitable for discussion, video viewing, and taking the final written exam. The classroom should be conveniently located for participants. It should also be equipped with the necessary teaching aids and materials.

Swimming Area

The Waterpark Lifeguarding module must be conducted at a waterpark that has one of the following attractions:
- Wave pool
- Speedslide with a runout
- Winding river
- Water slide with a catch pool

An adequate number of lifeguards with no duties other than supervising the class should be present during all water sessions.

Equipment and Supplies

At the beginning of each lesson is a list of required equipment and supplies. A master list of equipment for the module is found in Appendix G. Make sure all the equipment is ready and in working order before you teach the module.

All participants should have a copy of *Lifeguarding Today* (Stock No. 654110). The following video is required for this module: *Lifeguarding Today* (Stock No. 654114).

Testing and Certificates

On successful completion of the module, participants receive an *American Red Cross Course Completion* certificate (Cert. 3002) indicating Waterpark Lifeguarding. There is no validity period for the *Waterpark Lifeguarding* certificate.

To receive the course completion certificate for the American Red Cross Waterpark Lifeguarding module, the participant must—

- Demonstrate competency in each critical skill taught in the module. (See the Lifeguarding Skills Checklist, Appendix M, and the Lifeguarding Critical Skills Chart, Appendix N. For more information on critical skills, see Chapter 3.)
- Correctly answer at least 80 percent of the written examination questions (20 out of a total of 25 questions).

For more information on awarding certificates, completing records, and conducting course evaluations, see Chapter 6.

The Waterpark Lifeguarding Module Lesson Plan

Class Assignment prior to this lesson: Read Chapter 14 of *Lifeguarding Today* and complete the study questions.

Length: 5 hours

Equipment/Supplies: Name tags (optional); course roster; course outline; participant's manuals; video—*Lifeguarding Today;* VCR and monitor; chalkboard or newsprint (flip chart); chalk or markers; rescue tubes (one rescue tube per two participants); backboards with a minimum of three straps and a commercial head immobilizer attached (one per five participants); Lifeguarding Skills Checklist (Appendix M); copies of Waterpark Lifeguarding exams A and B and answer sheets for each participant (Appendix S); pencils; envelope or box; Participant Course Evaluation forms

Goal: Participants will gain the knowledge and skills needed to lifeguard effectively at a waterpark facility.

Objectives

After completing this module, participants should be able to—

1. Describe the difference between a waterpark and other types of multi-attraction aquatic facilities.

2. Describe a winding river and its surveillance issues.

3. Explain safety considerations for dispatching riders at a water slide, drop-off slide, speed slide, and free-fall slide.

4. Explain surveillance issues for a shallow catch pool, a deep catch pool, and a runout.

5. Explain surveillance issues for a wave pool.

6. Explain surveillance issues for deep- and shallow-water attractions.

7. List the eight recommended rules for water slides.

8. Explain the safety rules for speed slides and free-fall slides.

9. Demonstrate the compact jump from a height and the run-and-swim entry.

10. Demonstrate the walking assist, the front-and-back carry, and the beach drag.

11. Demonstrate a simple assist.

12. Demonstrate in-line stabilization techniques in a winding river, a catch pool, and a speed slide.

13. Demonstrate backboarding techniques used at a speed slide.

INTRODUCTION TO THE MODULE

Time: 15 minutes

Activity:

Name Tags
Course Roster

Course Outline

1. **Instructor and Participant Introductions**
   - Introduce yourself and welcome participants to the American Red Cross Waterpark Lifeguarding module.
   - Have participants introduce themselves by sharing their names, their reasons for taking this module, and their expectations.
   - Give a brief description of your background and credentials. Identify yourself as an American Red Cross instructor, and explain that this module is one of many courses and modules offered by the American Red Cross. Ask the participants to write their full names and addresses on the course roster so that you can complete the American Red Cross *Course Record* (Form 6418 and 6418A).

2. **Orientation to the Facility**
   - Point out the location of fire exits, telephones, rest rooms, and drinking fountains, and explain facility rules, if any.
   - Tell participants that they will need a swimsuit to participate in skill practice sessions.

3. **Course Schedule**
   - Distribute an outline that includes dates and times of class meetings, lesson content, and class assignments. Skill practice sessions and examinations should be clearly identified.

4. **Course Prerequisites**
   - To enroll in the Waterpark Lifeguarding module, participants must have a current *American Red Cross Lifeguard Training* certificate and a *CPR for the Professional Rescuer* certificate. If the participants' certificates were not checked at registration, check them at this time.

5. **Module Description**
   - Share the following goal statement with the class:
   The purpose of this module is to teach lifeguards the skills and knowledge needed to prevent and respond to aquatic emergencies at a waterpark facility.

6. **How Participants Will Learn**
   - Briefly explain that participants will learn through lectures, discussions, reading, group activities, and skill practice. This module is supported by video segments.

7. **Participant's Manual**
   - Identify the participant's manual for this module, American Red Cross *Lifeguarding Today,* and lead the participants through Chapter 14, "Waterpark Facilities." Instruct the participants in how best to use the manual to master the module content. Point out the following features of Chapter 14:
     - Objectives
     - Key Terms
     - Sidebars
     - Study Questions

   Lifeguarding Today, Chapter 14 "Waterpark Facilities" is required reading for this module.

8. **Module Completion Requirements**
   - Describe the American Red Cross requirements for successful module completion. To successfully complete this module, the participant must—
     - Correctly demonstrate the critical skills taught in the module.
     - Correctly answer at least 80 percent of the written examination questions (20 questions out of 25).

   Note: If there are academic requirements or state or local requirements beyond the minimum completion requirements set by the American Red Cross, explain them to participants at this time.

INTRODUCTION TO WATERPARK LIFEGUARDING

Time: 10 minutes

Video:

Tell participants they are going to see a video segment that will introduce them to the module. Show the introductory video segment "Waterpark Lifeguarding." (approx. 5 minutes)

Primary Points:

Lifeguarding Today page 262

- Many people visit waterparks every year. Most metropolitan areas have at least one waterpark; some cities have several. The popularity of these facilities has been increasing over the past 20 years.
- Most of what you learned in your Lifeguard Training course and in Chapters 1–12 of *Lifeguarding Today* applies directly to this module, including professionalism, team work, public relations, and rescue skills.

INTERACTING WITH THE PUBLIC

Time: 15 minutes

Activity:

Ask participants to name some of the factors that would make lifeguarding at a waterpark different from lifeguarding at a pool. Discuss situations and issues the lifeguard must be made aware of.

List factors and issues on the chalkboard or flip chart. Make sure the following points are covered:

- Rescues most likely will occur more often at a waterpark than at a pool because more patrons visit the facility daily.
- Many people who go to waterparks are not familiar with the different types of attractions and how the water moves within those attractions.
- Many waterpark patrons do not know how to swim.
- Rule enforcement is important for parents as well as children.
- Keep an eye out for anyone who may need help entering and exiting an attraction or who needs assistance after falling off an inner tube, being hit by a wave, or not being able to get all the way down a slide.
- Be alert for patrons who may suddenly become ill. Watch for patrons wearing medical alert bracelets or necklaces.
- Watch out for patrons who may be engaged in risky behavior or confrontations with other staff or patrons.

Activity:

Discuss ways to prevent the situations listed above in becoming emergency situations. Include the following points in the discussion:

- Give a clear explanation of the rules and enforce them firmly.
- Discuss the rules with large groups, and orient them to all attractions.
- Provide weak swimmers with life jackets if available.

INJURY PREVENTION

Time: 10 minutes

Primary Points:

Lifeguarding Today
page 264

Rules and Regulations

- Keep an eye out for patrons who may not be paying attention to signs or those who cannot read them.
- Some waterparks require riders to be a certain height to ride on particular attractions.
- Advise patrons of varying depths of water at different attractions.

■ Warning signs caution patrons with certain medical conditions that particular rides may not be advisable due to their health conditions.

Safety Checks

■ Take test rides on all attractions daily. Correct unsafe conditions before permitting patrons to use them.
■ Check equipment that patrons use.
■ Check all means of communication.
■ Make sure that all safety equipment is in good shape and in the appropriate place.

Primary Points:

Lifeguarding Today pages 264 & 265

Lifeguard Rotations

■ Lifeguard Rotations keep you alert and your surveillance skills sharp.
■ Rotations are usually based on the
  ■ Locations of lifeguard stations.
  ■ Number of patrons typically using the attractions.
■ How long lifeguards stay at a station and how often they have breaks depend on the facility.

Primary Points:

Lifeguarding Today page 265

Weather

■ If a storm approaches, tell the supervisor.
■ Follow the emergency action plan at your facility when severe weather threatens.

Primary Points:

Lifeguarding Today page 265

SURVEILLANCE

Time: 45 minutes

Video:

Show the Waterpark Lifeguarding video segment: "Waterpark Surveillance." (approx. 17 minutes)

Primary Points:

Lifeguarding Today pages 264 & 265

There are three general principles for patron surveillance at waterparks. These principles are—
■ Watch patrons as they enter and exit an attraction. This includes setting safe intervals between riders, called dispatch.
■ Keep patrons in view as long as possible. On some attractions, it may be difficult.
■ Be aware of the added risk of play structures. They need careful surveillance.

Winding Rivers

Primary Points:

Lifeguarding Today
page 266

- Lifeguards may be stationed at entrances and exits and at sitting or walking positions with overlapping areas of responsibility.
- Common rules and recommendations for winding rivers include—
  - Patrons should enter and exit the winding river only at designated locations.
  - Patrons should not jump or dive into the winding river.
  - Patrons should stay in tubes at all times.
  - Patrons should not swim in the winding river.
  - Patrons should not stack up tubes.
  - Only one person is allowed per tube, except when an adult is holding a small child.
    - The child should be wearing a life jacket in case the tube tips over.

Water Slides

Primary Points:

Lifeguarding Today
pages 267 & 268

- On some slides, people ride on an inner tube, raft, or mat. On other slides, no equipment is used.
- Usually only one person rides on an inner tube or raft unless the tube is made for more than one rider.
  - The correct riding position in a tube is feet first in a sitting position.
  - If you are not using equipment, then the position is face up and feet first.
- If you are positioned at the top of the slide, you need to make sure that patrons are tall enough to ride and that you are dispatching them at safe intervals.
- If you are positioned at the bottom of the slide, help patrons get out of the water and watch to see if riders are injured or startled.
  - Water flowing off a slide into a catch pool can create a hydraulic. A hydraulic is a condition in which water flows over an object, drops, and recirculates against the current, producing a strong downward force.
- If you are positioned in the middle of the slide, you may need to help riders if they get stuck or injured.
- Follow common guidelines for water slides at your facility.

Activity·

Discuss the following guidelines for guarding at water slides, and ask participants to give you reasons for each one.

- No swimsuit or shorts with metal rivets, buttons, or fasteners are allowed on the water slide.
- Eyeglasses, goggles, and sunglasses are not advised on the slide.
- Sliding is allowed in a feet-first, face-up position only.
- No running, standing, kneeling, rotating, or tumbling on slides, and no stopping in flumes or tunnels.
- No diving into catch pools.
- Exit the catch pool quickly.
- Do not cross in front of another slide when exiting the catch pool.

Drop-Off Slides

Primary Points:

Lifeguarding Today
page 268

- A drop-off slide ends with a drop of several feet into a catch pool.
- Make sure riders are sitting or lying in a feetfirst position.
- Riders may be surprised when they enter water deeper than they expected in the catch pool.

Speed Slides

Primary Points:

Lifeguarding Today
pages 268 & 269

- A speed slide is steep. Patrons may reach speeds of over 35 miles per hour.
- Only one person goes down the slide at a time, feetfirst, lying on the back with legs crossed at the ankles and arms crossed over the chest.
- Do not dispatch a rider until the previous rider has left the runout or catch pool.
- Patrons should be helped out of the water at the bottom because they may have become disoriented.
- Manufacturers of speed slides usually recommend the following:
  - The rider should not wear a life jacket because he or she may get caught or hung up.
  - Eyeglasses, goggles, and sunglasses are not advised.
  - Do not wear water shoes or sandals.

Free-Fall Slides

Primary Points:

Lifeguarding Today
page 269

- A free-fall slide is a speed slide with a nearly vertical drop that gives riders the sensation of falling.
- At the top of a free-fall slide, give riders the following specific directions:
  - Riders in line must stand back away from the slide.
  - Riders wait for the signal to start. (Signal only when you are sure the previous rider is out of the runout.)
  - Riders lie flat with ankles crossed and arms crossed over the chest.
  - Riders must not sit up for any reason until they have come to a complete stop.

Wave Pools

Primary Points:

Lifeguarding Today
page 269

- A wave pool produces waves of various heights, intervals, and patterns.
- Waves are created in three different ways, by—
  - An air pressure system.
  - A water pressure system.
  - Mechanical paddles.
- A wave cycle is often 10 minutes on and 10 minutes off. Learn the pattern of waves at your facility.
- Lifeguard rotation usually occurs when the waves are off.
- The number of lifeguards stationed depends on the—
  - Size and shape of the pool.
  - Number of people in the water.
- The emergency action plan should designate who pushes the emergency stop button to stop the waves, and when it should be pushed.
  - It should also designate who covers your zone when you are making a rescue.
- Most rescues take place where the waves break because patrons venture out there and weak swimmers can be knocked over by the waves.
- Wave pool users should enter only at the shallow end and should not dive into the waves.
- Keep the areas around ladders and railings clear of patrons so that others can exit quickly.

- Look out for weak swimmers falling off their inner tubes or rafts in deep water. Swimmers can be knocked down by a raft and be in trouble.
- Any time surfboards or boogie boards are allowed in the wave pool, nonsurfing patrons should stay out of the wave pool.

Kiddie Areas

Primary Points:

Lifeguarding Today
page 273

- Many waterparks have shallow areas for small children. These areas may have play equipment, such as—
  - Slides.
  - Fountains.
  - Swings.
  - Inflatable play equipment.
  - Climbing structures.
- Consistently enforce rules in these areas, such as height and age requirements.
- Lost children are often a problem. Encourage parental supervision.
- Small children may use the pool as a bathroom. Follow your facility's standard procedure for handling this problem.
- Be alert for children who are getting sunburned, and tell the child's adult guardian at once if you notice them getting sunburned.

Special Attractions

Primary Points:

Lifeguarding Today
pages 273–275

- Some waterparks have special activities such as—
  - Specialty slides.
  - Diving platforms.
  - Cable swings.
  - Hand-over-hand activities like ropes, nets, and rings.
- Some parks have shallow-water attractions, such as flat, floating structures tethered to the bottom, called "lily" pads. Participants try to walk from one to the other holding onto a rope.
- A rapids ride is a water attraction that simulates whitewater rafting. Lifeguards have to be situated to survey all parts of the ride.
- Riders can slide down a slide on a plastic sled. A lifeguard stationed at the top controls dispatch; a lifeguard at the bottom watches for sleds that collide or flip over.

PREPARING FOR EMERGENCIES

Time: 15 minutes

Primary Points:

Lifeguarding Today
pages 274 & 275

- The entire staff at the facility may be part of the safety team. Depending on the facility's size, the training may vary for different employees. Each staff member should know his or her role in the emergency action plan.
- Communication is essential to safety in a waterpark.
  - There are many means of communication that your facility may use, including—
    - A public address (PA) system.
    - Telephones.
    - Air horns.
    - Two-way radios.
    - Electrical lighting systems.
  - Your facility orientation or in-service training should teach you how and when to use them.

Activity:

Refer participants to the sample emergency action plan on page 275 in their *Lifeguarding Today* participant's manual.

Discuss some of the steps lifeguards would take that are unique to waterparks. Be sure to cover the following points:

- Once the emergency action plan is activated, a lifeguard would use the emergency stop button to stop waves at a wave pool.
- A lifeguard at the top of a slide would stop dispatch.
  - Communication between the lifeguard at the top and the one at the bottom is vital.
- At a deep-water attraction, all lifeguards would stand in their chairs to provide backup coverage.
- At a shallow-water attraction, lifeguards would move to cover all zones.

RESCUE SKILLS

Time: 20 minutes

Primary Points:

Lifeguarding Today
page 276

- You can use all the skills you learned in the American Red Cross Lifeguard Training course, as well as the new ones you will learn in this module. These include—
  - Entries.
  - Assists.

- Removal of the victim.
- Modifications for spinal injury management procedures.

■ The rescue tube is the most effective piece of lifeguarding rescue equipment.
- At waterparks, there may be times when you may not use a rescue tube at every station. These include when you are stationed—
  - At a shallow water attraction.
  - Beside a catch pool.
  - At the top of a slide.
  - At the bottom of a slide runout.

| Video: |

Show the Waterpark Lifeguarding video segment: "Rescue Skills." (approx. 16 minutes)

BREAK

Time: 10 minutes

Participants should change into swimsuits and prepare for the in-water skills practice.

SKILLS PRACTICE: WATERPARK RESCUE SKILLS

Time: 120 minutes

Entries (20 minutes)

Compact Jump

Primary Points:

The compact jump with a rescue tube should be used when entering from a height, such as a lifeguard stand or a head wall. At a wave pool, time your jump to land on the crest of a wave, not in the trough.

Activity:

Lifeguarding Today pages 276 & 277

Explain and demonstrate the compact jump into a wave pool. Guide the participants through the following steps:

1. Squeeze the rescue tube high against your chest with the ends under your armpits.
2. Jump out and away from the wall or lifeguard chair, with your knees bent and your feet together and flat.

> **SAFETY TIP:**
>
> A person using the compact jump can be injured by hitting the bottom of the pool. Therefore, make sure participants do not point their toes or enter the water with straight legs! Also emphasize that the participants hold the excess line to keep it from getting caught in the lifeguard chair or other equipment.

3. The buoyancy of the rescue tube helps bring you back to the surface.
4. When you surface, focus on the victim and begin your approach.
5. Have participants practice the skill until they feel comfortable performing it. Check off the participants' skills on the Lifeguarding Skills Checklist (Appendix M) as you watch them practice.

Run-and-Swim Entry

Primary Points:

Use the run-and-swim entry when entering the water from a gradual slope such as a wave pool.

Activity:

Lifeguarding Today
page 277

Explain and demonstrate the run-and-swim entry. Guide the participants through the following steps:
1. Hold the rescue tube in one hand and run into the water, lifting your legs to avoid falling.
2. When you reach the point where you can no longer run, put the rescue tube across your chest, lean forward, and start swimming.

> **SAFETY TIP:**
>
> Make sure that participants do not dive or plunge into the water, because it can result in serious injury.

3. Have participants practice the skill until they feel comfortable performing it. Check off the participants' skills as you watch them practice.

Assists (10 minutes)

Primary Points:

- Assists are the most common form of help you give patrons.
- To decide which kind of assist to use, consider—
  - The nature of the problem.
  - The person's condition.
  - The most effective strategy.

- Assists include—
  - Supporting patrons who are entering and exiting an attraction.
  - Helping patrons in or out of inner tubes or rafts.
  - Helping a tired swimmer in deep water reach shallow water.
  - Helping patrons who are stuck in a slide or who become frightened. (Sometimes you may have to climb up the slide to reach them or catch them when they come down.)
- Talking to the person during the assist is calming. If you see that a rescue is needed rather than an assist, activate the emergency action plan.

Simple Assist

Primary Point:

A simple assist may be as easy as helping someone to his or her feet.

Activity:

Explain and demonstrate two ways to make a simple assist. Assign partners or ask participants to find a partner. Guide participants through the following steps:

1. **Assist #1**—Keeping your rescue tube between you and the person who needs help, reach across the tube and grasp the person at the armpit to help maintain his or her balance.
2. **Assist #2**—If the person is underwater, grasp him or her under the armpits with both hands and help the person stand up.
3. Have participants practice these skills until they feel comfortable performing them. Have participants perform both skills several times and then change places with their partners and repeat the practice. Check off participants' skills as you watch them practice.

Removal From the Water (30 minutes)

Primary Point:

Lifeguarding Today page 279

There are three easy techniques for helping someone out of shallow water. These include the—
- Walking assist.
- Front-and-back carry.
- Beach drag.

Walking Assist

Primary Point:

Activity:

Lifeguarding Today page 279

Use the walking assist to help a conscious victim walk out of the water on a gradual slope, such as the entrance to a wave pool.

1. Place one of the victim's arms around your neck and across your shoulder.
2. Grasp the wrist of the arm that is across your shoulder, and wrap your free arm around the victim's back or waist to provide support.

3. Maintain a firm grasp and help the victim walk out of the water.
4. Have participants practice the skill until they feel comfortable performing it. Have participants perform the skill several times and then change places with their partners and repeat the practice. Check off participants' skills as you watch them practice.

Front-and-Back Carry

Primary Point:

Use the front-and-back carry with a large victim who is unconscious or who cannot get out of the water without help. Do not use this technique if you suspect the victim has a spinal injury.

Activity:

Lifeguarding Today
page 280

Explain and demonstrate the front-and-back carry. Assign or ask participants to work in groups of three (one victim, two lifeguards). Guide the participants through the following steps:

1. Get behind the victim and reach under the armpits. Grasp the victim's wrists, your right hand on the right wrist and your left hand on the left wrist. Cross the victim's arms across his or her chest.
2. The second lifeguard stands between the victim's legs, facing the same direction as you and the victim. The second lifeguard bends down and grasps the victim under the knees.
3. On signal, both lifeguards lift the victim and carry him or her out of the water.
4. Have participants rotate so that each participant has the opportunity to practice the skill. Have participants practice the skill until they feel comfortable performing it. Check off the participants' skills as you watch them practice.

Beach Drag

Primary Point:

The beach drag is a safe way to bring an unconscious victim or a person who is very heavy and unable to walk from the water. Do not use it if you suspect spinal injury.

Activity:

Lifeguarding Today
page 280

Explain and demonstrate the beach drag. Assign partners or ask participants to find a partner. Guide the participants through the following steps:

1. Stand behind the victim and grasp him or her under the armpits, supporting the head when possible with your forearms.
2. While walking backward, drag the victim toward shallow water.
3. Have participants perform the skill several times and then change places with their partners and repeat the practice. Have participants practice the skill until they feel comfortable performing it. Check off the participants' skills as you watch them practice.

Spinal Injury Management (60 minutes)

In-line stabilization and backboarding are difficult to perform in certain waterpark attractions. Moving water and confined spaces present problems.

Note: Depending on the facility where you are conducting this module, you may perform one or all of these spinal injury management skills. If you perform the entire procedure once in one skill, you need not practice immobilizing the victim on a backboard in the other skill(s). (If you perform all three of these skills, you may need to add additional time to this module.) Participants must perform one of these skills to successfully complete this module.

Spinal Injury Management in Winding Rivers

In a winding river, the current can pull or move the victim.

Explain and demonstrate spinal injury management in a catch pool. Assign or ask participants to work in groups of five (one victim, two lifeguards, two bystanders). Have participants repeat the skill, changing roles, so that each participant plays the role of the primary rescuer. Guide participants through the following steps:
1. Keep the victim's head pointing up-stream.
2. Establish in-line stabilization and turn the victim faceup.
3. Slowly turn the victim so that the current pulls the victim's legs around to point downstream.
4. Immobilize the victim on a backboard.
5. Once the victim is secure on the backboard, remove him or her from the water.

> **SAFETY TIP:**
> Make sure participants lift with their legs, not with their back, when practicing this skill. Improper lifting can cause injury.

6. Have participants practice the skill until they feel comfortable performing it. Check off the participants' skills when they assume the position of the primary rescuer and perform the skill correctly.

Primary Points:

Lifeguarding Today
page 281

Primary Point:

Activity:

Lifeguarding Today
page 281

Spinal Injury Management in a Catch Pool

Primary Points:

- The water in a catch pool moves with greater force than in a winding river. As soon as you suspect a spinal injury in a catch pool, signal other lifeguards to stop dispatch. If possible, signal someone to stop the flow of water.
- The force of the water in a catch pool often creates an eddy, a condition in which water flows opposite the main current.
- Move the victim to the calmest part of the catch pool. This is usually between two slides or, with one slide, in the middle of the catch pool.

Activity:

Lifeguarding Today
page 282

Explain and demonstrate spinal injury management in a catch pool. Assign or ask participants to work in groups of five (one victim, two lifeguards, two bystanders). Have participants repeat the skill, changing roles, so that each participant plays the role of the primary rescuer. Guide the participants through the following steps:

1. Establish in-line stabilization.
2. Turn the victim faceup.
3. Move the victim to the part of the catch pool where the water is calmest, which depends on whether there are two slides or one.
4. Immobilize the victim on a backboard.
5. Once the victim is secure on the backboard, remove him or her from the water.

SAFETY TIP:

Make sure participants lift with their legs, not with their back, when practicing this skill. Improper lifting can cause injury.

---

6. Have participants practice the skill until they feel comfortable performing it. Check off the participants' skills when they assume the position of the primary rescuer and perform the skill correctly.

Spinal Injury Management in a Speed Slide

Primary Point:

In a speed slide, the confined space creates challenges when performing spinal injury management.

Activity:

Lifeguarding Today
pages 282 & 283

Explain and demonstrate spinal injury management in a speed slide. Tell participants that this activity will be done as a group. Not everyone will practice as primary rescuer. Guide participants through the following steps:

Note: In making a rescue in a speed slide, the lifeguard immediately signals for dispatch to stop and for someone to turn off the water. The lifeguard then approaches the victim and assesses his or her condition.

1. Apply in-line stabilization to the victim.
2. Additional rescuers kneel along the outside of the slide. Place your hands beneath the victim with your arms and elbows inside the slide.
3. Lift the victim enough for the backboard to be slid under the victim.
4. An additional lifeguard slides the backboard from the feet to the head underneath the victim, making sure that the straps are not caught under the backboard and that the backboard is centered under the victim. Be careful to maintain in-line stabilization.
5. Lower the victim onto the backboard.
6. Using straps and a head immobilizer, secure the victim to the backboard. Lift the backboard out of the slide, and move the victim to safety.

SAFETY TIP:

Make sure participants lift with their legs, not with their back, when practicing this skill. Improper lifting can cause injury.

---

7. Have participants practice this skill three times or until they feel comfortable performing it. Change the primary rescuer each time the skill is practiced. Check off the participants' skills as you watch them practice.

BREAK

Time: 10 minutes

Participants should change into dry clothes and prepare for the final written exam.

FINAL WRITTEN EXAM AND CLOSING

Time: 30 minutes

Activity:

Written Exams
Answer Sheets
Pencils
Envelope or Box

1. Tell participants that they will now take a 25-question examination. They will have 20 minutes to complete the exam and must answer at least 20 questions correctly to pass. They may not use their participant's manuals to find the answers.
2. Hand out an examination and answer sheet to each participant.
3. Tell participants to write only on the answer sheet, mark answers clearly, and use pencil only (in case they want to erase or change an answer).
4. Tell them to check their answers before handing them in.
5. Tell them to come to you or raise one hand when they have finished the exam or have any questions.
6. Score the exams. The answer keys for both exams are at the end of this instructor's manual.

Note: As participants hand in their answer sheets and exams, quickly grade each exam and return it to the correct participant so that he or she can review any missed questions. If time allows, discuss with the class any exam items that were a problem. Collect all answer sheets and exams before the participants leave the class. If a participant fails the exam, ask him or her to see you after class to schedule a retest.

7. Give a copy of the Participant Course Evaluation form to each participant as he or she completes the written exam. Ask participants to leave the evaluations in a box or envelope you have provided near the door.

Note: Participants may have used the Participant Course Evaluation form at the back of their participant's manual when they took the Lifeguard Training course. You can obtain additional copies of these forms at your local American Red Cross unit.

8. Issue (or explain you will mail) an American Red Cross Waterpark Lifeguarding Course Completion Certificate to participants who scored 80 percent or better on the written exam and who successfully performed the critical skills in this module.
9. Thank all participants for attending the module.

10 the community water safety course

Course Outline

Community Water Safety

Activity	Approximate Time
Introduction to the Course	15 minutes
Introduction	10 minutes
Staying Safe While Having Fun	20 minutes
Preparing for Water Activities	30 minutes
Water Hazards	30 minutes
Aquatic Recreation	35 minutes
Taking Action in an Emergency	40 minutes
Providing Care Until Help Arrives	45 minutes
Closing	15 minutes
Community Water Safety, Total Time	**4 hours**

Note: Time does not include two optional videos and the in-water activities session.

The purpose of the American Red Cross Community Water Safety course is to provide information that will help people become safer and healthier in, on, and around the water.

Administrative Notes

The following points apply to this course:

Prerequisites

There are no prerequisites for enrollment in this course. If the optional in-water activities session is conducted, participants have the option of attending it. There are three levels of participation for those participating in the optional in-water activities session:

1. **Observers**—those who do not wish to enter the water and want to observe and participate in all activities that take place on land. Listening to the instructor and observing the in-water activities session increases an awareness and understanding of water safety.

2. **Life-jacket wearers or novice swimmers** — those who do not feel totally comfortable in the water yet wish to participate in water activities while wearing a life jacket. They must wear a Coast Guard-approved life jacket for the water activities. These participants practice in water up to chest-deep.

3. **Swimmers**—those who feel comfortable in deep water without a life jacket and who have passed the skills pretest for water activities. The skills pretest includes the following:

   - Enter shallow water; swim into deep water next to the edge of pool, dock, or lifeline for 10 yards; float or tread water for 1 minute; and return to shallow water on the back.

   - Jump into deep water, level off, and swim 10 yards to safety.

Course Length

This course is designed to be taught in a minimum of 4 hours. The instructor may add the 1-hour in-water activities session depending on the needs of the participants. This hour has not been included in the total course time.

Class Size

It is recommended that there be one instructor for every 10 participants in the class. If the class has more than 10 participants and you conduct the optional in-water activities session, there should be a co-instructor or instructor aide. Close supervision is required to ensure effective practice and the safety of participants. Furthermore, you can run a class more efficiently if you keep the class reasonably small, and you are less likely to exceed the allotted time periods for various activities.

Facilities

The course includes classroom activities requiring dry land space with a writing surface for each person. The optional in-water activities session requires a swimming facility, with shallow water, such as a pool. The shallow end of the pool should be a maximum of 4 feet deep.

If a waterfront or waterpark facility is used, it should be an open area free from surf or obstructions and have sufficient space for participants to perform the in-water activities.

Equipment and Supplies

At the beginning of each session is a list of required equipment and supplies. A master list of equipment for the course is in Appendix G. Make sure all the equipment is ready and in working order before you teach the course.

All participants should have a copy of American Red Cross *Community Water Safety* (Stock No. 654122). The following videos are optional for this course: American Red Cross *Home Pool Safety: It Only Takes A Minute* (Stock No. 329474) and American Red Cross *Water: The Deceptive Power* (Stock No. 329475).

Testing and Certification

There is no test, either written or of skills, at the end of this course. However, participants have the opportunity to answer the self-analysis questions located at the end of the *Community Water Safety* participant's manual. These questions are designed to help participants evaluate their retention and understanding of the information in the manual.

Participants who complete the course, whether they participate in the optional in-water activities session or not, may receive an American Red Cross *Course Completion* certificate (Cert. 3002) indicating *Community Water Safety*. There is no validity period for the *Community Water Safety* certificate.

For more information on awarding certificates, completing records, and conducting course evaluations, see Chapter 6.

The Community Water Safety Course Lesson Plan

Length:	4 hours (Optional in-water activities session is an additional 1 hour.)
Equipment/Supplies:	Name tags (optional); course roster; course outline; paper; pencils; participant's manuals; chalkboard or newsprint (flip chart); chalk or markers; different types of personal flotation devices; videos (optional)—*Water the Deceptive Power* and *Home Pool Safety: It Only Takes a Minute,* and VCR and monitor; *'Til Help Arrives* booklet (optional)
	Optional In-Water Activities Session: personal flotation devices (life jackets and vests), one per three participants; a shepard's crook, a rescue tube, a ring buoy, and a throw bag
Goal:	Participants will learn about various water environments and their potential hazards and become familiar with ways to remain safe and healthy while participating in aquatic activities.

Introduction to the Course

Time: 15 minutes

Activity:

Name Tags
Course Roster

Course Outline

1. **Instructor and Participant Introductions**
   - Introduce yourself and welcome participants to the American Red Cross Community Water Safety course.
   - Have participants introduce themselves by sharing their names and their reasons for taking this course and their expectations.
   - Give a brief description of your background and credentials. Identify yourself as an American Red Cross instructor, and explain that this course is one of many offered by the American Red Cross. Ask the participants to write their full names and addresses on the course roster so that you can complete the American Red Cross *Course Record* (Form 6418 and 6418A).
2. **Orientation to the Facility**
   - Point out the locations of fire exits, telephones, rest rooms, and drinking fountains, and explain facility rules, if any.

3. **Course Schedule**
   - Distribute a course outline that includes dates and times of class meetings and lesson content. The optional in-water activities session should be clearly identified, if you are going to conduct it.
   - If you are going to conduct the optional in-water activities session, explain to the participants that there will be an optional in-water activities session. Then explain that those participants who do not want to go into the water may listen, observe, and take part in activities that take place on land. All participants who wish to take part in any of the in-water activities must take a swimming test. Those who do not pass the test must wear life jackets and may not go into water over chest deep.
   - Tell participants that they will need a swimsuit if they want to participate in the in-water activities practice session.

4. **Course Description**
   - Share the following goal statement with the class:
     The purpose of this course is to present information about various aquatic environments and their potential hazards and to inform the general public on how to safely participate in aquatic activities.

5. **How Participants Will Learn**
   - Briefly explain that participants will learn through lectures, discussion, and activities. They may also watch videos.

6. **The Participant's Manual**
   - Identify the participant's manual for this course, American Red Cross *Community Water Safety,* and lead participants through it. Point out the following features:
     - Self-Analysis Questions
     - Glossary
   - Tell participants that they will be given time to answer the Self-Analysis questions both at the beginning of the course and at the end so that they can compare their answers.

7. **Course Completion**
   - Describe the American Red Cross requirements for successful course completion. To successfully complete this module, the participant must attend the entire course session.

Note: Participants will receive a course completion certificate regardless of whether they participate in an in-water activities session or not.

Introduction

Time: 10 minutes

Activity:

Paper
Pencils

1. Hand out paper and pencils to the participants.
2. Tell participants that they have 10 minutes in which to answer the Self-Analysis questions. Tell them to jot down brief answers so that they can compare them with the answers they give at the end of the course.

STAYING SAFE WHILE HAVING FUN

Time: 20 minutes

Activity:

1. Ask participants to tell you some of the aquatic facilities they use and the aquatic activities they enjoy. Write some of these on the chalkboard or flip chart.
2. Quote Commodore Longfellow's saying—"Water can be a good friend or a deadly enemy." Ask participants to tell you some of the dangers they associate with their water activities.
3. Tell participants that staying safe while enjoying the water is what this course is about. They will not only learn how to stay safe and prevent drowning and injury in pools and other water environments, but they will also learn how to stay safe and help themselves in unexpected situations.

Drowning and Spinal Injury Risks

Primary Points:

Community Water Safety pages 4 & 5

- Drowning and spinal injury are the two major hazards in aquatic recreation.
- Drowning is the fourth leading cause of death from unintentional injury in the United States.
- Drowning has decreased in guarded facilities.
- Children under 5 and young adults from ages 15 to 24 have the highest rates of drowning.
- Headfirst entries into shallow water result in approximately 1,000 disabling back and neck injuries a year.
- Young adult males, ages 15 to 30, are the most frequent victims of these spinal injuries. The injuries result from diving into shallow water and striking the head on the bottom or an unexpected object.

PREPARING FOR WATER ACTIVITIES

Time: 30 minutes

Primary Points:

*Community Water
Safety*
page 7

Primary Points:

*Community Water
Safety*
pages 7–11

■ Be prepared by knowing what hazards to look for in specific water environments.

■ Be prepared by knowing how to rescue yourself or another person and how to give first aid to someone in an emergency.

Safety in the Water

People engaging in aquatic activities should follow these water-safety guidelines:

■ Learn the safety steps you should take before starting any activity in or near the water.

■ Learn about swimming, boating, and first aid, and be sure that others in your group also are informed.

　■ Contact your local American Red Cross chapter for information about swimming and first aid courses.

　■ Check with the Coast Guard and other organizations about boating and other aquatic courses.

■ Know what to do in case of a water emergency.

■ Choose a safe place for water recreation.

■ Use Coast Guard-approved life jackets when boating.

■ Look for potential water hazards.

■ Know local weather conditions and how to find out what is forecasted.

■ Know how to prevent, recognize, and care for hypothermia and heat emergencies.

■ Be familiar with the basic safety tips whenever you swim in any body of water. Some of these tips include—

　■ Never swim alone.

　■ Watch out for the dangerous "toos"—too tired, too cold, too far from safety, too much sun, and too much hard playing.

■ Stay out of the water when you are overheated.

■ Do not chew gum or eat while you swim.

■ Learn the correct way to dive, and know when it is safe to dive.

■ Use common sense about swimming after eating. In general, you do not have to wait an hour after eating before swimming. However, if you have had a large meal, let digestion start before you begin.

Note: Refer participants to page 7 of their Community Water Safety participant's manual for more safety tips.

Primary Points:

Community Water Safety
pages 7–9

Weather

- Look at the weather conditions before you and others enter the water.
- Avoid being in the water during storms, fog, or high winds.
- Do not swim after a storm in a lake or river if the water seems to be flooding. Currents may become strong, the water may become cloudy, and new obstacles in the water can be dangerous.
- Always check weather reports before participating in outdoor aquatic activities.
- Watch the sky for rolling dark clouds or clouds with cauliflower-like tops. They indicate a coming storm.
- Always leave the water at the first flash of lightning, sound of thunder, or onset of rain.

Primary Points:

Community Water Safety
page 10

Life Jackets

- To stay safe in and around the water, one should learn how to swim and should wear a life jacket or have one readily available.
- Make sure the life jacket is Coast Guard-approved, is in good condition, and fits properly.
- Make sure it is best suited to the water activity you plan to participate in.

Note: Refer participants to page 10 in their Community Water Safety participant's manual for descriptions of the five types of personal flotation devices.

Activity:

Personal Flotation Devices

Have participants look at the various flotation devices and try them on. Show participants how to tell if a device fits properly.

Primary Points:

Community Water Safety
page 11

Alcohol

- Drinking alcohol and participating in water activities can be very dangerous. Alcohol—
  - Affects your balance and makes you more likely to fall into the water.
  - Makes it harder to stay warm, even though you might feel warm after your first drink.
  - Affects your judgment (such as deciding to attempt a headfirst entry into shallow water).
  - Slows your movement and impairs your vision.
  - Can reduce your swimming skills, even if you're an excellent swimmer.

Diving

Primary Points:

Community Water Safety
page 11

- Diving can be fun and a safe activity if the following safety principles are followed:
  - Learn how to dive properly from a qualified instructor.
  - Always follow safety rules—never make exceptions.
  - Obey "No Diving" signs, which always indicate the area is unsafe for headfirst entries.
  - On the beach, do not run and enter waves headfirst.
  - Never dive into cloudy or murky water.
  - Do not use alcohol or other drugs.
  - Resist peer pressure to participate in any dangerous activities.

Note: Refer participants to page 11 in their Community Water Safety participant's manual for more safe-diving tips.

Staying Healthy

Primary Points:

Community Water Safety
page 12

- Staying healthy around the water means that you prevent problems even before you go into the water—and even if you do not go in.
  - Even though you may be protecting yourself from drowning and other injuries, you need to protect yourself from other problems, such as sun damage.
  - Small children and others who cannot take care of themselves need your help to protect their health.

Protecting Your Skin

Primary Points:

Community Water Safety
page 12

- Too much sun can lead to sunburn, skin cancer, and premature aging.
  - Limit the amount of direct sunlight by staying out of the sun between 10:00 am and 2:00 pm.
  - Protect your skin with a sunscreen with an SPF (sun protection factor) of at least 15. Use a water-resistant sunscreen if you are going to be in the water.

Protecting Your Eyes

Primary Points:

Community Water Safety
page 12

- Use sunglasses to protect your eyes from UV (ultraviolet) sun rays.
  - Be sure to wear sunglasses that absorb 90 percent of UV sunlight.

Protecting Your Ears

Primary Points:

Community Water Safety
pages 12–14

- Swimmer's ear can be prevented if you follow these basic tips:
  - After swimming, get the water out of your ears. Shake your head, tilt your head, and hop up and down on one foot, or use a towel to gently wipe the outer ear. You can also use a hair dryer on a low setting.
  - Eardrops can help dry the ear canal after swimming.
  - If you swim frequently, wear a swim cap or wetsuit hood, especially for surfing or sailboarding. This can help prevent ear problems caused by exposure to wind and cold water.
  - Do not use wax-type ear plugs. They may damage the ear canal and make infection more likely. Silicone earplugs give better protection.
  - Ask your doctor how to flush out your ears using warm water and an ear syringe.
  - Do not scratch, touch, or put anything into your ears.

Preventing Heat Emergencies

Primary Points:

Community Water Safety
page 14

- Heat exhaustion can be caused by strenuous work or exercise in the heat.
  - Heat stroke usually occurs when people ignore the signals of heat exhaustion (cool, pale, moist, or red skin, headache, nausea, dizziness, faintness, or exhaustion) and stay in the heat.

Preventing Hypothermia

Primary Points:

Community Water Safety
pages 14 & 15

- Hypothermia occurs when the body's warming mechanisms cannot maintain normal body temperature and the inner core cools.
- Cold water exposure can cause hypothermia.
- Protect yourself from hypothermia in the following ways:
  - When you are near cold water, remember that cold water is dangerous even if you do not intend to go in.
  - Do not go on or near the water unless you can get help quickly in an emergency.
  - Wear a Coast Guard-approved life jacket while boating and fishing on or near cold water.
  - In cooler weather, wear rain gear or insulated clothes.
  - Wear layers of clothes.
  - Carry matches in a waterproof container. You may need to build a fire to warm up after a fall into cold water.
  - Do not drink alcohol to stay warm. Although at first it may give a feeling of warmth, it actually increases loss of body heat.

Cramps

Primary Points:

Community Water Safety
page 16

- Cramps occur when your muscles become tired or cold from swimming or other activity.
- Changing the position of the limb and massaging the area often relieves the cramp.

Exhaustion

Primary Points:

Community Water Safety
page 16

- Exhaustion may occur when you no longer have the energy to keep swimming or move in the water.
- Prevent exhaustion by resting often while participating in aquatic activities.

Seizure Disorders

Primary Points:

Community Water Safety
page 16

- Seizures can occur in water.
- Epilepsy is a common type of seizure disorder.
- Anyone with a seizure disorder should always swim with someone who knows about his or her condition and in guarded areas.
- Children should be supervised by a responsible adult who knows how to treat their condition.

Helping in an Emergency

Primary Points:

Community Water Safety
pages 16–17

1. Explain that it is important to be prepared for emergencies when swimming in areas where there is no lifeguard on duty. Discuss with participants some ways of being prepared. Cover the following points:
   - Have an emergency signal—some way to let others know that there is an emergency and help is needed.
   - Have safety equipment with you.
   - Know what to do in case of emergencies.
   - Keep a first aid kit in your car and at home.
     - Take it with you on any type of outdoor activity.
     - Learn what needs to be in it.
2. Tell participants to look at Figure 2–13 on page 17 of their participant's manual. Discuss the contents of a first aid kit with them.

Note: You may want to have a first aid kit available to show the participants. You can pass the kit around and let the participants examine the contents.

WATER HAZARDS

Time: 30 minutes

Primary Points:

Community Water Safety
page 19

Video:
(optional)

- Every water site and activity has its own unique qualities and potential hazards.
- Being able to recognize these hazards and knowing what to do when you encounter them can prevent problems from occurring.

Show the video: *Home Pool Safety: It Only Takes a Minute.* (approx. 21 minutes)

Pools and Spas

Primary Points:

Community Water Safety
pages 19 & 20

- Every year, 300 to 400 children under age five drown in either home pools or unguarded pools, nationwide.
- Fences that are four-sided and three-sided (using house as fourth side), along with self-locking gates and doors, may help keep children out of home pools and spas.
- Adult supervision of children is essential.
- Spas also present hazards.
- Spa temperatures should not be over 104 degrees. Time spent in the spa should be limited to 15 minutes or less.
- Follow these additional guidelines for spa safety.
  - Never use a spa after drinking alcohol.
  - Do not let children under age 5 use a spa. Young children are more prone to overheating because their bodies cannot regulate temperatures well.
  - Do not let children of any age use a spa unsupervised.
  - Hot water can cause health problems in people who are susceptible to certain ailments or who have certain conditions.
    - Do not use a spa if you are pregnant or suffer from high or low blood pressure, heart disease, seizures, or diabetes.
    - Check with your doctor before using a spa if you are taking medications.
    - Check with your doctor if you have a chronic medical condition to find out if hot water could aggravate it.
  - If you own a spa, post the emergency telephone number for the Emergency Medical Services (EMS) system by your telephone. Keep a cordless telephone near the spa.

Activity:

Ask participants to suggest a list of safety rules for a home pool and for a spa. These rules can include no running, no diving, or no electrical appliances, such as a radio, near the pool or spa.

Waterparks

Primary Points:

Community Water Safety
pages 20 & 21

- Waterparks are popular aquatic facilities that have specific hazards. When visiting a waterpark, participants should—
  - Be sure the area is well supervised by lifeguards before you or others in your group enter the water.
  - Read all posted signs. Follow the rules and directions lifeguards give. Ask questions if you are not sure about a correct procedure.
  - When you go from one attraction to another, note that the water depth may be different and read the rules to see how the attraction should be used.
  - Before you start down a water slide, get in the correct position—face up and feet first.

Buckets and Bathtubs

Primary Points:

Community Water Safety
page 21

- Fifteen percent of home drownings have been in bathtubs and other small containers of water.
- Never leave a child alone with containers filled with water. Do **not** leave a child alone in a bathtub. Keep bathroom doors closed; empty cleaning buckets immediately after use.

Lakes, Ponds, and Rivers

Primary Points:

Community Water Safety
pages 21–25

- In any open water, you may encounter potentially dangerous conditions that differ from what you are used to. These include—
  - Murky water.
  - Shallow water.
  - An area where there is no lifeguard on duty.
- Before entering the water in a new area, check out the water conditions.

Note: Refer participants to page 23 of their Community Water Safety participant's manual for a list of factors to consider when selecting safe swimming areas.

- **River Currents**
  - River currents are often unpredictable and fast moving because of bottom changes.
  - Stay out of rivers or creeks after heavy rains because of the dangers of rising waters and flooding.
- **Hydraulics**
  - A hydraulic is water that flows down over an object in the water, causing a strong downward force that can trap you.
  - The water surface may look calm and can fool a person looking from the surface.
  - Stay out of areas where water drops off, such as edges and waterfalls.
- **Dams**
  - Avoid all water activities both above and below a dam.
- **Underwater Obstacles**
  - Always enter open water slowly, carefully, and feetfirst because rocks, stumps, and remains of old structures may be present.

Note: Refer participants to the sidebar "The Old Swimming Hole" on page 22 in their Community Water Safety participant's manual and suggest that they read it, if they have not already done so.

- **Flooding**
  - Levees have saved many communities from flooding, but they cannot protect against record rains and record high water levels.
  - Heavy rains in a short period of time can lead to flash flooding.
  - Avoid drainage ditches. After a heavy rain, they can quickly turn into raging rivers that can take a human life.
  - Avoid driving through flooded roadways or over flooded bridges.
  - Stay out of underpasses that can quickly flood near intersections or railroad crossings.
- **Aquatic Life**
  - Some aquatic plants and animals may be dangerous.
    - If you become entangled in aquatic plants, do not panic but try to swim slowly and gently away, with a current if there is one.
    - If you encounter any aquatic life while swimming, swim slowly away from it.

Oceans

Primary Points:

Community Water Safety
pages 25–28

Ocean beaches are popular places. At the beach and the ocean, you need to watch out for hazards, such as waves, currents, and other water conditions.

- Guarded ocean beaches often use flags to signal water conditions. A red flag means the area is unsafe.
- Do not swim at unguarded beaches because of potential dangers.
- **Waves**
  - Any swimmer can be knocked over by a wave breaking close to shore.
  - Children playing at the water's edge can be knocked down and pulled into the water by a sudden, large breaking wave.
- **Ocean Currents**
  - Drift or side currents move parallel to the shore.
  - Undertows move down the slope of the beach, straight out, and under incoming waves.
  - Rip currents move straight out to sea beyond the breaking waves.
    - If a current carries you parallel to shore, try to swim toward shore while moving along the current. If you are being carried away from shore, swim out of the current, not against it, by moving parallel to the shore. Once you are free, turn and swim toward shore.
- **Aquatic Life**
  - You can be stung by stepping or swimming near a jellyfish or Portuguese man-of-war.
  - Before going into any ocean, find out what local marine life may be dangerous, how to avoid it, and how to care for any injuries.

Note: First aid for stings is described in Chapter 6 of Community Water Safety.

Activity:

Ask participants to describe to you any dangers they have experienced with lakes, ponds, rivers, and oceans.

Camps and Group Trips

Primary Points:

Community Water Safety
pages 28 & 29

- Water activities at camps and during field trips require attention to safety.
- Parents should check a camp waterfront and find out how it is supervised before enrolling a child.
- Camp waterfronts should be supervised by trained personnel.
- The camp should have a buddy system.

- When planning a group trip, tell the facility about—
  - The size of your group.
  - The general ages of group members.
  - The swimming abilities of group members.
  - When you plan to arrive.
- Review the rules and regulations.
- Do not take a group, especially children, to open water unless you are sure there is enough lifeguard supervision and the conditions are safe.

AQUATIC RECREATION

Time: 35 minutes

Primary Points:

Community Water Safety
page 31

Video:
(optional)

Primary Points:

Community Water Safety
pages 31–35

It is important to gain knowledge and receive instruction before participating in boating, water sports, or white-water rafting.

Tell participants that they are going to see a video about various aquatic environments and what can happen in them. Show the video: *Water the Deceptive Power.* (approx. 31 minutes)

Boating

- Anyone going boating should know how to swim and operate a boat safely.
  - Find a boating course in your area. Check with the American Red Cross, the U.S. Power Squadron, the U.S. Coast Guard Auxiliary, United States Sailing, the American Canoe Association, or marinas and recreational facilities in your area.
- Drinking alcohol while boating is dangerous.
  - More than 50 percent of drownings from boating incidents involve alcohol.
  - Drinking and boating can kill. Do not endanger yourself or others. Stay sober while boating.
- Safety equipment
  - Check federal and state laws for equipment required for the type of boat you will be using.
  - Before going boating, make sure that your boat has all the necessary safety equipment on board and in working condition.

Note: Refer participants to page 32 of Community Water Safety for a list of safety equipment that should be on a boat.

- Navigational rules
  - Boat operators must learn and obey navigational rules to keep boating safe and enjoyable.
  - Navigational rules determine right-of-way.
  - When you approach a boat head on—
    - Keep to your right.
    - Boats sailed or rowed have the right-of-way. A sailboat always has the right-of-way over a powerboat.
  - Crossing paths
    - The boat on the right has the right-of-way. The boat on the left must slow down, change course, or pass behind the other boat. A sailboat always has the right-of-way over a powerboat.
  - Overtaking
    - The boat being passed has the right-of-way. The passing boat may pass on either side after giving the proper signal with the horn.
  - Learn the rules for exiting and entering a marina. Obey speed rules and the rules for small or no-wake zones near docks, piers, or crowded boat ramps.
  - Learn how to disembark and board a boat from a dock or shoreline.
    - Wear nonskid shoes.
    - Watch for waves or boat wakes that may throw you off balance.
    - Tell those already on board that you are about to board or disembark.
    - Have another person hold and help stabilize the boat while you board or disembark.
    - Be careful not to step on equipment.
    - Keep your weight low in the hull of the boat to keep the boat stable.
  - When docking a boat, make sure it is tied at the front and back.
  - Step ahead as close to the center of the boat as you can.
  - Hold the side of the boat as you shift your weight.
  - Sit on the dock first if the dock is much higher than the boat.
  - At the beach or shore, make sure the boat is floating before you step in.
  - To disembark, reverse steps.

- To change positions in a small boat—
  - Only one person should move at a time.
  - Keep the weight low and as near the center of the boat as possible.
  - Keep the boat trimmed by balancing the weight of one passenger against another.
  - In heavy waves, change positions only when necessary to correct the balance.
- Float plan
  - If you are planning to be out in a boat for a few hours or longer, leave a written float plan with a responsible person.
  - A float plan should contain—
    - Boat number and name.
    - Boat size, make, and capacity.
    - Number of engines, horsepower, and type of fuel used.
    - Number of persons on board and their names, addresses, and telephone numbers.
    - Type of radio equipment on board.
    - Departure date, time, and location.
    - Destination.
    - Date and time that you want the Coast Guard notified if you fail to reach your predetermined destination.

Sailboarding

Primary Points:

Community Water Safety
page 35

- To remain safe, always wear a Coast Guard-approved life jacket and monitor water and weather conditions for possible problems.
- You will enjoy sailboarding more if you take lessons from a qualified instructor.

Surfing

Primary Points:

Community Water Safety
page 35

- Take lessons from an experienced person.
- Never surf alone.
- Look out for other surfers, swimmers, jetties, reefs, and debris in the water.

Snorkeling and SCUBA

Primary Points:

Community Water Safety
page 36

- When snorkeling, you use fins to move quickly through the water, a snorkel to help you breathe, and a mask so that you can see clearly under the water.

- To snorkel safely, follow these guidelines:
  - Practice in shallow water.
  - Check the equipment carefully, and know how it functions.
  - Learn how to clear water from the snorkel when treading water.
  - Learn how to put your mask back on when you tread water.
  - Be careful not to swim too far from shore or the boat or be carried off by a current.
  - Never snorkel alone.
  - Practice snorkeling in a pool or shallow water before venturing into open water.
- SCUBA divers wear a mask and fins and carry a compressed air supply and regulator for breathing.
- SCUBA divers also use buoyancy compensators, wetsuits, weights, and instruments to monitor depth, time, and directions under water.
- Many SCUBA organizations offer safe and effective SCUBA courses for individuals wanting to dive.
- Take lessons from a certified instructor.
- Follow these guidelines:
  - Get a medical examination and take a swim test before learning SCUBA diving.
  - Once certified, do not dive in rough or dangerous waters or in environments for which you are not trained. Ice, cave, and shipwreck diving require special training. One can easily get lost or trapped and run out of air.

Water Skiing

Primary Points:

Community Water Safety
page 37

- Learn any specific federal, state, and local regulations for water skiing in your area.
- Be sure the boat and ski equipment are in good shape.
- Always turn the motor completely off when you approach a fallen skier.
- Watch for other boats and skiers in the area, and avoid getting too close.
- Wear a Coast Guard-approved life jacket when water skiing.
- Always make sure a "spotter" is on the boat to watch the skier.

Tubing and Rafting

Primary Points:

Community Water Safety
page 37

- When rafting or tubing, always wear a Coast Guard-approved life jacket and protective headgear.
- Monitor water clarity, temperature, and currents, as well as weather conditions, for possible problems.

- Do not go tubing or rafting after a heavy rain.
- If you raft with a tour company, make sure the guides are qualified. Check with your local chamber of commerce for accredited tour companies and guides.

Fishing and Hunting

Primary Points:

Community Water Safety
page 37

- When fishing or hunting near water, dress properly for the weather.
- Always wear a Coast Guard-approved life jacket.
- Watch your footing when you walk next to water.
- Do not mix alcohol with activities near the water.

Ice Activities

Primary Points:

Community Water Safety
pages 37 & 38

- Learn about ice and what precautions to take to protect yourself.
- The following conditions can cause weak or thin spots in the ice:
    - Springs or fast-moving water
    - Wind and wave action
    - Water bubblers (devices designed to keep the water near boat docks from freezing thick)
    - Objects protruding through the ice, such as tree stumps
- To prevent ice emergencies, follow these guidelines:
    - Check the ice thickness before you go out. To be safe, ice should be solid and at least 4 inches thick. Remember, the ice might not be the same thickness over the entire area of a lake, pond, or bog.
    - Solid, 4-inch-thick ice is generally safe to walk or skate on but not thick enough to drive a vehicle on.
    - Ice activities are safer on small, shallow bodies of water without a current. Ice will be more solid on this water.
    - Look for objects sticking up through the ice, and avoid these areas.
    - Don't go out on ice that has recently frozen, thawed, and then frozen again.
        - This happens in the spring and early winter as temperatures change often.
        - Wait until the outside temperature has been below freezing long enough so that at least 4 inches of solid ice form over the entire area.
    - Always stay with at least one other person.
    - Tell someone where you will be and when you intend to return.
    - Wear warm clothes. Polypropylene, Capalene, or wool works well for holding warm air next to your body and for insulation, even when wet.

- Carry matches in a waterproof container. You may need to build a fire to warm up after a fall into cold water.

TAKING ACTION IN AN EMERGENCY

Time: 40 minutes

Primary Points:

Community Water
Safety
page 40

- Even with the best precautions, water emergencies occur.
- You may also be in a situation when either you or someone else may need help.
- By learning rescue techniques, you can help yourself and others in an emergency.

Activity:

Ask participants to tell you about any water emergencies they have experienced. Ask what participants did to help themselves or others.

Self-Rescue in Warm Water

Primary Points:

Community Water
Safety
pages 40–43

- In warm water, you can use survival floating and survival swimming to stay on the surface and make your way to safety.
- Survival floating is a face-down floating technique.

Note: Refer participants to Figure 5–1, A and B, and to the steps for performing survival floating on page 40 in the their participant's manual.

- **Survival Swimming**
  - Use this method when you need to move to safety.

Note: Refer participants to Figure 5–2, A and B, and to the steps for performing survival floating on page 41 of their participant's manual.

- **Self-Rescue When Clothed**
  - Many types of clothing, such as a shirt or jacket and even boots, will actually help you float and will help protect you from cold water.
  - If you fall into the water, you may be able to trap air in the shoulders of your shirt or jacket to help keep afloat while you paddle toward safety.

Note: Refer participants to Figure 5–3, A and B, and to the steps for using a jacket or shirt for flotation on pages 41 and 42 of their participant's manual.

Self Rescue in Cold Water

Primary Points:

Community Water Safety
pages 42–46

- If you fall into cold water, you need to conserve body heat as well as prevent hypothermia by trying to get out of the water as quickly as possible.
- Winter clothes can actually help you float. Heavy clothes also help delay hypothermia.
- If you fall into cold water wearing a life jacket —
  - Keep all clothes on, especially your hat, to help retain your body heat.
  - Keep your face and head above the surface.
  - If you swim in cold water, try to conserve energy by keeping your arms under water while you swim.
  - If safety is more than a few strokes away, float and wait to be rescued.
- If you are wearing a life jacket while waiting to be rescued, you can do the following:
  - Get into the H.E.L.P. (heat escape lessening) position:
    - Draw your knees up to your chest, hold your upper arms to your sides, and fold your lower arms up or across your chest. Keep your face forward and out of the water.
    - Don't use the H.E.L.P. position in swift water. In swift water, you should always go down the current feetfirst.
  - Two or more people can use the huddle position.
    - Put your arms around each other's shoulders so that the sides of your chests are together.
- If you fall into cold water without a life jacket—
  - Keep all clothes on and move as little as possible to conserve heat and energy.
  - Swim only if you are close enough to reach shore safely.
  - After reaching safety—
    - Remove wet clothing.
    - Move to a warmer environment.
    - Rewarm your body gradually.

Falling Through the Ice

Primary Points:

Community Water Safety
page 46

- Resist the urge to try to climb back out. Reach forward but do not push down on the ice.
- Get into a floating position on your stomach. Bend your knees to help trap air in your pant legs or your boots.
- Reach forward onto the broken ice, but do not push down on it. Use a breaststroke kick or some other kick to push yourself up onto the ice.

- Do not stand up once you get back onto the ice. Crawl or roll away from the broken area with your arms and legs spread as far out as possible.
- Call for someone to extend or throw something to you. Use it to pull yourself along. Do not stand on the ice.
- Once you are safe, follow the guidelines for preventing hypothermia.

Falling Out of a Boat

Primary Points:

Community Water Safety
page 46

- If the boat is still afloat, climb back into it if you can do so safely, or hold onto the side while someone slowly paddles the boat to safety.
- If the boat capsizes, turn the motor off and stay with the boat. Only leave the boat if it is in danger of catching on fire or if there is a life-threatening emergency.
- Hold onto the hull of the boat or sit on or in it. You can paddle a small capsized boat to safety. In cold water, get as much of your body as possible into the boat.

Helping Others

Primary Points:

Community Water Safety
page 49

- You can learn basic skills to aid a person in trouble in the water, but always remember, your safety comes first.
- If you cannot easily help the person, call for professional help.

Emergency Medical Services

Primary Points:

Community Water Safety
page 49

- The Emergency Medical Services (EMS) system is a network of professionals who will respond to the emergency, take care of the victim, and transport the victim to get further medical treatment if necessary.
- When an emergency happens, you or someone else must call 9–1–1 or the emergency number in your community to contact the EMS dispatcher, who will take your information and summon professionals to the scene.

Recognizing an Emergency

Primary Points:

Community Water Safety
pages 49 & 50

- Not all emergencies are obvious. It is important to be able to recognize an emergency.
- Being able to recognize that a person is having trouble in the water may help save that person's life.
- Watch for anything that seems unusual.
- There are two kinds of water emergency situations: a swimmer in distress and a drowning person.

- A swimmer in distress may be too tired to get back to shore, but can stay afloat and breathe, and may be able to call out for help. That person may be treading water or holding onto a line for support. Someone who is trying to swim but not making progress may be in distress.
- A person in distress may begin to drown if not helped soon.
- Most drowning people do not call for help. They spend their energy trying to keep their heads above water.
- An active drowning person's arms are pressing down, trying to keep his or head above the water to breathe. The body is vertical in the water. The person cannot call out for help.
- A passive drowning victim is not moving and will be floating facedown on the bottom or near the surface of the water.

Note: Refer participants to Table 5–1 on page 50 in their participant's manual, which compares the characteristics of swimmers, distressed swimmers, and drowning victims.

Deciding to Act

Primary Points:

Community Water Safety page 51

- Once you know there is an emergency, you have to decide to act—and how to act.
- To prepare for the moment when you have to make a decision to act, think about all the different emergency situations and what you might do. Do not hesitate to act because—
  - Of other people at the scene.
  - The victim is a stranger or different from you in some way.
  - Of the injury or illness itself.
  - You fear catching any disease from the victim. It is extremely unlikely that you would catch a disease from rescuing someone or giving first aid.
  - You are afraid of doing something wrong.
- Once you decide to act, make sure the scene is safe and you will not endanger yourself.

Calling for Help

Primary Points:

Community Water Safety pages 51 & 52

- If the victim is out of the water, call a lifeguard immediately if you are at a guarded facility. If the victim is in the water, assist the person to safety and then call EMS.
  - Make sure you stay on the phone until the dispatcher has finished asking you all the questions.

1. Ask participants how they might react if they saw a person who was obviously in an emergency situation.
2. Ask participants how they think people tend to react in general when faced with an emergency situation.
3. Ask participants why people sometimes take no action to help others in an emergency situation. Answers may vary but should include some of the following:
   - Lack of knowledge of what to do
   - Fear of doing something wrong
   - Fear for personal safety
   - Fear of the person who is in trouble or injured
   - Fear of a lawsuit

Out-of-Water Assists

Activity:

Ask participants to tell you how they might try to assist someone who was in trouble in the water without going in the water themselves. List some of their ideas on the chalkboard or flip chart.

Primary Points:

Community Water Safety
page 52

- Without going into the water, you can help a person who is in trouble in the water by using a reaching or throwing assist.

Note: Refer participants to Figures 5–16 and 5–17 on page 52 of their participant's manual.

Reaching Assists

Primary Points:

Community Water Safety
pages 52 & 53

- To perform a reaching assist, brace yourself firmly and reach out to a person in the water with an object such as a tree branch, a pole, a paddle, or any other object that will extend your reach. Community pools, pools at hotels and motels, and recreational areas often have reaching equipment such as an aluminum or fiberglass pole with a large hook at one end, called a shepherd's crook.
- You can lie flat on a pool deck or a pier and reach out with your arm.
- If you are already in the water, firmly grasp the pool ladder, overflow trough or some other secure object, and extend the other arm or one leg.

Throwing Assists

Note: Refer participants to Figures 5–18, A and B, and 5–19 on page 53, and to Figures 5–20, 5–21, and 5–22 on page 54 of their participant's manual.

Primary Points:

Community Water Safety
pages 53–55

■ If someone is beyond your reach, you can throw a piece of equipment, such as a heaving line, ring buoy, throw bag, rescue tube, or other device to the victim and pull him or her to safety.

In-Water Assists

Note: Refer participants to Figure 5–24, A and B, on page 55 of their participant's manual.

Wading Assists With Equipment

Primary Points:

Community Water Safety
pages 55 & 56

■ If the water is shallow enough so that you can stand with your head out of the water, wade into the water to assist the person. Take a buoyant device with you and extend it to the person. You can use a rescue tube, ring buoy, buoyant cushion, kickboard, life jacket, tree branch, pole, air mattress, paddle, or another object that floats. Do not go into the water if a current or a soft bottom makes wading dangerous.

■ Always keep the buoyant device between you and the victim.

■ Once the victim has grasped the object, either pull the victim to safety or let it go and tell the victim to kick to safety.

■ If the victim is lying motionless and facedown in the water, he or she is probably unconscious. If the water is not over your head, wade into the water with a buoyant device and turn the person face up. Then bring the person to the side of the pool or the shoreline and remove him or her from the water.

Walking Assist

Note: Refer participants to Figure 5–25 on page 56 of their participant's manual.

Primary Points:

Community Water Safety
page 56

■ If the victim is in shallow water where he or she can stand, place one of the victim's arms around your neck and across your shoulder, grasp the wrist of that arm with your other hand, and help the person out of the water.

| Primary Points: |
| Community Water Safety page 56 |

Beach Drag

Note: *Refer participants to Figures 5–26 and 5–27 on page 56 of their participant's manual.*

- You may use the beach drag with a victim in shallow water on a sloping shore or beach. This method works well with a heavy or unconscious victim.
  - Stand behind the victim, and grasp him or her under the armpits. Support his or her head on your forearms, if possible, and walk backwards, slowly dragging the victim toward the shore.

Helping Someone Who Has Fallen Through Ice

| Primary Points: |
| Community Water Safety page 57 |

- If a person falls through the ice, never go out onto the ice yourself to attempt a rescue. Instead, follow these guidelines:
  - Send someone to call EMS personnel immediately.
  - From a secure place on land, try a reaching or throwing assist.
  - If you can do it safely, pull the victim to shore. If you cannot, talk to the victim and make sure he or she is as secure as possible until help arrives.

PROVIDING CARE UNTIL HELP ARRIVES

Time: 45 minutes

| Activity: |

Discuss with participants the various kinds of emergencies that can occur around the water and may require first aid. List some of them on the chalkboard or flip chart.

| Primary Points: |
| Community Water Safety page 59 |

Til' Help Arrives **booklet**

- People may need first aid because of injuries or sudden illnesses that may occur in or around the water.
- In an emergency situation, remember to call 9–1–1 or the local emergency number as soon as you see there is an emergency. Optional—Show participants the booklet *Til' Help Arrives,* and explain that it describes basic steps of care a person can give an injured or suddenly ill person until more advanced help arrives.
- Contact your local American Red Cross unit about available first aid and CPR courses.

Specific Emergencies

Rescue Breathing

Primary Points:

Community Water Safety pages 59 & 60

■ If a person is not breathing, you will need to breathe air into the person to supply him or her with the oxygen needed to survive.

■ If you rescue a person and he or she is not breathing, bring the person out of the water as quickly as possible.

■ To find out whether the person is breathing, position the person on his or her back on a flat surface and use the head-tilt/chin-lift to open the airway.

■ Put your ear close to the person's mouth and nose. Watch to see if the chest rises and falls. If you cannot see, hear, or feel any signs of breathing, then the person is not breathing.

■ Have someone call EMS personnel. Begin the steps for rescue breathing by making a seal with your mouth over the victim's mouth, pinching the victim's nose shut, and blowing slow breaths into the victim. Watch as the chest gently rises and falls, which shows that your breaths are going into the victim. Check for a pulse. If the victim has a pulse but is still not breathing, continue rescue breathing.

Activity:

1. Using a co-instructor, an instructor aide, or a volunteer participant as victim, demonstrate the head-tilt/chin-lift. Explain that this maneuver moves the tongue away from the back of the throat so that it cannot block the airway.

2. Demonstrate looking, listening, and feeling for breathing.

Air Blockage

Primary Points:

Community Water Safety page 60

■ When a person's air passage becomes blocked, your goal is to open the airway as quickly as possible.

■ If the airway is obviously obstructed, give abdominal thrusts until you clear the airway.

Activity:

Explain and demonstrate how to give abdominal thrusts (Heimlich Maneuver), using a co-instructor, an instructor aide, or volunteer participant as the victim. Show the hand position on a standing victim. Do not give actual abdominal thrusts.

Heat Emergencies

■ Heat Cramps

- Heat cramps are painful muscle spasms, usually in the arms and legs. Have the victim rest in a cool place and drink cool water. Do not give the victim salt tablets or salt water.

■ Heat Exhaustion

- A person may be experiencing heat exhaustion if—
  - The skin is cool, moist, pale, or red, and the person has a headache or feels nauseated, faint, dizzy, or exhausted.
- To give care—
  - Move the person to a cool environment.
  - Have the person rest and drink a half glass of cold water every 15 minutes.
  - Put cool, wet cloths on skin, loosen tight clothing, and remove any clothing soaked with sweat.
  - If the victim does not improve in 30 minutes or begins to vomit, refuses water, or becomes unconscious, call EMS personnel immediately. Heat stroke may be developing.

■ Heat Stroke

- This condition is life-threatening. The victim of heat stroke will not sweat and will have hot, red, dry skin and very high body temperature. Breathing may be rapid and shallow. The victim may vomit or lose consciousness.
  - Remove the victim from the sun or hot environment.
  - Cool the victim. Apply cool, wet cloths, such as towels or sheets, to the victim's body if you have not already done so. If you have ice packs or cold packs available, put them on the victim's wrists, ankles, neck, and armpits. Do not apply rubbing alcohol, which can worsen the condition.

Hypothermia

- Anyone in cold water or in wet clothes for a long time may develop hypothermia. Signals include feeling weak, confusion, irregular pulse, bluish lips, numbness, slurred speech, shivering, and semiconsciousness or unconsciousness.
- To care for a person who may have hypothermia—
  - Handle the victim very gently and monitor breathing.
  - Remove wet clothes, dry the victim, and move him or her to a warm environment. Do not warm the victim too quickly, such as by immersing him or her in warm water. Rapid warming may cause heart problems. Remember that hypothermia can be life-threatening.

- Wrap the victim in blankets or put on dry clothes.
- If the victim is alert, give him or her warm liquids to drink. Do not give the victim alcohol or caffeine.

Bites and Stings

Insect Stings

Primary Points:

Community Water Safety
pages 64–67

- If you go to open-water areas, you may come in contact with insects, snakes, or aquatic life that may sting or bite.
- Some people have a severe reaction to an insect sting that may be life-threatening.
- If the stinger is still in the skin, remove the stinger as soon as possible by scraping it away from the skin with your fingernail or a plastic credit card.
- Do not use tweezers.
- Wash the area with soap and water, and cover it to keep it clean. Apply a cold pack to reduce swelling.
- Watch for signs of an allergic reaction.
  - The person may experience hives, itching, rash, weakness, nausea, vomiting, dizziness, and breathing difficulties that include coughing and wheezing.
  - The throat and tongue may swell and impair breathing.
  - Watch the person carefully if you see any of these signs of an allergic reaction. If the person has any difficulty breathing or says his or her throat is closing, call EMS personnel immediately. If the person has a kit with medication in it to counteract the allergic effects of an insect bite, help the person use it, if necessary.

Marine Life

- Some types of fish and certain jellyfish may give you a painful sting.
  - Soak the injured part in vinegar as soon as possible. You can use baking soda or alcohol as an alternative. Do not rub the wound or apply ammonia or fresh water.
  - Flush a wound from a sting ray, sea urchin, or spiny fish with tap or ocean water. Soak the injured part in nonscalding hot water for about 30 minutes. Watch the person in case he or she has an allergic reaction. If so, call EMS personnel immediately.

Snakes

- If someone has been bitten by a snake, wash and immobilize the injured area, keeping it lower than the heart.
- Do **not** apply ice, a tourniquet, or electric shock.
- Seek medical attention as soon as possible.

Splinters, Fishhooks, and Other Objects in a Wound

Primary Points:

Community Water Safety
page 67

- Remove splinters with tweezers, and wash and cover the site to keep it clean.
- If a fishhook or a piece of wood, glass, or metal is stuck in a wound, don't remove it. Place dressings and clean cloths around the object to keep it from moving. Get medical help.
- If a fishhook is not imbedded but has cut the skin, stop the bleeding with direct pressure on the cut, and cover it with a sterile dressing. The victim should check with his or her physician to see if a tetanus shot is needed.

Seizures

Primary Points:

Community Water Safety
page 68

- A seizure (sometimes called a convulsion) is a temporary loss of consciousness with, in some cases, uncontrolled muscle contractions.
- A person who has a seizure in the water can suddenly become unconscious and submerge.
- A seizure may have the following characteristics:
  - The victim may have a peculiar sensation preceding the seizure lasting a few seconds. He or she may hear, see, smell, or taste something peculiar or not there, may feel pain, or may have a sensation warning him or her to move to safety.
  - A sudden rigidity of the person's body, sometimes after a high-pitched cry.
  - Loss of consciousness.
  - Uncontrolled muscular movement, during which the victim may lose bladder and bowel control. The victim may also salivate, hold his or her breath, and clench the jaw. The heart rate increases.
  - A state of drowsiness and confusion after the seizure. Then the victim gradually regains consciousness and may complain of a headache.
- First aid for someone having a seizure includes the following:
  - Protect the victim from injury. If on land, clear the area of any hard or sharp objects and loosen any tight clothing.

- Do not try to restrain a victim having muscular contractions.
- Do not put anything in the victim's mouth. If on land, turn the victim on the side if needed to let saliva or vomit drain out.
- Have someone call EMS personnel.
- Stay with the victim until EMS personnel arrive. Monitor the victim's breathing. If the victim stops breathing, start rescue breathing.
- Help the victim rest and feel comfortable. Be reassuring and supportive. Protect the victim's privacy by keeping onlookers at a distance.

Spinal Injury

Primary Points:

Community Water Safety
pages 68–72

- The spine is a strong, flexible column of bones called vertebrae. It supports the head and trunk and protects the spinal cord. The spinal cord is a bundle of nerves that run through the vertebrae and go out to all parts of the body. Any injury to the spine can damage these nerves and cause paralysis or death. An injury can happen anywhere along the back or neck up to the head, but neck injuries most commonly result from headfirst entries into the water.
- If you are unsure whether a person has a spinal injury, think about what the person was doing and what happened to cause the injury. The following are situations in which a spinal injury is possible:
  - Any fall from a height greater than the victim's height
  - Any person found unconscious for an unknown reason
  - Any serious head injury
  - Any injury from an entry from a diving board or water slide, or from diving from a height (such as a bank or a cliff)
  - Diving into shallow water
- If the person is conscious, ask how he or she is feeling. The following symptoms may also indicate a spinal injury:
  - Pain along the spine at the site of the injury
  - Loss of movement in the hands and feet, arms and legs, or below the injury site
  - Loss of sensation or tingling in the arms, legs, hands, or feet
  - Disorientation
  - Back or neck shape looks wrong
  - Bruise over the spine
  - Impaired breathing
  - Obvious head injury
  - Fluid or blood in the ears

■ Special Spinal Injury Techniques

- ■ If the person is in the water, you must try to keep the person's head and neck from moving and get the person to safety. Before you try to do this, check to see if a lifeguard or other person trained in these techniques is present.

Activity:

Refer participants to page 71 to the section "General Guidelines for Care" in their participant's manual. Review these guidelines. Tell the participants that they can use these general guidelines to care for a victim in shallow water by themselves or with the help of a bystander.

CLOSING

Time: 15 minutes

Activity:

Paper
Pencils

1. Hand out paper and pencils and ask participants to reanswer the self-analysis questions and compare the answers they gave this time with the answers they gave before the course began.
2. If the optional in-water activities session is being conducted, tell participants they will have a 10-minute break for those who wish to change into swimsuits for the in-water activities session. Other participants can be dismissed at this time. Thank them for attending the course and hand out course-completion certificates. If you do not have the certificates with you, tell participants that certificates will be mailed to them.

OPTIONAL IN-WATER ACTIVITIES SESSION

Time: 60 minutes

Activity:

Personal Flotation Devices

Conduct the swimming pretest for those who wish to participate in the in-water session. To pass the swimming test, participants must—

1. Enter shallow water; swim into deep water next to the edge of pool, dock, or lifeline for 10 yards; float or tread water for 1 minute; and return to shallow water on their backs.
2. Jump into deep water, level off, and swim 10 yards to safety.

On the basis of the swimming test results, hand out life jackets to the participants who did not pass the test and to those who did not take the test but wish to participate wearing life jackets.

Reaching Assist

- Firmly brace yourself on a pool deck or pier, and reach out to the victim with any object that will extend your reach, such as a pole, an oar or a paddle, a tree branch, a shirt, a belt, or a towel.
- When the victim grasps the object, slowly and carefully pull him or her to safety, keeping your body low and leaning back.
- If you have no object with which to reach the victim, lie flat on the pool deck or pier and extend your arm to him or her. If you are already in the water, hold onto the pool ladder, overflow trough, or some other secure object with one hand and extend your arm or one leg to the victim. Do not release your grip at the edge or swim out into the water.

1. Have participants practice reaching a floating object with a shephard's crook and recovering it. Using a "swimmer" partici- pant as a victim, have participants practice reaching assists using various objects such as a reaching pole, a kickboard, or a towel.
2. Have participants hold onto a ladder or some other stable object and practice extending an arm or leg to a victim.

Throwing Assist

When performing a throwing assist—

- Get into a stride position (the leg opposite your throwing arm in front of the other leg). This position lets you keep your balance when you throw the equipment.
- Bend your knees.
- Step on your end of the line with your forward foot.
- Try to throw the device just beyond the victim but within reach.
- Throw the device so that any wind or current will bring it back to the victim.
- When the victim has grasped the device, slowly pull him or her to safety. Lean back away from the victim as you pull.

Using a co-instructor, instructor aide, or "swimmer" participant as victim, have participants practice throwing assists. Be sure that they remember to throw the object slightly beyond the victim and to lean back as they pull the victim to safety.

Wading Assist With Equipment

Primary Points:

Community Water Safety
pages 55 & 56

- If the water is shallow enough that you can stand with your head out of water, wade into the water.
- Take a buoyant object and extend it to the victim. Return to safety.
- If the victim is face down in the water, and you have no reason to suspect a spinal injury, turn the victim over to a face-up position. Return to the side of the pool or the shoreline.

Activity:

Rescue Tube

Using a co-instructor, instructor aide, or a "swimmer" participant, have participants practice a wading assist with equipment in chest-deep water.

Walking Assist and Beach Drag

Primary Points:

Community Water Safety
page 56

- **Walking Assist**
  - Place one of the victim's arms around your neck and across one shoulder.
  - Grasp the wrist of the arm that is across your shoulder, and wrap your free arm around the victim's back or waist.
  - Maintain a firm grasp, and help the victim walk out of the water.
- **Beach Drag**
  - Stand behind the victim, and grasp him or her under the armpits, supporting the victim's head with your forearms.
  - While walking backward slowly, drag the victim toward the shore.
  - Remove the victim completely from the water, or at least to a point where the head and shoulders are well out of the water.
  - You may use a two-person drag if another person is present to help you.

Activity:

Demonstrate the walking assist and the beach drag. Have participants practice in pairs and in groups of three, with participants taking turns being the victim.

Spinal Injury Management

Primary Points:

Community Water Safety
pages 69–72

- Call 9–1–1 or your local emergency number or be sure someone else has called.
  - Minimize movement of the victim's head, neck, and back.
    - Try to keep the victim's head in line with the body. Do this without pulling on the head.

- Position the victim faceup at the surface of the water. This may require you to bring a submerged victim to the surface and to a face-up position. Keep the victim's face out of the water to let him or her breathe.
- Check for consciousness and breathing once you have stabilized the victim's spine. A victim who can talk or is gasping for air is conscious and breathing.
- Support the victim with his or her head and spine immobilized until help arrives.

Activity:

Using a co-instructor, an instructor aide, or a "swimmer" participant, demonstrate the hip/shoulder support and the head splint, including rotating a face-down victim faceup. Include the following points:

- **Hip and Shoulder Support**
  - This method helps limit movement to the spine. Use it for a victim who is face up. Support the victim at the hips and shoulders to keep the face out of the water.
  - Approach the victim from the side, and lower yourself to chest depth.
  - Slide one arm under the victim's shoulders and the other under the hip bones. Support the victim's body horizontally, keeping the face clear of the water.
  - Do not lift the victim, but support him or her in the water until help arrives.
- **Head Splint**
  - This method provides better stabilization than the hip/shoulder support. Use it only for a victim facedown at or near the surface. This victim must be turned faceup to breathe.
  - Approach the victim from the side.
  - Gently move the victim's arms up alongside the head. Do this by grasping the victim's arms midway between the shoulder and elbow. Grasp the victim's right arm with your right hand. Grasp the victim's left arm with your left hand.
  - Squeeze the victim's arms against his or her head. This helps keep the head in line with the body.
  - With your body at about shoulder depth in the water, glide the victim slowly forward.
  - Continue moving slowly, and rotate the victim toward you until he or she is faceup. This is done by pushing the victim's arm that is closer to you under water while pulling the victim's other arm across the surface.

- Position the victim's head in the crook of your arm with the head in line with the body.
- Maintain this position in the water until help arrives.

CLOSING

Activity:

Briefly review the in-water activities with the participants. Thank all participants who attended the optional in-water activities session.

11 the head lifeguard course

Course Outlines

Head Lifeguard

Lesson 1 — The Roles and Responsibilities of the Head Lifeguard

Activity	Approximate Time
Introduction to the Course	10 minutes
Roles and Responsibilities of the Head Lifeguard	15 minutes
Minimizing Risks	30 minutes
Aquatic Injury Prevention	70 minutes
Selecting Lifeguards	25 minutes
Training	25 minutes
Closing	5 minutes
Lesson 1, Total Time	**3 hours**

Lesson 2 — Team Building, Public Relations, and Emergency Response

Activity	Approximate Time
Review of Previous Material	5 minutes
Building a Lifeguard Team	45 minutes
Interacting With the Public	45 minutes
Emergency Response	25 minutes
Looking to the Future	15 minutes
Final Written Exam and Closing	45 minutes
Lesson 2, Total Time	**3 hours**

The purpose of the Head Lifeguard course is to provide lifeguards with career development training that includes injury prevention, selection and training of lifeguards, team building, interaction with patrons, and emergency-response planning.

Administrative Notes

The following points apply to this course:

Prerequisites

Current American Red Cross *Lifeguard Training* certificate (Cert. 653460) or a current lifeguard training certificate from another nationally recognized organization. Contact your local American Red Cross unit about reviewing and approving prospective candidates who do not hold a current American Red Cross *Lifeguard Training* certificate, but hold a lifeguard training certificate from another organization.

Course Length

This course is designed to be taught in a minimum of 6 hours. The course is presented in two 3-hour class sessions.

Since the times allotted in the lesson plans do not include relief breaks, you may have to build additional time into the course.

Class Size

It is recommended that there be one instructor for every 15 participants in the class. If the class has more than 15 participants, you should have a co-instructor or aide. You can run a class more efficiently if you keep the class reasonably small, and you are less likely to exceed the allotted time periods for various activities.

Facilities

Classroom Space

The lessons in the Head Lifeguard course require classroom space suitable for discussion and taking the final written exam. The classroom should be conveniently located for participants. It should also be equipped with the necessary teaching aids and materials.

Equipment and Supplies

At the beginning of each lesson is a list of required equipment and supplies. A master list of equipment for the course is in Appendix G. Make sure all the equipment is ready and in working order before you teach the course.

All participants should have a copy of *Head Lifeguard* (Stock No. 654119). There are no supporting videos for this course.

Before each lesson, it is advisable that instructors prepare the newsprint (flip charts) with the information and diagrams needed for the activities in each class session.

Note: You may wish to use an overhead projector for the course lectures and activities. You can prepare transparencies showing the key points listed in these lesson plans and the facility diagrams needed for the activities.

Testing and Certificates

On successful completion of the course, participants receive an American Red Cross *Course Completion* certificate (Cert. 3002), indicating Head Lifeguard. There is no validity period for the *Head Lifeguard* certificate.

To receive the course completion certificate for the American Red Cross Head Lifeguard course, the participant must—

- Fully attend and participate in the course.
- Correctly answer at least 80 percent of the written examination questions (32 correct out of a total of 40 questions).

For more information on awarding certificates, completing records, and conducting course evaluations, see Chapter 6.

Lesson 1
The Roles and Responsibilities of the Head Lifeguard

Class Assignment prior to this lesson: Read Chapters 1, 2, 3, 4, and 5 of *Head Lifeguard.*

Length: 3 hours

Equipment/Supplies: Name tags, course roster, course outline, participant's manuals, chalkboard or newsprint (flip chart), chalk or markers, Facility Floor Plans (Appendix J)

Goal: Participants will become aware of the roles, characteristics, and responsibilities of a head lifeguard. In addition, participants will become familiar with how to minimize risks, prevent injuries, and select and train lifeguards.

Objectives

After completing this lesson, participants should be able to—

1. List five leadership characteristics necessary for a head lifeguard.

2. Explain the three types of responsibilities of a head lifeguard, and describe nine legal considerations for head lifeguards.

3. List at least six components of proper supervision that measure a head lifeguard's standard of care.

4. List five reasons for keeping records and reports.

5. List the four components of the risk-management process and at least five categories of potential emergencies at an aquatic facility.

6. Explain how a head lifeguard can help protect patrons from injury through communication.

7. Describe two ways to regulate a facility's patron load.

8. List three methods for developing a lifeguard schedule.

9. List seven factors that can determine the location of a lifeguard station, and explain the reasons for elevated, ground-level, and boat lifeguard stations.

10. Explain the advantages and disadvantages of zone coverage.

11. Explain the importance of rotating lifeguards.

12. Explain how the five types of programs and the different types of special-use pools and structures can affect patron surveillance.

13. List four health, sanitation, and facility security items that should be included in a facility's policies and procedures manual.

14. List five areas of a facility that should be inspected daily, and describe six precautions that a head lifeguard and facility management can take to help eliminate or decrease vandalism.

15. Describe the head lifeguard's role in selecting lifeguards.

16. List three skill areas a lifeguard applicant should be tested on during the preemployment process.

17. Describe the head lifeguard's role in interviewing lifeguard applicants.

18. List five characteristics of an effective lifeguard, and explain how behavioral interviewing helps assess an applicant's characteristics.

19. List eight items to include in an orientation for new lifeguards.

20. Explain how to plan and schedule in-service training, and describe five areas and skill practices that can be covered in in-service training.

21. Explain the four steps to use to give corrective feedback when evaluating a lifeguard's skills.

22. List five aspects of an emergency situation to focus on in a simulation.

23. Describe two ways to conduct an in-service review of rules, regulations, policies, and procedures.

24. Explain how to conduct new and review certification courses during in-service training.

25. Explain why lifeguards need a fitness program and how to help staff maintain their fitness at peak levels.

INTRODUCTION TO THE COURSE

Time: 10 minutes

Name Tags

Course Roster

1. **Instructor and Participant Introductions**
   - Introduce yourself and welcome participants to the American Red Cross Head Lifeguard course.
   - Have participants introduce themselves by sharing their names and their reasons for taking this course and their expectations.
   - Give a brief description of your background and credentials. Identify yourself as an American Red Cross instructor, and explain that this course is one of many offered by the American Red Cross. Ask the participants to write their full name and address on the course roster so that you can complete the American Red Cross *Course Record* (Form 6418 and 6418A).

2. **Orientation to the Location**
   - Point out the locations of fire exits, telephones, rest rooms, and drinking fountains, and explain facility rules, if any.

3. **Course Schedule**
   - Distribute a course outline that includes dates and times of class meetings, lesson content, and class assignments. The written examination should be clearly identified.

4. **Course Prerequisites**
   - To enroll in the Head Lifeguard course, participants must have a current American Red Cross *Lifeguard Training* certificate or a current lifeguard training certificate from another nationally recognized organization. If the participants' lifeguard training certificates were not checked at registration, check them at this time.

5. **Course Description**
   - Share the following goal statement with the class:
   The purpose of this course is to provide lifeguards with career development training that includes injury prevention, selection and training of lifeguards, team building, interaction with patrons, and emergency-response planning.

6. **How Participants Will Learn**
   - Briefly explain that participants will learn through lectures, discussions, reading, and group activities.

7. **Participant's Manual**
   - Identify the participant's manual for this course, American Red Cross *Head Lifeguard,* and lead the participants through it. Instruct the participants how best to use the manual to master the course content. Point out the following features of *Head Lifeguard:*
     - Objectives
     - Key Terms
     - Sidebars
     - Study Questions
     - Appendixes
     - Glossary

   Head Lifeguard is required reading for this course.

8. **Course Completion Requirements**
   - Describe the American Red Cross requirements for successful course completion. To successfully complete this course, the participant must—
     - Fully attend and participate in the course.
     - Correctly answer at least 80 percent of the written examination questions (32 questions out of 40).

Note: If there are academic requirements or state or local requirements beyond the minimum completion requirements set by the American Red Cross, explain them to participants at this time.

ROLES AND RESPONSIBILITIES OF THE HEAD LIFEGUARD

Time: 15 minutes

Primary Points:

Head Lifeguard
page 2

- A head lifeguard is a lifeguard in a supervisory position in a facility's chain of command.
- As head lifeguard, you will—
  - Take charge of the lifeguard team, and be assertive in asking lifeguards to fulfill their primary duties.
  - Make decisions and lead meetings.
  - Help lifeguards understand their responsibilities and duties.
  - Build a good working relationship with your supervisor.
- Where you fit in the chain of command depends on your facility.
  - The head lifeguard is typically at the middle level of the chain of command.
  - In some small facilities, the head lifeguard is also the facility manager.
  - Check with your supervisor to see exactly where you fit in the chain of command.

Characteristics of a Head Lifeguard

Primary Points:

Head Lifeguard
page 4

- A head lifeguard needs to have the same characteristics as a lifeguard, such as reliability, a positive attitude, courtesy, and consistency.

The head lifeguard also needs—
- The ability to lead, to command respect, and to motivate others.
- Problem-solving and decision-making skills.
- Self-confidence and initiative.
- Interpersonal and "people management" skills.
- A professional attitude and appearance.

Responsibilities

Primary Points:

Head Lifeguard
page 4

- As head lifeguard, you have three types of responsibilities:
  - Ensuring the safety of both the lifeguard team and facility patrons, which includes—
    - Identifying and correcting hazards.
    - Educating patrons about the facility's rules and regulations.

- Developing emergency action plans.
- Handling problem situations.
■ Supervising and training lifeguarding staff, which includes
  - Testing and interviewing lifeguard applicants.
  - Planning and providing job-related training.
  - Scheduling staff.
  - Delegating responsibility.
  - Improving staff performance.
  - Communicating and interacting with the lifeguard team.
  - Serving as a liaison between your supervisor and the lifeguard team.
■ Supervising the safety inspection, general care, and cleaning of the facility, which includes—
  - Maintaining equipment.
  - Reporting any unsafe conditions and equipment to the facility manager immediately.

MINIMIZING RISKS

Time: 30 minutes

Primary Points:

Head Lifeguard page 10

■ As a head lifeguard, you accept management responsibilities.
■ You are legally responsible for your actions as well as those you supervise.

Primary Points:

Head Lifeguard page 10

Legal Considerations
■ A lawsuit is a legal procedure for settling a dispute.
  - If your facility has an incident involving a death or disability, such as a drowning or spinal injury, a lawsuit may result.
■ Becoming familiar with certain legal principles helps you understand liability.

Primary Point:

Head Lifeguard page 11

Duty to Act
■ As a result of their job definition, lifeguards and head lifeguards have a duty to act if an emergency occurs at the facility.

Standard of Care

Primary Points:

Head Lifeguard page 11

■ The public expects a certain standard of care of lifeguards and head lifeguards.
  - This standard of care is based on training guidelines developed by national lifeguard training organizations and on state or local laws or regulations.

- You must perform to a standard of care expected of a person with your training and working in your position.
- If you fail to act or to live up to the standard of care established for you, and this failure causes damage to another person, you are negligent.
- This applies to your actions and also to the actions of the lifeguard team you supervise. This standard of care includes whether—
  - Adequate supervision is present.
  - The supervisor is aware of a dangerous condition.
  - All staff have proper training or certification.
  - Policies and procedures are understood and enforced.
  - Supervisor(s), lifeguards, and patrons communicate appropriately.
  - Patrons understand and adhere to safety practices.
  - Supervisor(s) and lifeguards understand limits for participants in specific activities.
  - Adequate instructions and appropriate skill progressions are given in aquatic activity classes.
  - Adequate indications of dangers are given, and protective devices are used as required.
  - Equipment and the facility are checked appropriately.

Negligence

- Negligence is the failure to follow a reasonable standard of care, resulting in damage or injury.

Good Samaritan Laws

- Many states have Good Samaritan laws that offer general protection to those providing emergency care. These laws generally protect individuals if they are not grossly negligent, act in good faith, and act within the scope of your training.
- Since Good Samaritan laws differ from state to state, some of these laws may not provide coverage to individuals who have a duty to respond. Find out what your state's Good Samaritan laws are, and see to what degree they will protect you and your staff.

Consent

- Before providing care, you must first obtain the victim's consent. To obtain consent you should—
  - State your level of training.
  - Explain what you think may be wrong.

Primary Point:

Head Lifeguard
page 12

Primary Points:

Head Lifeguard
page 12

Primary Points:

Head Lifeguard
page 12

- Explain what you plan to do. At this point, a conscious, alert victim can decide whether to grant his or her informed consent for care.
- A person who is unconscious, confused, or seriously ill or injured may not be able to grant his or her consent. In these cases, the law assumes the person would want care. This is called implied consent.
  - When a parent or guardian is not present, you also have implied consent for minors who obviously need emergency assistance.

Refusal of Care

Primary Point:

Head Lifeguard
page 13

- If someone refuses your offer to provide care, you should honor the request. If he or she refuses your offer of help, try to have a witness hear the refusal. Your facility may have a form for documenting a patron's refusal.

Abandonment

Primary Point:

Head Lifeguard
page 13

- Once you or your lifeguards begin to provide care, you can not leave your victim until someone with equal or greater training takes over. Usually your obligation ends when the victim is turned over to more advanced medical personnel such as EMTs. If you leave the victim before this point, you can be legally responsible for abandonment.

Confidentiality

Primary Point:

Head Lifeguard
page 13

- Respect the victim's privacy by maintaining confidentiality. Do not discuss the victim's condition, care, or circumstances with anyone other than law enforcement or EMS personnel.

Record Keeping

Primary Points:

Head Lifeguard
page 14

- Many aquatic facilities require that records and reports be kept, such as—
  - Daily logs.
  - Preemployment forms.
  - Working reports.
  - Incident report forms.
  - In-service training records.
  - Lifeguard evaluation forms.

  The purposes of records and reports include—
  - Providing information for decisions about equipment, schedules, personnel, procedural changes, and facility improvements

- Providing information for research on the causes and prevention of injuries and fatalities
- Providing the basis for budget recommendations and future expenditures and their justification to management
- Complying with state and local laws requiring specific records about sanitation and maintenance
- Providing an accurate and legal document should legal action occur.

Risk Management

Primary Points:

Head Lifeguard
pages 14–16

- Risk Management is identifying and eliminating or minimizing dangerous conditions that can cause injury and financial loss. The risk management process has four components:
    1. Identify risks
    2. Evaluate the risks
    3. Select the methods to address the risks
    4. Implement procedures to help protect against loss
- Identify risks by surveying and inspecting your facility and considering potential emergencies. Then select the methods to address them. Consider the following categories:
    - Equipment
    - Structures
    - Environment
    - Evacuation
    - Communications
    - Care
    - Crowd control
    - Rescue
    - After hours
- Evaluate risks by reviewing previous records and reports and by analyzing past emergencies, including staff response.
- Implement procedures and changes to eliminate, reduce, or transfer risks, such as—
    - Hiring new personnel for additional job functions.
    - Rehearsing emergency action plans.
    - Documenting all training and incidents at the facility.

Activity:

1. Take the participants on a tour of the facility at which you are conducting the course.
2. Have the participants make a list of hazards or potential hazards and the safety precautions they can identify.

3. After the tour, return to the classroom and have the participants discuss their lists.

AQUATIC INJURY PREVENTION

Time: 70 minutes

Primary Points:

Head Lifeguard
page 20

- One of your most important duties as head lifeguard is to ensure that your lifeguards implement the three aquatic injury control strategies:
  - Communication
  - Patron Surveillance
  - Facility Surveillance

Communication

Primary Points:

Head Lifeguard
page 20

- Communication strategies help protect patrons from injury and death.
- Warning signs help prevent injuries.
- Post rules and regulations at all entrances to your facility.
- Do not assume that all patrons will read and understand posted rules. Rules that are clear to you may not be equally clear to all patrons.
- Rules and regulations are usually based on health codes, local ordinances, and facility policies.
- Rules of conduct for patrons fall into two categories:
  - General behavior expected of patrons.
  - Specific behaviors expected when using specific equipment.
- Be sure lifeguards can identify and correct rule infractions without neglecting surveillance duties.
- If necessary, you should be available to explain the rationale for a rule.

Patron Surveillance

Primary Point:

Head Lifeguard
page 21

- Patron loads, lifeguard-to-patron ratios, programming of activities, structures within the facility, and special-use pools are all factors you must consider in patron surveillance.

Patron Loads

Primary Points:

Head Lifeguard
page 21

- Patron load refers to the maximum number of individuals allowed either in the water or in the facility at any time.
  - Some state and local health codes have regulations.
  - You and the facility manager may establish patron load.

You need to have a way of regulating the number of patrons. This can be done through—

- A periodic head count.
- The cashier keeping track of patrons entering the facility.

Staffing

Primary Points:

Head Lifeguard
page 21

- Some state and local health codes specify certain ratios of lifeguards to patrons.
  - You and your management may set a ratio of lifeguards to patrons.
  - Past records may help you determine the number of guards needed at certain times during the day and/or season.
  - If patron load is large, you may need more lifeguards. If additional lifeguards are unavailable, you may have to close part of the facility.

Scheduling

Primary Points:

Head Lifeguard
pages 21–23

- When scheduling lifeguards—
  - Make sure adequate staff are present to supervise activities.
  - Make schedules at least two weeks in advance.
  - When preparing a schedule, consider—
    - Types of activities planned.
    - Age and skill level of participants.
    - Special-use groups.
- The following are three methods for developing a staff schedule:
  - Hire staff to fill designated shifts.
  - Post shifts that need to be filled, and let staff sign up for them, then assign the shifts that aren't taken.
  - Assign shifts based on set criteria or factors such as—
    - Seniority.
    - Best work record.
    - Ability to do other jobs.
- When you schedule—
  - Establish a fair and uniform system and stick to it.
  - Put the process in writing in the policies and procedures manual.
  - Schedule so that staff can get adequate rest between shifts.
  - Post schedules in a standard and conspicuous place.
  - Emphasize that once a schedule is posted, the lifeguards have a contractual agreement for services to be performed.
  - Use a set system for shift substitutions and be sure that substitutes only come from approved staff.
  - Lifeguards should report in time to be ready for their first assignment or rotation.

Stationing Lifeguards

Primary Points:

Head Lifeguard
pages 23 & 24

- Lifeguard surveillance may be done from the deck, the beach, or the water.
- Lifeguard stands should be located where lifeguards can observe patrons easily and react quickly.
- When determining where to locate lifeguard stations, consider the following:
  - Size and shape of the facility
  - Depth of the water
  - Number of patrons in the facility
  - Movement of the sun and wind
  - Condition (clarity) of the water
  - Size of the deck or dock area
  - Type of activity

Elevated stations

- Elevated stations provide a better vantage point for scanning.
- In large open-water facilities, lifeguards may need binoculars.
- In camps, the lifeguard in the elevated station acts as a lookout and directs lifeguards on the ground.

Ground-level stations

- In some small facilities, lifeguards are stationed at ground or deck level, in specific areas, or moving around the entire area.

Boat stations

- In open-water areas, one or two lifeguards may be stationed in a boat at the outer edges of the swimming area with first aid equipment and a rescue tube.

Activity:

**Facility Floor Plans
Appendix J**

1. Break participants into two groups.
2. Pass out one copy of a floor plan to each group.
3. Designate the number of lifeguards available for that facility (2, 3, 4, 5, etc.)
4. List conditions on each diagram, such as number of patrons, types of activities, and structures.
5. Have each group mark the appropriate location of lifeguard stations and indicate whether they are elevated or ground level.
6. Have each group explain their placements.

Surveillance

- Communication and cooperation with lifeguards in adjacent areas helps to ensure safety.
- Lifeguards should continuously scan back and forth, covering their total area of responsibility.
- Observe the surface and under the water with each scan.
- If a patron goes underwater, watch to make sure he or she resurfaces.
- Be sure to watch the area directly in front of and below the lifeguard stand.

Zone coverage

- No lifeguard should have a zone that requires a scan of more than 180 degrees.
- Zones should be overlapping because lifeguards can concentrate on a limited area, and overlapping zones allow double coverage.
- Disadvantages of overlapping zones include a possible need for more staff and confusion about lifeguards' area of responsibilities.
  - To minimize these disadvantages in large swimming areas—
    - Concentrate swimmers in a few sections of the swimming area.
    - Ensure lifeguards are aware of their specific areas.
    - Establish effective communications among lifeguards.

Total coverage

- Use this method only if a small number of patrons are in the water and only when two lifeguards are on duty, one on surveillance duty and the other completing assigned tasks.

Backup coverage

- If a lifeguard must enter the water to perform a rescue, lifeguards who remain out of the water must supervise a larger area.
- They may need to move to a better vantage point.
- The backup lifeguard(s) must survey both (all) areas of responsibility.

1. Draw up on newsprint or on a chalkboard diagrams of two large pool facilities.

Note: You can use the facility floor plans in Appendix J, as a model for the two diagrams. You may also want two prepare these diagrams before the start of this class session to save time.

2. Give conditions, such as size of pool, number of lifeguards available, number of patrons, and structures.
3. Have the class discuss the locations of lifeguard stations and the zones, showing where zones overlap on one diagram.
4. Using the second diagram, have the class discuss and identify changes in zones for backup coverage when a lifeguard goes into the water to make a rescue.

Rotation

Primary Points:

Head Lifeguard
pages 26–29

- Rotation helps maintain staff alertness.
- Rotating lifeguards must maintain constant surveillance of the zone of responsibility.
- The incoming lifeguard assumes a position that allows him or her to scan the area while the outgoing lifeguard comes down off the stand.
- The lifeguard being relieved scans while the relieving lifeguard gets on the stand or into the appropriate position.
- Rotations should take place on a regular schedule.
  - Lifeguards should not be on the stand for more than 1 hour without a break.
- Do not rotate all lifeguard stations simultaneously.

Programming

Primary Points:

Head Lifeguard
pages 29–32

- Programming affects the number of lifeguards on duty and the training and preparation of these lifeguards.
- It also affects the development of emergency action plans for the various activities.
- Facility management can conduct various activities at the same time by dividing the swimming area into sections.
- All sections require a lifeguard on duty for that activity.
- The common types of programs at aquatic facilities include—
  - Instructional Programs, such as infant and preschool swimming, lifeguard training, and SCUBA diving.
  - Competitive Programs, such as high school swimming, United States Swimming, and water polo.
  - Recreational Programs, such as open swimming, water basketball, and family swimming.
  - Fitness Programs, such as water aerobics, water walking, and lap swimming.
  - Service and Self-Development Programs, such as arthritis classes, physical therapy, and rehabilitation.

Activity:

Newsprint
Markers

1. List the five types of programs on newsprint.
2. Discuss with participants the types of safety concerns and hazards connected with these instructional programs. Refer participants to pages 29–32 in the *Head Lifeguard* participant's manual.

Special-Use Pools and Structures

Primary Points:

Head Lifeguard
pages 32–37

- Provide specialized in-service training for special-use pools and structures in your facility.
- Types of pools and structures include—
  - Lane lines.
  - Bulkheads.
  - Deep pools.
  - Water polo pools.
  - Diving pools.
  - Wading pools.
  - Water slides.
  - Play structures.
  - Spas.
  - Therapy pools.

Activity:

Newsprint
Markers

1. Select three types of pools from the list of special-use pools and structures. List these three types of pools as headings on newsprint.
2. Have participants generate a list of rules to post at each pool.
3. List these rules under each heading.

Facility Surveillance

Primary Points:

Head Lifeguard
page 37

- Your facility's policies and procedures manual should include the following information about health, sanitation, and security of the facility:
  - Safety checklists for daily, weekly, or monthly inspections
  - Outline of maintenance and repair procedures
  - Areas of the facility to be cleaned on a daily, weekly, or monthly schedule and cleaning procedures
  - Checklist for closing the facility

Safety Inspections

Primary Points:

Head Lifeguard
pages 37–43

- Ensure that all recreational and rescue equipment is inspected daily.
- Follow facility procedures for an identified hazard.
- When performing a safety check, inspect all areas open to patrons, including locker rooms, showers, toilets, deck areas, structures, and pool(s).

- At waterfront facilities, check beach area and docks.
- If your facility has water slides or play structures, your inspection should include these structures too.

Facility Maintenance

Primary Points:

Head Lifeguard
pages 43 & 44

- The following is a daily maintenance routine.
  - Before opening the facility—
    - Check the bottom for hazards.
    - Clean the bathhouse.
    - Skim the water surface to remove debris.
    - Brush the pool walls and vacuum.
    - Rake the beach area.
    - Empty trash containers.
    - Clean the office.
    - Check lifelines.
    - Hose deck or dock areas.
  - During hours of operation—
    - Inspect areas for sunbathing.
    - Inspect locker rooms.
    - Inspect toilets and showers.
    - Replenish needed supplies.
  - At closing—
    - Check bottom of swimming area for objects.
    - Disinfect the locker room.
    - Put lost and found articles in a designated area.
    - Return equipment to the proper area.
    - Turn off all unnecessary lights.
    - Turn on security lights.
    - Check windows, doors, and gates.

Pool Water

Primary Points:

Head Lifeguard
page 44

- You should be able to clearly view the pool bottom and easily recognize racing lines and drain covers.
- If pool chemistry is your responsibility, you should take a pool operator course.
- In general, chemical levels are checked at least four times a day.
- Outdoor pools may require more checks as a result of environmental factors.

Chemical Handling and Safety

Primary Point:

Head Lifeguard
page 44

- Your employer must provide training and specific information about chemicals you handle.

Electrical Safety

Primary Points:

Head Lifeguard
pages 44 & 45

- All electrical devices should be connected to the power supply only from a ground fault interrupter.
- Rooms and boxes containing electrical equipment should stay locked.

Incident and Injury Chart

Primary Points:

Head Lifeguard
page 45

- The chart shows where and when incidents and injuries have happened.
- This record may help you and facility management determine causes and devise a plan to prevent them.

Facility Security

Primary Points:

Head Lifeguard
pages 45–48

- Access to the pool area should be restricted to times when a lifeguard is on duty.
- The door from the locker room to the swimming area should be locked until a lifeguard opens it.
- Instructors should not allow class members into the water until the lifeguard signals readiness.
- At the end of the day, have your lifeguards scan the bleachers, deck, water, and pool bottom.
- They should also check rest rooms and other areas for patrons.
- All doors should be locked and tested.

Activity:

1. Have a prepared diagram of a pool facility, including bleachers and doors, on newsprint.
2. Have participants indicate all the areas that need to be checked for security.
3. Ask participants: "What could happen if you do not check the facility for security?" Answers may include the following:
   - Someone could enter after hours and steal equipment from the facility
   - Someone could enter and vandalize the facility
   - Someone could enter the water while the lifeguard was not on duty
4. Discuss the possible consequences if the above situations occurred.

Vandalism Protection

Primary Point:

Head Lifeguard
page 48

- The facility can take precautions to eliminate or decrease the occurrence of vandalism.

Note: Refer participants to page 48 in the Head Lifeguard participant's manual for specific precautions.

SELECTING LIFEGUARDS

Time: 25 minutes

Primary Points:

Head Lifeguard
page 52

■ Your role in selecting lifeguards for employment depends on the facility.
■ In many facilities, the head lifeguard helps assess applicants.

The Selection Process

Primary Points:

Head Lifeguard
page 52

■ Applicants should meet age and certification requirements, demonstrate various competencies and knowledge, and have certain personality characteristics.
■ The preemployment process begins when an applicant completes the application form for employment.
■ Reviewing the application before the interview and preemployment testing process will help you understand the applicant's work history, abilities, and certifications.
■ Keep all information in the application confidential.

Age and Certification Requirements

Primary Points:

Head Lifeguard
pages 52 & 53

■ Lifeguard age, level of training, and certification criteria are established by the facility and state or local ordinances.
■ Before employment, lifeguard applicants must show proof of age and current certifications.
■ Keep copies of certificates on file.
■ Monitor certificate expiration dates.
■ Be familiar with the different types of lifeguard certifications to help with screening and assigning lifeguard positions.
■ Know what specific skills and knowledge are needed for different positions in the facility.

Preemployment Testing

Primary Points:

Head Lifeguard
pages 53 & 54

■ Preemployment testing includes assessing and evaluating applicant's skills and knowledge.
■ Current certifications do not guarantee that the person has maintained his or her skills and knowledge.
■ Knowledge is assessed through written tests.

- You can test decision-making skills using scenarios or simulations.
- Minimum rescue skills required include entering the water, swimming to a victim, using equipment to rescue a victim, and moving the victim to safety.
- You may want to use the rescue skills listed in Appendix F of the *Head Lifeguard* participant's manual.

Note: Refer participants to page 135 and 136, Appendix F, in the Head Lifeguard participant's manual.

- First aid and CPR skills are a critical aspect of an effective lifeguard's skills.
- You can use the skills in the American Red Cross Lifeguard training course and the CPR for the Professional Rescuer course for first aid and CPR skills screening.
- You can set up scenarios or simulations for the testing process.

Interviewing

Primary Points:

Head Lifeguard
pages 55–57

- As head lifeguard, you may conduct interviews with lifeguard applicants.
- Before the interview, review the candidate's written and skills tests and identify any needs for additional training.
- You may decide that you can give training where deficiencies exist.
- In the interview, you determine if the applicant has the characteristics needed to be an effective lifeguard. These include —
  - Reliability.
  - Decision making.
  - Courtesy and consistency.
  - Positive attitude.
  - People skills.
- Use behavioral interviewing to help you assess personal characteristics of lifeguard applicants:
  - Ask applicants to describe events that have happened in their lives, for example, emergency situations.
  - Ask if he/she had ever cared for a child when an emergency occurred.
  - Ask: "How did you determine who would do what?"
    "Were you able to get the job done?"
    "Did you or the other person argue?"
- When interviewing, you must follow certain legal guidelines.
- Be familiar with federal, state, and local legislation and issues relating to the Americans with Disabilities Act.

1. Have the class prepare a list of 10 interview questions.
2. List the interview questions on newsprint.
3. Discuss the list and evaluate the questions as to whether they are non-discriminatory, using Appendix G (page 137) in *Head Lifeguard* as a guide.
4. Have participants rephrase or eliminate any discriminatory questions.

Newsprint
Markers

Lifeguard Selection

■ The final selection process should depend on—
  ■ Applicant's previous experience.
  ■ Results of written and skills preemployment tests and interview.
■ The facility may have other determining factors, as well, such as drug tests and physical exams.
■ Talk with your supervisor or the personnel department to learn your exact role in the hiring process.

Primary Points:

Head Lifeguard
page 57

TRAINING

Time: 25 minutes

Primary Points:

Head Lifeguard
page 60

■ Facility management is responsible for ongoing training of its lifeguards.
■ You may be responsible for planning and conducting training sessions.
■ Training sessions should cover key skills, facility procedures, and conditioning.
■ Lifeguards' ability to react quickly and correctly develops and improves with experience, practice, and proper training.

Orientation

Primary Points:

Head Lifeguard
pages 60–62

■ Orientation gives the new lifeguard his or her first impression of the job.
■ Review job descriptions and responsibilities.
■ Tour the facility and discuss the following:
  ■ Hazardous areas
  ■ Location of rescue equipment
  ■ Location of phones and first aid supplies
  ■ Zones or areas lifeguards cover
  ■ Location and meaning of facility signs
  ■ Lifeguard lounge or break area
■ Discuss personnel policies.

- You may cover some or all of the following:
  - Communication techniques
  - Emergency action plans
  - Security systems
  - Facility opening and closing procedures
  - Public relations
  - How to prevent disease transmission
  - Weather-related problems
  - Maintenance procedures
  - Proper handling of chemicals and related safety procedures

In-Service Training

Primary Points:

Head Lifeguard
page 62

- In-service training should occur often throughout the season or year.
- Decide on the goals and objectives for each session.
- Cover topics and skills that help the staff grow professionally.
- Make an effort to make your in-service training fun, informative, and challenging.

Activity:

1. Discuss one or two different locations, for example, a waterfront, a waterpark, a community aquatic facility.
2. Have the participants, as a group, design an in-service training plan for each specific facility. Have them choose specific rescue skills training and specific public relations training.
3. Have the participants describe why they chose specific activities and training.

Evaluation of Staff Lifeguarding Skills

Primary Points:

Head Lifeguard
page 63

- Use in-service training to periodically evaluate the skills of lifeguards.
- Compile a list of lifeguarding skills needed at the facility.
- Before evaluating lifeguards, organize them for effective skill practice and performance.
- Evaluate the lifeguards on each skill identified on your list.
- Be sure to give feedback on their performance.
  - Steps for constructive feedback include—
    - Describing what you observed.
    - Telling the lifeguard what was done correctly and then describe any critical errors.
    - Suggesting how to improve.
    - Allowing time for questions.
    - Giving an opportunity to practice correctly.

Emergency Procedures

Primary Points:

Head Lifeguard
pages 63–66

- Review the facility's emergency action plans (EAPs) with staff periodically.
- Have lifeguards walk through the emergency action plans.
- Talk about victim recognition, lifeguard reaction time, backup availability, and available support personnel.
- Concentrate on the following five aspects of an emergency during emergency simulations:
  - Identification of the situation
  - Individual responsibilities
  - Emergency communications
  - Backup coverage
  - Records and reports

Rules and Regulations

Primary Points:

Head Lifeguard
page 66 & 67

- Periodically review facility rules and regulations with lifeguards.
  - This helps to make sure that the lifeguards understand the reasons for the rules.
- Explain how lifeguards should deal with patrons who break rules.

Policies and Procedures

Primary Points:

Head Lifeguard
page 67

- Review policies and procedures during in-service training.
- Explain to the lifeguards the impact of new policies and procedures on them and the facility.

Legislation

Primary Points:

Head Lifeguard
page 67

- Some laws and regulations require you to give specialized training.
- If you cannot give this training yourself, you may need to bring in experts in that field.
- You should become familiar with all laws and regulations that affect you and your lifeguarding staff.

Special Events

Primary Points:

Head Lifeguard
page 67

- Post events with dates in the facility office in a list or on a calendar.
- For special events, lifeguard location, surveillance, rotation, and zone coverage may differ from day-to-day operations.
- Give instructions to explain specific changes from normal policies.
- If possible, give specialized training for special events.

Patron Relations

Primary Points:

Head Lifeguard
pages 67 & 68

- Your role as head lifeguard includes providing customer service training and monitoring how the staff gives that service.
- Give your lifeguards these customer service tips:
  - Give efficient service.
  - Give an impression of helpfulness.
  - Use a team philosophy.
  - Show genuine interest in patrons.
  - Answer requests promptly.
  - Give personalized service.
  - Do not abuse your authority.
  - Be thoroughly familiar with facility operations and policies.
  - Be professional.

Professional Development

Primary Points:

Head Lifeguard
pages 68 & 69

- In-service training is an excellent way to give new and review certification courses to your staff.
- A long course can be spread out through several in-service training sessions.
- If you are not an instructor, contact your local unit of the American Red Cross for help in locating an instructor.
- Include new training required by federal and state regulations.
- Offer advanced levels of training to your lifeguards, such as the American Red Cross Emergency Response course.
- Other professional development courses and modules could include—
  - American Red Cross Oxygen Administration module.
  - American Red Cross Preventing Disease Transmission.
  - American Red Cross Waterpark Lifeguarding.
  - American Red Cross Waterfront Lifeguarding.
  - American Red Cross Safety Training for Swim Coaches.
  - American Red Cross Water Safety Instructor.
  - American Red Cross Head Lifeguard course.
  - American Red Cross instructor courses in first aid and CPR.

Developing a Lifeguard Fitness Program

Primary Points:

Head Lifeguard
pages 69–72

- Lifeguard fitness is critical for patron safety. As head lifeguard, you may be responsible for developing a fitness program for your lifeguards.
- Conditioning should be ongoing throughout the season or year.

- Reward your lifeguards for participating in ongoing conditioning training.
- Keep records and post charts of the yardage each lifeguard swims.
- Issue certificates of achievement for specified yardage achieved.
- You may require a minimum number of yards each lifeguards on a weekly, monthly, or seasonal basis.

In-Service Training Reports

Primary Points:

Head Lifeguard
page 72

- Keep records of all in-service training sessions.
- Keep these records on file for at least three years for future reference and inspection.

Note: *Refer participants to Appendix I, page 141, in the Head Lifeguard participant's manual for a sample in-service training record form.*

CLOSING

Time: 5 minutes

Activity:

Respond to any questions from the participants.

Assignment:

Read Chapters 6, 7, 8, and 9 of *Head Lifeguard* and complete the study questions at the end of each chapter.

Lesson 2 — Team Building, Public Relations, and Emergency Response

Class Assignment prior to this lesson: Read Chapters 6, 7, 8, and 9 of *Head Lifeguard*.

Length: 3 hours

Equipment/Supplies: Chalkboard or newsprint (flip chart); chalk or markers; copies of Head Lifeguard exams A and B and answer sheets for each participant (Appendix S); pencils; envelope or box

Goal: Participants will learn how to effectively build a strong lifeguard team, how to interact with the public, and how to plan for emergencies. In addition, participants will learn about careers that are available to them in the future.

Objectives

After completing this lesson, participants should be able to—

1. Describe the head lifeguard's role as liaison between management and lifeguards.
2. Explain how a head lifeguard's leadership style affects the lifeguard team.
3. Describe three benefits of teamwork, and explain how developing and accomplishing goals benefits a lifeguard team.
4. Describe five tips a head lifeguard can use for effective communication.
5. Describe the six-step approach for solving problems.
6. Explain how recognition can motivate a lifeguard team member and describe seven techniques for building a lifeguard team and improving leadership skills.
7. Explain how to correct a lifeguard's problem behavior.
8. Explain the purpose of evaluating lifeguards and describe at least eight evaluation criteria.
9. List and explain at least five general guidelines for developing a positive relationship with patrons.
10. Explain at least five general principles for dealing with problem situations, and explain the five-step approach to resolve conflict.
11. Explain how a head lifeguard deals with violence.
12. Explain how a head lifeguard deals with a problem situation involving groups.

13. Explain why one must look beyond cultural differences when supervising patrons, and list four guidelines for working with patrons who do not speak English.

14. List two aspects of cultural behavior relevant to lifeguarding situations.

15. Describe three general categories of disabilities.

16. Explain the responsibilities of the head lifeguard and support personnel during an emergency.

17. Explain the importance of communication during an emergency, and describe four items to discuss after practicing an emergency action plan.

18. Explain the purpose and importance of an incident report and list six categories of information to be included on an incident report form.

19. Describe seven examples of procedures to follow after an emergency.

20. Explain what critical incident stress is and the effects it can have on a lifeguard or head lifeguard.

21. Recognize the signs of critical incident stress, and describe six ways that a head lifeguard can cope with stress.

22. Explain the purpose of critical incident stress debriefing (CISD).

23. Explain how the experience and knowledge gained as a head lifeguard can be beneficial in future careers.

24. List at least five career opportunities in the aquatics field and five career opportunities in the recreation field.

25. List three college degrees to consider for a future career in aquatics.

REVIEW OF PREVIOUS MATERIAL

Time: 5 minutes

Review

Primary Points:

- A head lifeguard is a lifeguard who has a supervisory position in a facility's chain of command.
- One of the responsibilities of a head lifeguard is to meet the standards of care of the profession.
- Other responsibilities of a head lifeguard include—
  - Minimizing risks.
  - Preventing injuries.
  - Assisting in lifeguard selection.
  - Training staff.

BUILDING A LIFEGUARD TEAM

Time: 45 minutes

Primary Points:

Head Lifeguard
page 76

- As head lifeguard, you are the leader of the lifeguard team.
- As the team leader, you have a supervisory role to—
  - Help lifeguards improve their performance.
  - Correct a problem behavior.
  - Conduct periodic performance evaluations.

Liaison With Management

Primary Points:

Head Lifeguard
page 76

- The head lifeguard serves as a liaison between the lifeguards and facility management.
  - The head lifeguard brings any major problems to the facility manager, such as—
    - Maintenance problems.
    - Unresolved conflicts.
    - Serious difficulties with patrons.
    - All serious emergencies.
  - The head lifeguard brings issues of concern from the lifeguards to management and also represents management to the lifeguards. The head lifeguard must understand management's philosophy and the policies of the facility.

Activity:

1. Ask participants to list possible concerns of lifeguards or incidents occurring at a facility that could be appropriate to bring to the attention of management.
2. Ask participants which of these issues might be able to be handled by the lifeguards and the head lifeguard without going to management.
3. Ask participants to identify potential areas of concern in which management will expect the head lifeguard to intercede.

Leadership Style

Primary Points:

Head Lifeguard
pages 76 & 77

Leadership style involves how you interact with and lead the lifeguards. No one style is automatically right or wrong. The way you make decisions, with the group or independently, will depend on the issue, your personality, and the personalities of lifeguards.

1. Ask participants to discuss the following three issues commonly addressed by a head lifeguard. They are—
   - Requests for a change in work schedule.
   - Uniform selection.
   - Assignment of lifeguard stands.
2. Ask them how they would handle each issue.

Developing the Lifeguard Team

- Teamwork is a shared sense of spirit.
- Teamwork has three main benefits:
  - A team can do its work and accomplish its goals more efficiently than a group of individuals working separately.
  - Team members are better motivated to do a good job.
  - Everyone has more fun cooperating and working as a team.
- Building a team requires a great deal of effort.
- Developing and accomplishing goals benefits a lifeguard team, as—
  - Team members understand the accomplishment of their goal depends on the cooperation of all members.
  - The group begins to depend on and appreciate each member.
  - When they accomplish a goal, team members recognize each other for their contribution.
  - Recognition from the facility management further develops team cohesion and motivation.
- The head lifeguard needs the following skills to manage the team:
  - Communication
  - Problem solving and decision making
  - Delegation
  - Motivation and recognition

Communication

- Communication is important for the head lifeguard as the liaison between the lifeguard team and management.
- The following are guidelines to help promote effective communication:
  - Avoid speaking in a monotone or mumbling.
  - Speak in a nonthreatening tone of voice.
  - Use appropriate and familiar terms and vocabulary.
  - Focus on the listener and the subject.
  - Do not use body language or facial expressions that are distracting, threatening, or inappropriate.

- Become a good listener. Do not try to interpret what someone is saying, and really listen.
- Make sure your communication is effective. Ask for feedback, repeat what you think you heard.

Note: Refer participants to page 79 in the Head Lifeguard participant's manual for more tips on effective communication.

Problem Solving and Decision Making

Primary Points:

Head Lifeguard
pages 79 & 80

- Problem-solving skills develop more easily for those who—
  - Respect others.
  - Are optimistic.
  - Are willing to work toward finding a solution.
  - Consider creative options.
  - Recognize that conflict can lead to creative solutions.

Follow these six steps to approach problem solving.
1. Identify the problem.
2. Identify all possible solutions; solicit the help of your lifeguard team to identify potential solutions.
3. Evaluate the alternatives.
4. Select the solution.
5. Implement the solution. Communicate with everyone involved so that everyone knows the course to be taken.
6. Evaluate the solution after a trial period. If the solution does not work, return to Step 3, reevaluate the possibilities, and try an alternative solution.

Delegation

Primary Point:

Head Lifeguard
page 81

Delegation is entrusting others with tasks for which you are responsible. A head lifeguard duty that is delegated is still the responsibility of the head lifeguard.

Motivation and Recognition

Primary Points:

Head Lifeguard
pages 81 & 82

- The head lifeguard must create a work environment conducive to the accomplishment of lifeguard team goals. To achieve these goals, the head lifeguard will need to motivate his or her team members. Recognition of a job well done enhances team motivation.
  - Recognition might take the following forms:
    - Certificates of appreciation
    - Merit pay
    - Employee of the week, month, or year
    - Special mention in facility publications

1. Ask participants to describe how they feel when recognized for their effort.
2. Ask participants if those feelings motivate them to continue with their effort.
3. Ask how employees might react when they realize their efforts will be recognized.
4. Ask participants what motivates them to do a good job.

Team Building

Techniques for building a lifeguarding team and improving your leadership skills include—

- Checking things out yourself.
- Holding regular meetings.
- Participating in social events with staff.
- Eliciting public feedback.
- Having lifeguards evaluate you.
- Personally conducting new employee orientations.
- Making yourself available and approachable.

Supervising the Lifeguard Team

- You are responsible for correcting the problem behavior of a lifeguard team member.
- You also have an additional responsibility of conducting periodic performance evaluations.

Improving Performance

- When correcting problem behavior, follow these principles to reduce the problem(s) positively:
  - Do not approach the problem behavior from a confrontational standpoint.
  - When talking to a lifeguard on any issue, address the situation, problem, or behavior, not the person.
  - Discuss the matter in private, if possible.
  - Keep a positive relationship with your employees. Be honest and sincere, and show respect for the person.

Evaluation

- The purpose of evaluation is to recognize what the lifeguard does well and assess what improvement is needed.
- Evaluation should be an ongoing, daily process.
- Base evaluations on standards and expectations that should be in policies and procedures manual.

The Lifeguard Evaluation Form

Note: Refer participants to the Sample Lifeguard Evaluation Form (Appendix J) on page 142 in the Head Lifeguard participant's manual.

Primary Points:

Head Lifeguard
page 85

- The form is used to document a Lifeguard's performance.
- Lifeguards should have their own copy of the completed form.
- Lifeguards are evaluated on the basis of specific criteria, such as job knowledge of all responsibilities and lifeguarding skills.
- A number of different methods can be used for evaluating, such as using a numerical scale or ratings, poor, excellent, and so on.
- The facility usually has procedures for handling lifeguards with poor evaluations and no signs of improvement.

INTERACTING WITH THE PUBLIC

Time: 45 minutes

Primary Points:

Head Lifeguard
page 90

- Effective communication with the public is crucial in lifeguarding.
- You are both an important contact for patrons at your facility and a role model for the lifeguards you supervise.
- Be prepared to address the cooperative as well as the uncooperative patrons.

Interacting Positively With the Public

Primary Points:

Head Lifeguard
page 90

- Use the following general guidelines to develop a positive relationship with patrons:
  - Treat people as you would like to be treated.
  - Be professional at all times.
  - Avoid unnecessary conversation with other employees or patrons while on duty.
  - When interacting with patrons, speak clearly and make direct eye contact.
  - Take all suggestions and complaints seriously, and follow up as necessary.
  - Do not make promises you cannot keep.
  - Keep interactions brief and direct.
  - Enforce rules fairly and consistently.
  - Take a sincere interest in all patrons.

Facility Policies for Interaction

Primary Points:

Head Lifeguard
page 91

- Know the policies and guidelines for interacting with patrons at your facility.
- Communicate these policies and guidelines to your lifeguard team through your words and actions.
- Review any material on public relations with your lifeguards.

Preventing Problems

Primary Points:

Head Lifeguard
page 91 & 92

- You and your lifeguard team can positively influence the behavior of patrons through—
  - Appearance and behavior.
  - Posting rules.
  - Consistent enforcement of rules and regulations.

Responding to Problems

Primary Points:

Head Lifeguard
page 92

- Problems may still occur when—
  - A patron who is generally cooperative breaks a rule or behaves in a manner that must be corrected.
  - An uncooperative patron, for whatever reason, intentionally breaks rules and does not cooperate with your positive attempts to correct the situation.
- Follow these general principles for handling problem situations:
  - Anticipate problems.
  - Do not overreact.
  - Focus on the behavior, not the individual.
  - Respect the patron's feelings.
  - Be firm, fair, and friendly.
  - Do not pretend to know everything.
  - Use suspension as a last resort.

Uncooperative Patrons

Primary Points:

Head Lifeguard
page 93

- Make sure lifeguards know to contact you if a conflict occurs with an uncooperative patron.
- If an uncooperative patron persists in problem behavior, regardless of the causes, you must act right away.
- Before you assume a patron is being uncooperative, make sure he or she understands the rules. There may be a language barrier.

Activity:

1. Ask participants to identify situations in which generally cooperative patrons might need to have a behavior corrected.
2. Ask participants to provide examples of situations in which a patron might be viewed as uncooperative.

3. Ask participants to describe ways of approaching the situation. Reinforce the general principles for handling a problem situation.

Conflict Resolution

Primary Points:

Head Lifeguard
page 93 & 94

■ Follow these principles if uncooperative behavior escalates into conflict:
  ■ Plan ahead before intervening in the conflict.
  ■ Follow the policies and procedures in the facility's manual.
  ■ Try to resolve the conflict.
  ■ If you are having difficulty handling a situation, pass the problem up the chain of command.
■ Use the five-step approach to resolve conflict.
  1. Cool off—Wait until those involved are calm enough to talk about the problem.
  2. Identify the problem—Each person involved needs to say what the problem is.
  3. Identify the feelings—Elicit specific feelings.
  4. Identify what is wanted—The first person needs to state what he or she wants to happen.
  5. Resolve the conflict—Use one or more of the conflict management strategies listed on page 94 of the *Head Lifeguard* participant's manual.

Activity:

1. Ask participants to share examples of conflict situations they may have experienced.
2. Ask participants to describe how the conflict was resolved.
3. Ask participants if the resolution was effective.
4. Have participants brainstorm to develop effective ways to resolve the conflict utilizing the five-step approach.

Dealing With Violence

Primary Points:

Head Lifeguard
pages 94 & 94

■ The potential for violent acts does exist in the aquatic environment.
  ■ Violent acts include—
    ■ Fist fights.
    ■ Assaults.
    ■ Pushing.
    ■ Threats with weapons.
    ■ Aggressive taunting.
    ■ Molestation.
    ■ Rape.
    ■ Drive-by shootings.

- The facility's emergency action plan should have policies and procedures for dealing with violent acts.
- Follow these guidelines when handling a violent situation:
  - Call for immediate assistance as outlined in your facility's emergency action plan.
  - Remove bystanders from the area.
  - Stay at least 6 feet away from the violent individual.
  - Do not approach a violent patron alone. Have a backup.
  - Assess the situation before intervening.
  - If a weapon is present, immediately evacuate patrons from the area or provide cover within the facility.

Problems With Groups

Primary Points:

Head Lifeguard
page 95

When approaching a group causing a problem, follow these guidelines:

- Offer a friendly, accepting attitude and environment.
  - Be sure the group knows the rules and regulations to be enforced.
  - Treat each member as an individual.
  - Learn their language; understand their language and idioms.
  - Never embarrass or "call one down" in front of his or her group.
  - Do not back a group or individual into a corner without giving the group or person an honorable way out.
  - Be willing to listen.
  - Make patrons feel responsible for reaching a positive outcome.

Cultural Diversity

Primary Points:

Head Lifeguard
pages 95 – 97

- Cultural diversity can involve behavior or traits related to age, gender, race, ethnicity, religion or spirituality, sexual orientation, socioeconomic conditions, and other factors.
- One of your roles as a head lifeguard includes developing a climate in your facility that accepts differences, respects and values others, and encourages the human dignity of all.
- Although cultural differences may result in varying appearances and behaviors of patrons, culture is irrelevant when a person is drowning. Your lifeguard team must always look for instinctive, universal behaviors.
- Cultural behavior that is relevant to lifeguarding includes —
  - "Appropriate" clothing for swimming.
  - Language.

- Follow these guidelines when interacting with non-English-speaking patrons:
  - Use your attire to let the person know you are a lifeguard.
  - Try to communicate in English.
  - Speak slowly and clearly.
  - Attempt a second language if you know one.
  - Seek another individual to serve as translator.

Activity:

1. Ask participants to write down on a piece of paper any request a lifeguard might commonly make of a patron, for example, "Please do not dive into shallow water."
2. Assign partners or ask participants to find a partner. One partner is the lifeguard and the other is the patron.
3. Ask the participants who are the lifeguards to communicate the request they wrote down to their partner. The participant must communicate this request without speaking or writing it down.
4. Once the partner (patron) has figured out the request, have participants switch roles and repeat the activity.
5. Allow five minutes for this activity.
6. Once you have reassembled the class, ask participants to relate this experience to a patron who might not speak English or to a patron who might be unable to hear.

Patrons With Disabilities

Primary Points:

Head Lifeguard
pages 97–101

- A disability is a loss, absence, or impairment of sensory, mental, or motor function.
- Mainstreaming is the process of including people with disabilities in the same programs and activities as the nondisabled.
- The Americans with Disabilities Act ensures that people with disabilities have access to a wide range of opportunities and services.
- Patrons may be disabled in sensory function, mental function, or motor function.

Activity:

Newsprint
Markers

1. Write each functional disability on newsprint or on a chalkboard. These include sensory function, mental function, and motor function.
2. Have participants name types of problems they might encounter with each functional disability.
3. Discuss how to interact with people with functional disabilities.

EMERGENCY RESPONSE

Time: 25 minutes

Primary Points:

Head Lifeguard
page 104

- You may develop different emergency action plans for the types of emergencies that might occur in your facility.
- Effective plans are thoroughly reviewed, practiced, and evaluated.

Types of Emergencies

Primary Points:

Head Lifeguard
page 104

There are five general groups of emergencies—
- Aquatic emergencies include—
  - Distressed swimmers.
  - Drowning.
  - Spinal injuries.
- Medical emergencies include—
  - Heart attack.
  - Stroke.
  - Sudden illness.
- Facility emergencies include—
  - Fire.
  - Power failure.
  - Chemical spill.
  - Failure of the phone system.
- Weather related emergencies include—
  - Violent winds.
  - Tornadoes.
  - Lightning.
  - Earthquakes.
  - Flash floods.
  - Mud slides.
- People-related emergencies include—
  - Missing person.

Responsibilities

Primary Point:

Head Lifeguard
pages 105 & 106

- During an emergency, all staff at the facility may have a responsibility.

Lifeguarding Responsibilities

Primary Points:

Head Lifeguard
page 105

- The head lifeguard may decide what staff have the following key responsibilities during an emergency:
  - Covering the rescuer's area
  - Clearing the swimming area

- Calling EMS personnel or other support if necessary
- Meeting EMS personnel
- The head lifeguard must ensure the emergency actions plan functions as intended.
- Responsibilities of the head lifeguard during an emergency include deciding who has continuing responsibility for—
  - Ensuring that someone completes an incident report after the emergency.
  - Inspecting the equipment or facility after an incident.
  - In the case of a missing person, determining when and where to start a search.

Support Personnel

Primary Points:

Head Lifeguard
pages 105 & 106

- All full- and part-time staff should know their role in the facility EAP, as well as their position on the chain-of-command chart.
- Outside support includes EMS personnel, fire fighters, law enforcement personnel, poison control centers, the chemical supply company, the power company, and others.

Activity:

1. Ask participants to identify why one person, the head lifeguard, decides who takes action in an emergency situation. Ask them to imagine what it would be like if several people were in charge.
2. Ask participants to discuss the five key responsibilities involved in emergency response. Encourage the participants to identify why each is important to the success of the emergency action plan.

Communication

Primary Points:

Head Lifeguard
page 106

- The success of an emergency action plan depends on good communication. Every plan should specify—
  - Who communicates with whom.
  - Who is responsible for each communication.
  - When communication should occur.
- The chain-of-command chart should identify who needs to be notified in specified emergencies and who is to talk with the media, the public, and the family of the victim.

Emergency Preparedness

Primary Points:

Head Lifeguard
pages 106 & 107

■ To work effectively when an emergency does occur, emergency action plans must be practiced. After a practice, discuss the following points:
  ■ Reaction time
  ■ Visibility
  ■ Backup
  ■ Internal support personnel
  ■ External support personnel

Activity:

Newsprint
Markers

1. Write the five points to review after practicing an emergency action plan on newsprint or on a chalkboard.
2. Ask participants to explain how each of these key points affects emergency response.

After an Emergency

Primary Points:

Head Lifeguard
page 107

■ Certain follow-up procedures have to be completed after an emergency, such as deciding if lifeguards can return to surveillance, reporting the incident to management, and completing necessary reports.
■ After an emergency, you, management, and other staff should evaluate the effectiveness of the emergency action plan. Identify what worked and what could be done better.
■ Correct weak areas and build on strengths.
■ Walk staff through any new version of an emergency action plan as soon as possible.

Incident Reports

Primary Points:

Head Lifeguard
pages 107–109

■ Incident reports document what occurred in the emergency or problem situation.
■ Incident reports—
  ■ Can be used in court if there is legal action taken against the facility.
  ■ May reveal, over time, hazards present at the facility.
  ■ Identify what problems are most likely to occur.
  ■ Fulfill state and local government agencies requirements to report accidents at the facility.

Incident reports should include the following:
■ Information about the victim
■ Information about the rescue and assistance or care given
■ Information about conditions at the time of injury

- Information about the cause of injury
- Information about the rescuers
- Information on witnesses' statements

Critical incident stress

Primary Points:

Head Lifeguard
pages 110–112

- A critical incident is an emergency involving serious injury or death. It can cause critical incident stress.
- If this stress is not managed, it may lead to a serious condition called post-traumatic stress disorder.
- Critical incident stress may result in—
    - Anxiety.
    - Depression.
    - Sleeplessness.
    - Nausea.
    - Restlessness.
    - Loss of appetite.
- The head lifeguard should recognize the following signs of critical incident stress reactions:
    - Confusion
    - Lowered attention span
    - Poor concentration
    - Denial
    - Guilt
    - Depression
    - Anger
    - Change in interactions with others
    - Increased or decreased eating
    - Uncharacteristic excessive humor or silence
    - Unusual behavior

Activity:

Ask participants to identify signs of critical incident stress and discuss with them how these reactions might affect a lifeguard's performance.
- You can do several things to reduce the effects of stress:
    - Use quick relaxation techniques, such as deep breathing.
    - Eat a good meal.
    - Avoid alcohol and drugs.
    - Drink plenty of water.
    - Review the event, and clear up any uncertainties.
    - Get enough rest.
    - Exercise.
    - Attend a critical incident stress debriefing.

- Critical incident stress debriefing (CISD) brings together people suffering critical incident stress with trained mental health professionals and peers.
- Critical incident stress debriefing provides those suffering from critical incident stress the opportunity to share and understand their feelings and learn to cope with the outcome of the critical incident.

LOOKING TO THE FUTURE

Time: 15 minutes

Primary Points:

Head Lifeguard
page 116

- The position of head lifeguard may be the first step of your journey on a career path into aquatics or recreation.
- The skills and knowledge you acquire as a head lifeguard continue to be of value to you as you move on in your future career. Key skills include—
  - Risk management skills.
  - Staff selection and training.
  - Leadership skills.

Career Opportunities in Aquatics

Primary Points:

Head Lifeguard
pages 116–118

- Employment as a head lifeguard can lead to many opportunities in the aquatics field, such as—
  - Pool Manager (Aquatic Facility Manager).
  - Aquatics Director/Superintendent/ Supervisor.
  - Aquatics and Sports and Leisure Clubs Director.
  - Aquatics Programmer/Coordinator.
  - Instructional Specialists/Swim Coach.
- Other opportunities available in the aquatics field include—
  - Aquatics consultant.
  - American Red Cross Water Safety specialist.
  - Developer of aquatic materials.
  - Aquatics and safety lecturer.
  - Graduate assistant.

Career Opportunities in Recreation

Primary Points:

Head Lifeguard
pages 118 & 119

- Aquatics is a part of the overall field of recreation.
- Your experience as a head lifeguard can help you if you choose to make a career in recreation, such as—
  - Parks and recreation director.
  - Recreation program supervisor.

- Recreation center/facility manager.
- Recreation specialist.
- College degrees are a requirement for many positions in recreation, such as degrees in—
  - Recreation (Leisure Studies).
  - Physical Education (Human Performance).
  - Health Education.
    - Check with colleges and universities to see what programs and degree tracks they have to offer. Professional organizations and associations listed in Appendix C (page 127) of the *Head Lifeguard* participant's manual can also provide information on accredited programs.

Other Careers

Primary Points:

Head Lifeguard
pages 119

- From your experience in first aid and CPR training as a head lifeguard you may develop an interest in emergency medicine with positions such as an emergency medical technician (EMT) or a paramedic.
- You can use your experience, supervisory skills, and education you gain as a head lifeguard in virtually any career you choose.

FINAL WRITTEN EXAM AND CLOSING

Time: 45 minutes

Activity:

Written Exams
Answer Sheets
Pencils

1. Tell participants that they will now take a 40-question examination. They will have 35 minutes to complete the exam and must answer at least 32 questions correctly to pass. They may not use their participant's manuals to find the answers.
2. Hand out an examination and answer sheet to each participant.
3. Tell participants to write only on the answer sheet, mark answers clearly, and use pencil only (in case they want to erase or change an answer).
4. Tell them to check their answers before handing them in.
5. Tell them to come to you or raise one hand when they have finished the exam or have any questions.
6. Score the exams. The answer keys for both exams are at the end of this instructor's manual.

Note: As participants hand in their answer sheets and exams, quickly grade each exam and return it to the correct participant so that he or she can review any missed questions. If time allows, discuss with the class any exam items that were a problem. Collect all answer sheets and exams before the participants leave the class. If a participant fails the exam, ask him or her to see you after class to schedule a retest.

7. Refer participants to the back of their *Head Lifeguard* participant's manuals for a copy of the Participant Course Evaluation form. Ask participants to complete the form and leave it in the box or envelope you have provided near the door.

8. Issue (or explain you will mail later) an American Red Cross *Head Lifeguard Course Completion* certificate to participants who scored 80 percent or better on the written exam and who attended all class sessions.

9. Thank all participants for attending the course.

10. Make arrangements to retest any participants who did not successfully pass the written exam.

12 the lifeguarding instructor aide course

T he purpose of the Lifeguarding Instructor Aide course is to provide training for individuals who wish to assist lifeguarding instructors in conducting American Red Cross Lifeguard Training courses. The Lifeguarding Instructor Aide course also provides an excellent opportunity for lifeguards who do not meet the minimum age requirement for the Lifeguarding Instructor course, but who would like to further their lifeguard training.

Lifeguarding Instructor Aides receive credit for the volunteer hours they spend in Lifeguard Training courses. This information is included on the *Course Record* each time an aide assists with a course, and the local Red Cross unit keeps a record of the aide's contribution.

Training Options

You can train Lifeguarding Instructor Aides in two ways. The Lifeguarding Instructor Aide course is designed for 6 to 10 aide candidates. The apprenticeship program discussed later in this chapter can be used to train one or two aides at a time, as needed.

Objectives of Lifeguarding Instructor Aide Training

Regardless of the method used, training should enable aide candidates to understand the roles and responsibilities of a lifeguarding instructor aide, including the clerical, instructional, supervisory, and maintenance duties.

Administrative Notes

The following points apply to the Lifeguarding Instructor Aide training:

Prerequisites

Lifeguarding Instructor Aide

Individuals who hold a current *American Red Cross Lifeguard Training* certificate and *CPR for Professional Rescuer* certificate, and exhibit a strong sense of maturity and responsibility are eligible to be trained as Lifeguard Instructor Aides.

Waterfront Lifeguarding Option

Individuals who have American Red Cross Lifeguarding Instructor Aide certification (if the option was not held in conjunction with the original Lifeguarding Instructor Aide course) and American Red Cross Waterfront Lifeguarding certification.

Waterpark Lifeguarding Option

Individuals who have American Red Cross Lifeguarding Instructor Aide certification (if the option was not held in conjunction with the Lifeguarding Instructor Aide course) and American Red Cross Waterpark Lifeguarding certification.

Note: If participants do not meet the prerequisites for the Lifeguarding Instructor Aide course or options, they can still participate in the course or options, but they won't receive certification, and their roles as aides will be limited to clerical and maintenance responsibilities.

Course Length

This course is designed to be taught in a minimum of $11\frac{1}{2}$ hours. The basic course content is presented in 5 sessions of 2 hours each and a fifth session of $1\frac{1}{2}$ hours. These sessions cover the material and skills in the Lifeguard Training course. Two optional sessions of 2 hours each may also be taken by aide candidates who wish to assist in the Waterfront Lifeguarding or Waterpark Lifeguarding modules. Each session includes classroom discussion, video, and demonstration, practice, and practice teaching of lifeguarding skills.

Class Size

One instructor is recommended for every 10 aide candidates in the course. If the class has more than 10 aide candidates, there should be a co-instructor. Close supervision is required to ensure effective practice and the safety of participants. Furthermore, you can run a class more efficiently if you keep the class reasonably small, and you are less likely to exceed the allotted time periods for various activities. If you have fewer than six aide candidates, consider conducting an apprenticeship program.

Facilities

The course includes activities requiring a classroom and a writing surface for each person, and water activities requiring a swimming facility such as a pool and a nonsurf waterfront or waterpark for the optional sessions. For scheduling purposes, it may be necessary to rearrange the sequence of sessions or to devote an entire session to classroom activities and another to water activities. Breaks are short, so advise aide candidates to come to the sessions with their swimsuits on, to be ready for the practice sessions.

Equipment and Supplies

Appendix G is a list of required equipment and supplies. Make sure all the equipment is ready and in working order before you teach the course.

Evaluation

To complete the course successfully, aide candidates must—
■ Attend and participate enthusiastically in all sessions.
■ Be able to correctly demonstrate the skills in the Lifeguard Training course.
■ Complete the Lifeguarding Instructor Aide test and answer sheet at the end of this lesson. *(Note: Aide candidates need not score a certain grade on the test. It is offered as a review tool for the course.)*

Apprenticeship Program

In an apprenticeship program, you cover the material appropriate for the course(s) or module(s) in the American Red Cross Lifeguarding program with which the aides will be assisting. Apprenticeship training also includes a discussion of—
■ Course objectives, both content and skill.
■ Course materials and their use.
■ The role of the aide in assisting with practice sessions.
■ Responsibilities of the instructor and aide.

During the apprenticeship, you should plan time to help the aide candidates improve their skills. Provide opportunities for the aide candidates to observe successful lifeguarding instructors and other lifeguarding instructor aides.

Certificates

Aide candidates who successfully complete the Lifeguarding Instructor Aide course, apprenticeship program, or options are eligible to receive an *Aide Certificate* (Cert. 3003). They may then assist lifeguarding instructors in conducting the courses for which they are trained.

Note: If they did not successfully complete the Lifeguarding Instructor Aide course, apprenticeship program, or options, they can still assist with lifeguarding instructors, but they won't receive certification, and their roles as aides will be limited to clerical and maintenance responsibilities.

Complete the certificates accurately. Be sure to indicate the course(s) of the American Red Cross Lifeguarding program with which the aide may assist, for example, "Lifeguard Training," "Waterfront Lifeguarding," "Waterpark Lifeguarding."

When the lifeguarding instructor aides have finished their training, thank them for participating and urge them to take active roles in the American Red Cross Lifeguarding program. Encourage them to participate in instructor courses when they are eligible.

Reporting

Report the results of the Lifeguarding Instructor Aide course, apprenticeship program, or options on the *Course Record* (Form 6418 and Form 6418A). On the *Course Record* enter the course name and course code number. The following is a list of the course names and course code numbers:

Course Name	Course Code Number
Lifeguard Training	3460A
Waterfront Lifeguarding	3461A
Waterpark Lifeguarding	3462A

Turn the *Course Record* in promptly to your local Red Cross unit.

For more information on awarding certificates, completing records, and conducting course evaluations, see Chapter 6.

Course Materials

Participant's Materials

Each aide candidate will need the following:
- *American Red Cross Lifeguarding Today* (Stock No. 654110)
- *American Red Cross CPR for the Professional Rescuer* (Stock No. 652048)
- Notebook and pencil
- Swimsuit and towel

Instructor's Materials and Equipment

- American Red Cross Identification
- *American Red Cross Lifeguarding Today* (Stock No. 654110)
- *American Red Cross Lifeguarding Instructor's Manual*
- *American Red Cross Instructor Candidate Training Manual* (Stock No. 329741)
- *Course Record* (Form 6418 and Form 6418A)

Class Materials and Equipment

- The following American Red Cross videos are recommended:
  - *Lifeguarding Today* (Stock No. 654110)
  - *American Red Cross CPR for the Professional Rescuer* (Stock No. 652051)
  - *American Red Cross Community First Aid* (Stock No. 625035)
  - *Instructor Candidate Training* (Stock No. 329740) or *General Orientation* (Stock No. 321867)
- Half-inch videocassette recorder (VCR) and monitor, if you show videos
- Rescue tubes (one rescue tube per two participants)
- Rescue boards (one rescue board per five participants) —**Waterfront Lifeguarding Option only**

- Backboards with a minimum of three straps and a commercial head immobilizer attached (one backboard per five participants)
- Adult, child, and infant manikins (one manikin for every two or three participants)
- Decontamination supplies: decontaminating solution, gauze pads, soap and water, baby bottle brush, basins or buckets, nonsterile disposable gloves, goggles, and any accessories recommended by the manikin manufacturer
- Blankets or mats (one for every two or three participants)
- Resuscitation masks
- Bag-valve masks
- Triangular bandages
- Gauze
- Roller gauze
- Splinting supplies
- *American Red Cross Aquatics Catalog* (Stock No. 654129), one per participant
- *Aide Certificates* (Cert. 3003), one per participant

Role and Responsibilities of Lifeguarding Instructor Aides

Be sure the aide candidates understand that they play a valuable role in the instructional process. They need to work cooperatively with the lead instructor to ensure that participants receive a positive and safe learning experience. Lifeguarding instructor aides have a responsibility to uphold the standards of the American Red Cross Lifeguarding program and to represent the American Red Cross in a positive manner at all times.

Lifeguarding instructor aides may assist lifeguarding instructors in several ways:

- **Clerical.** Aides can prepare class attendance rolls, call the roll at class time, and update lifeguarding skills checklists.
- **Supervisory.** Aides can assign partners for practice sessions, assist with general class control, and act as safety lookouts.
- **Instructional.** Because of their lifeguard training, aides can be especially helpful in assisting with courses by demonstrating skills, helping participants who need individual assistance, and conducting many aspects of practice sessions under the supervision of the instructor.
- **Maintenance.** Aides can be helpful in distributing, collecting, and storing equipment and supplies. In addition, they can help minimize or remove hazards in and around the swimming areas.

Course Outlines

Lifeguarding Instructor Aide Course Outline

Session 1

Activity	Approximate Time	Method	Resources
Introduction and registration	10 minutes	L	
Objectives of Lifeguarding Instructor Aide training	10 minutes	L/D	*IM*, p. 347
Duties and responsibilities of a Lifeguarding Instructor Aide	10 minutes	L/D	*IM*, p. 350
Overview of the American Red Lifeguard Training Program	20 minutes	L/D	*IM*, Chapters 1–6
Video: "Rescue Skills"	15 minutes	AV	*Lifeguarding Today* video
Break	5 minutes		
Demonstration of— ■ Extension assist from deck ■ Entries ■ Approaches ■ Swimming extension rescue ■ Active victim rear rescue ■ Multiple victim rescue ■ Passive victim rear rescue	15 minutes	Demo	*IM*, Chapter 7, Lesson 6
Practice of rescue skills listed above Aide candidates practice teach. Instructor helps aide candidates learn to recognize common errors and to provide corrective feedback.	30 minutes	P	
Closing	5 minutes	L/D	
Session 1, Total time 2 hours			

IM = Instructor's Manual   AV = Audiovisual   D = Discussion
L = Lecture   P = Practice   Demo = Demonstration

Lifeguarding Instructor Aide Course Outline

Session 2

Activity	Approximate Time	Method	Resources
Review Session I	5 minutes	L	
Video: "Controlling Bleeding and "Splinting"	18 minutes	AV	*Community First Aid* video
Practice of First Aid skills Aide candidates practice teaching. Instructor helps aide candidates learn to recognize common errors and to provide corrective feedback.	30 minutes	P	
Video: "Rescue Skills Part 2"	7 minutes	AV	*Lifeguarding Today* video
Break	5 minutes		

Demonstration of—
■ Feet-first surface dive
■ Submerged victim rescue
■ Removal from the water—
  ■ 2-lifeguard lift
  ■ 1-lifeguard lift
	20 minutes	Demo	*IM*, Chapter 7, Lesson 7

Practice of rescue skills listed above Aide candidates practice teach. Instructor helps aide candidates learn to recognize common errors and to provide corrective feedback.	30 minutes	P	
Closing	5 minutes	L/D	
Session 2, Total time 2 hours			

IM = Instructor's Manual   AV = Audiovisual   D = Discussion
L = Lecture   P = Practice   Demo = Demonstration

Lifeguarding Instructor Aide Course Outline

Session 3

Activity	Approximate Time	Method	Resources
Review of Session 2	5 minutes	L	
Video: "Rescue Breathing"	9 minutes	AV	*CPR for the Professional Rescuer* video
Practice of rescue breathing skills Aide candidates practice teach. Instructor helps aide candidates learn to recognize common errors and to provide corrective feedback.	15 minutes	P	
Video: "Clearing an Obstructed Airway, Adult and Child"	9 minutes	AV	*CPR for the Professional Rescuer* video
Practice of obstructed airway, adult adult and child Aide candidates practice teaching. Instructor helps aide candidates learn to recognize common errors and to provide corrective feedback.	15 minutes	P	
Video: "Clearing an Obstructed Airway, Infant"	7 minutes	AV	*CPR for the Professional Rescuer* video
Practice of obstructed airway, infant Aide candidates practice teach. Instructor helps aide candidates learn to recognize common errors and to provide corrective feedback.	15 minutes	P	
Break	5 minutes		

continued

Activity	Approximate Time	Method	Resources
Video: "Using a Resuscitation Mask"	6 minutes	AV	*CPR for the Professional Rescuer* video
Practice use of resuscitation mask Aide candidates practice teaching. Instructor helps aide candidates learn to recognize common errors and to provide corrective feedback.	10 minutes	P	
Video: "Using a Bag-Valve-Mask"	4 minutes	AV	*CPR for the Professional Rescuer* video
Practice use of bag-valve mask Aide candidates practice teaching. Instructor helps aide candidates learn to recognize common errors and to provide corrective feedback.	15 minutes	P	
Closing	5 minutes	L/D	
Session 3, Total time 2 hours			

IM = Instructor's Manual AV = Audiovisual D = Discussion
L = Lecture P = Practice Demo = Demonstration

Lifeguarding Instructor Aide Course Outline

Session 4

Activity	Approximate Time	Method	Resources
Review of Session 3	8 minutes	L	
Video: "Adult CPR"	6 minutes	AV	*CPR for the Professional Rescuer* video
Practice of Adult CPR Aide candidates practice teaching. Instructor helps aide candidates learn to recognize common errors and to provide corrective feedback.	20 minutes	P	
Video: "Child CPR"	6 minutes	AV	*CPR for the Professional Rescuer* video
Practice of Child CPR Aide candidates practice teaching. Instructor helps aide candidates learn to recognize common errors and to provide corrective feedback.	20 minutes	P	
Break	5 minutes		
Video: "Infant CPR"	4 minutes	AV	*CPR for the Professional Rescuer* video
Practice of Infant CPR Aide candidates practice teaching. Instructor helps aide candidates learn to recognize common errors and to provide corrective feedback.	20 minutes	P	

continued

Activity	Approximate Time	Method	Resources
Video: "Two-Rescuer CPR"	6 minutes	AV	*CPR for the Professional Rescuer* video
Practice of Two-Rescuer CPR Aide candidates practice teaching. Instructor helps aide candidates learn to recognize common errors and to provide corrective feedback.	20 minutes	P	
Closing	5 minutes		
Session 4, Total time 2 hours			

IM = Instructor's Manual   AV = Audiovisual   D = Discussion
L = Lecture   P = Practice   Demo = Demonstration

Lifeguarding Instructor Aide Course Outline

Session 5

Activity	Approximate Time	Method	Resources
Review of Session 4	5 minutes	L	
Video: "Spinal Injury Management"	23 minutes	AV	*Lifeguarding Today* video
Break	5 minutes		
Demonstration of in-line stabilization techniques—shallow and deep water	15 minutes	Demo	*IM*, Chapter 7 Lessons 9 & 10
Practice of in-line stabilization techniques—shallow and deep water Aide candidates practice teaching. Instructor helps aide candidates learn to recognize common errors and to provide corrective feedback.	20 minutes	P	
Demonstration of backboarding techniques—shallow and deep water	15 minutes	Demo	*IM*, Chapter 7 Lessons 9 & 10
Practice of backboarding techniques shallow and deep water Aide candidates practice teaching. Instructor helps aide candidates learn to recognize common errors and to provide corrective feedback.	30 minutes	P	
Review	7 minutes	L/D	
Session 5, Total time 2 hours			

IM = Instructor's Manual   AV = Audiovisual   D = Discussion
L = Lecture   P = Practice   Demo = Demonstration

Lifeguarding Instructor Aide Course Outline

Session 8

Activity	Approximate Time	Method	Resources
Review of Session 5	10 minutes	L	
Review of role and responsibility of Lifeguarding Instructor Aide	15 minutes	L/D	*IM*, p. 350
Representing the Red Cross	15 minutes	L/D	*ICT*, pp. 101–104
Video: "Behind the Scenes"	10 minutes	AV	Segment from *Instructor Candidate Training or General Orientation*
Final test and review	20 minutes	T	
Discussion of other leadership opportunities in the Lifeguarding Program	10 minutes	L/D	American Red Cross *Aquatics Catalog*
Certification and evaluation	10 minutes	L/D	*Aide Certificates*

Lesson 6, Total time   1 hours, 30 minutes

IM = Instructor's Manual   *ICT* = Instructor Candidate Training Participant's Manual
AV = Audiovisual   D = Discussion   L = Lecture
P = Practice   Demo = Demonstration   T = Test

Waterfront Lifeguarding
Optional Session 7

Activity	Approximate Time	Method	Resources
Review of Session 6 or introduction	5 minutes	L	
Video: Waterfront Lifeguarding—*"Rescue Skills"*	15 minutes	AV	*Lifeguarding Today* video
Break	5 minutes		
Demonstration of waterfront rescue skills	25 minutes	Demo	*IM*, Chapter 8
Practice of waterfront rescue skills Aide candidates practice teaching. Instructor helps aide candidates learn to recognize common errors and to provide corrective feedback.	60 minutes	P	
Certification and closing	10 minutes	L/D	*Aide Certificates*
Session 7, Total time 2 hours			

IM = Instructor's Manual   AV = Audiovisual   D = Discussion
L = Lecture   P = Practice   Demo = Demonstration

Waterpark Lifeguarding
Optional Session 8

Activity	Approximate Time	Method	Resources
Review Session 6 or introduction	5 minutes	L	
Video: Waterpark Lifeguarding— "Rescue Skills"	15 minutes	AV	*Lifeguarding Today* video
Break	5 minutes		
Demonstration of waterpark rescue skills	30 minutes	Demo	*IM*, Chapter 9
Practice of waterpark rescue skills Aide candidates practice teaching. Instructor helps aide candidates learn to recognize common errors and to provide corrective feedback.	55 minutes	P	
Certification and closing	10 minutes	L/D	*Aide Certificates*
Session 8, Total time 2 hours			

IM = Instructor's Manual   AV = Audiovisual   D = Discussion
L – Lecture   P = Practice   Demo = Demonstration

Name _____

IMPORTANT: Read all instructions before beginning this test.

INSTRUCTIONS: Mark all answers in pencil on this sheet. The questions on this test are multiple choice. Read each question slowly and carefully, then fill in the blank with the letter of your answer. If you wish to change an answer, erase your first answer completely. Return this test to your instructor when you are finished.

1. _____ The minimum age required to enroll in an American Red Cross Lifeguarding course is—

   A. 15 years of age.

   B. 16 years of age.

   C. None.

   D. Any age, as long as the student has finished the seventh grade.

2. _____ The best reason for everyone to be aware of safe diving rules is to—

   A. Prevent possible spinal injury.

   B. Avoid legal problems.

   C. Prevent double drowning.

   D. Encourage participation in competitive diving.

3. _____ A lifeguarding instructor aide can issue student—

   A. Certificates.

   B. Diplomas.

   C. Authorization.

   D. None of the above.

4. _____ The role and responsibilities of a Lifeguarding Instructor Aide include all of the following **except**—

   A. Providing clerical assistance to the instructor.

   B. Providing medical assistance to the instructor.

   C. Providing supervisory assistance to the instructor.

   D. Providing teaching assistance to the instructor.

5. _____ The minimum age required to enroll in an American Red Cross Lifeguarding Instructor course is—

A. 5 years of age.

B. 17 years of age.

C. Any age, as long as the participant can swim well.

D. No age requirement.

6. _____ A lifeguarding instructor aide can assist an instructor in all of the following ways except—

A. Preparing equipment.

B. Giving demonstrations.

C. Providing participants with corrective feedback.

D. Accepting sole responsibility for the participants.

7. _____ A lifeguarding instructor aide is responsible for following a facility's emergency action plan (EAP). An EAP includes all of the following except—

A. Having posted procedures on how to call 9–1–1.

B. Having safety equipment and a well-stocked first aid kit readily available.

C. Having an emergency signal.

D. Knowing how to perform emergency medical techniques.

8. _____ An effective skill demonstration must—

A. Be clearly visible to all participants.

B. Show as many angles of the skill as possible.

C. Be performed as slowly as possible.

D. All of the above.

9. _____ You should wear or display American Red Cross identification—

A. Whenever you teach American Red Cross health and safety courses.

B. Only when you are teaching at your local American Red Cross unit.

C. Only when you are teaching in a recreational pool setting.

D. Only when lifeguarding at a pool.

10. _____ The _____ you develop as a lifeguarding instructor aide can help prepare you for careers other than in the aquatic field.

A. Skills

B. Certificate

C. Friends

D. Money

American Red Cross
Lifeguarding Instructor Aide

1. **A** The minimum age required to enroll in an American Red Cross Lifeguarding course is—
   A. 15 years of age.
   B. 16 years of age.
   C. None.
   D. Any age, as long as the student has finished the seventh grade.

2. **A** The best reason for everyone to be aware of safe diving rules is to—
   A. Prevent possible spinal injury.
   B. Avoid legal problems.
   C. Prevent double drowning.
   D. Encourage participation in competitive diving.

3. **D** A lifeguarding instructor aide can issue student—
   A. Certificates.
   B. Diplomas.
   C. Authorization.
   D. None of the above.

4. **B** The role and responsibilities of a Lifeguarding Instructor Aide include all of the following **except**—
   A. Providing clerical assistance to the instructor.
   B. Providing medical assistance to the instructor.
   C. Providing supervisory assistance to the instructor.
   D. Providing teaching assistance to the instructor.

5. __B__ The minimum age required to enroll in an American Red Cross Lifeguarding Instructor course is—

A. 5 years of age.

B. 17 years of age.

C. Any age, as long as the participant can swim well.

D. No age requirement.

6. __D__ A lifeguarding instructor aide can assist an instructor in all of the following ways except—

A. Preparing equipment.

B. Giving demonstrations.

C. Providing participants with corrective feedback.

D. Accepting sole responsibility for the participants.

7. __D__ A lifeguarding instructor aide is responsible for following a facility's emergency action plan (EAP). An EAP includes all of the following except—

A. Having posted procedures on how to call 9–1–1.

B. Having safety equipment and a well-stocked first aid kit readily available.

C. Having an emergency signal.

D. Knowing how to perform emergency medical techniques.

8. __D__ An effective skill demonstration must—

A. Be clearly visible to all participants.

B. Show as many angles of the skill as possible.

C. Be performed as slowly as possible.

D. All of the above.

9. __A__ You should wear or display American Red Cross identification—

A. Whenever you teach American Red Cross health and safety courses.

B. Only when you are teaching at your local American Red Cross unit.

C. Only when you are teaching in a recreational pool setting.

D. Only when lifeguarding at a pool.

10. __A__ The _____ you develop as a lifeguarding instructor aide can help prepare you for careers other than in the aquatic field.

A. Skills

B. Certificate

C. Friends

D. Money

section c: appendixes

Administrative Terms and Procedures

For further information on any of the following terms and procedures, ask your Instructor Trainer or contact your local Red Cross unit.

Instructor—A member of a select group of individuals authorized to serve as agents of the Red Cross by teaching American Red Cross basic courses and imparting knowledge and skills consistent with American Red Cross policies, procedures, standards, and guidelines.

Red Cross Unit—Any Red Cross chapter, field service territory, or SAF station.

Certified—Receipt of a completion certificate when a participant has met all minimum course requirements of a Red Cross course.

Authorized—To be accepted by a local Red Cross unit to teach a Red Cross course in that unit's jurisdiction. To become authorized, the *Health and Safety Instructor Certificate* (Form 5736) and the *Instructor Agreement* (Form 6574) must be signed by you and a Red Cross unit official from your unit of authorization.

Reauthorization—The act of being authorized again by teaching or co-teaching at least one of the specified lifeguarding, water safety or CPR courses during your authorization period. You will receive a *Health and Safety Instructor Authorization Certificate* (C-3005) when you are reauthorized.

Extended Authorization—When you wish to teach on a temporary basis within another Red Cross unit's jurisdiction, you must contact that unit to get your instructor certificate endorsed for extended authorization. You must also notify that unit prior to any teaching activity and observe any procedures specific to that unit.

Transfer of Authorization—If you relocate for any reason, your authorization may be accepted by the Red Cross unit in your new jurisdiction. Contact your new Red Cross unit for further information on how the Red Cross can transfer your teaching records to your new location.

Suspension/Withdrawal of Authorization—The local Red Cross unit grants an Instructor authorization to teach. It is also the Red Cross unit's responsibility to suspend or withdraw the Instructor authorization for due cause. Due cause, generally, means that the Instructor does not or will not abide by the standards, policies, or procedures of the Red Cross organization and its programs or in some way abuses the position of an authorized Red Cross Instructor.

Teaching Records—Your Red Cross unit of authorization maintains your teaching and training records for the purpose of reauthorization, awards, and recognition, etc.

Course of Record—A course for which a properly completed, duly signed *Course Record* (Form 6418) and, if necessary, a *Course Record Addendum* (Form 6418A) have been submitted to and accepted by a Red Cross unit in the jurisdiction in which the course was conducted.

Minimum Enrollment for Courses—Each course must have enough participants to provide course participants with sufficient skill practice to accomplish the course objectives. Therefore, you must obtain prior permission from your local Red Cross to conduct a course with fewer than six participants. Courses must have a minimum of six participants enrolled, not necessarily passing.

Co-Teach—To share full or 100 percent participation in course leadership with one or more co-instructors. Co-teaching is also known as team teaching.

Instructor Aide—An individual who successfully completes instructor aide training to help an instructor with a basic course.

Instructor Agreement (Form 6574)—A form signed by Red Cross instructors before being authorized to teach a Red Cross course. It explains the rights and responsibilities of both the instructor and the Red Cross unit of authorization.

Instructor Agreement for American Red Cross Courses

The American Red Cross agrees to —

- Provide the quality training needed to help you carry out your instructor responsibilities to prepare for, conduct, report on, and evaluate Red Cross courses.
- Provide in good condition the appropriate materials, supplies, and equipment needed to meet the requirements of each course you teach.
- Provide timely updates of information and skills when appropriate.
- Establish and explain all national and local policies, regulations, and procedures that relate to your instructor responsibilities, including the American Red Cross Code of Conduct (contained in this Appendix).
- Provide effective, timely support and guidance.
- Provide supervision for and evaluation of your teaching performance.

As an American Red Cross instructor, I agree to —

- Follow all the current policies, regulations, and procedures of the American Red Cross related to the conduct and administration of Red Cross courses, including the American Red Cross Code of Conduct.
- Accept supervision and evaluation of my instructor responsibilities by the American Red Cross.
- Recognize that the completion of an appropriate instructor training course is only a prerequisite of appointment as a Red Cross instructor and that the authorization to teach is granted only by receiving an instructor authorization issued by the appropriate Red Cross unit.
- Teach only those courses I am authorized to teach, and only within those jurisdictions in which I am authorized, as scheduled in coordination with the appropriate Red Cross unit.
- Follow through on all classes assigned to me, including teaching the complete curriculum for each Red Cross course, completing required records in a timely and accurate manner, and providing appropriate course certificates or other recognition to participants as specified by the service.
- Recognize that Red Cross materials are copyrighted and may be reproduced only with the permission of the American Red Cross at national headquarters.
- Identify myself as a Red Cross representative and the course materials as those of the Red Cross, and in general, act as an agent of the Red Cross in all matters related to the use of my instructor authorization.
- Recognize that this agreement remains in effect as long as my Red Cross instructor's authorization remains current.

American Red Cross Code of Conduct

The American Red Cross is a charitable not-for-profit organization dedicated to providing service to those in need. The American Red Cross has traditionally demanded and received the highest ethical performance from its volunteer and paid staff. The conditions, however, under which American Red Cross services are being provided have changed dramatically over the past several years and will continue to change. Trends external to the American Red Cross, most notably economic trends and the resulting cost containment efforts in all sectors of the economy, mandate that renewed attention be given to the conduct of those individuals who represent this organization.

In an effort to maintain the high standard of conduct expected of the American Red Cross with respect to the management of its own affairs and to enable the American Red Cross to continue to offer services required by those in need, the American Red Cross adopts the following Code of Conduct applicable to all volunteer and paid staff.

No volunteer or paid staff shall:

1. Authorize the use of or use for the benefit or advantage of any person, the name, emblem, endorsement, services, or property of the American Red Cross, except in conformance with American Red Cross policy;
2. Accept or seek on behalf of himself or any other person, any financial advantage or gain of other than nominal value offered as a result of the volunteer or paid staff member's American Red Cross affiliation.
3. Publicly utilize any American Red Cross affiliation in connection with the promotion of partisan politics, religious matters, or positions on any issue not in conformity with the position of the American Red Cross;
4. Disclose any confidential Red Cross information that is available solely as a result of the volunteer or paid staff member's affiliation with the American Red Cross to any person not authorized to receive such information or use to the disadvantage of the American Red Cross any such confidential information, without the express authorization of the American Red Cross;
5. Knowingly take any action or make any statement intended to influence the

conduct of the American Red Cross in such a way as to confer any financial benefit on such a person or on any corporation of entity in which the individual has a significant interest or affiliation; or
6. Operate in any manner that is contrary to the best interest of the American Red Cross.

In the event that the volunteer or paid staff member's obligation to operate in the best interests of the American Red Cross conflicts with the interests of any organization in which he has a financial interest or with which he is affiliated, the individual shall disclose such conflict to the American Red Cross as soon as he becomes aware of it, shall absent himself from the room during deliberations, and shall refrain from voting in connection with the matter. The individual shall not permit his presence at the meeting to be counted in determining whether there exists a quorum.

American Red Cross Unit

Signature of Representative

Title of Representative

American Red Cross Instructor

(Print name)

Signature of Instructor

Date

Form 6574
(Rev. 4/91)

Authorized Provider Agreement For American Red Cross Instructional Courses

This agreement is between

_____
(name of corporation or other organization or
individual contrator)

(hereafter referred to as the Authorized
Provider)

and the

_____
(Name of Red Cross unit)

of The American National Red Cross
(hereafter referred to as the Red Cross).

The agreement is effective from
_____ until_____

unless renewed by agreement of the parties
for the period to be determined between them.

It may be terminated by either party with 30
days' written notice to this effect.

In the event of such termination, neither party
will have any further liability to the other
party under this agreement.

A. This auhorization is limited to the geographic jurisdiction of this/these Red Cross unit(s):

_____
(Name[s] of unit[s])

_____

B. Under the terms of this agreement, the Red Cross agrees to the following:

1. To support the training of the employees, members, and/or clients of the Approved Provider in the following Red Cross training courses:

_____
(List by name)

_____

2. To train as instructors those representatives of the Authorized Provider whom the Authorized Provider appoints, if those representatives meet Red Cross prerequisites for prior training and/or experience.
3. To issue Red Cross instructor certificates once those representatives successfully complete the required training.
4. To authorize the instructors in paragraph B.3., above, to teach Red Cross courses within the geographic area indicated in paragraph A., above.
5. To support and evaluate these instructors in an effective and timely manner.
6. To make available such needed equipment (listed as an appendix to this agreement) as the Authorized Provider

does not itself own and maintain and the Red Cross local unit can supply.

7. Upon receipt of the course schedule, to provide in quantities equal to numbers of students scheduled, all needed materials, including textbooks, workbooks, instruction manuals, training films, and course records.

8. To provide instructors with all policies and procedures to be followed, including all updates and revisions, in a timely manner.

9. To provide instructors with additional Red Cross training and retraining as appropriate to ensure that these instructors have the benefit of the most recent advances in the subject.

10. To maintain all course records on behalf of the Authorized Provider for at least five years.

11. To arrange for completed certificates to be delivered to individual course participants within _____ week(s) of course completion.

12. To maintain a close and ongoing supportive relationship with the Authorized Provider, the instructors, and other contacts of the Authorized Provider.

13. To guarantee, for the period of the contract, the prices noted on the attached price list. (The price incorporates Red Cross costs for course books, films, other materials, record keeping, certificate processing, program research and development, administration, promotion assistance, instructor training and support, etc.).

14. To invoice the Authorized Provider at the time course materials are delivered to the Authorized Provider.

C. Under terms of this Agreement, the Authorized Provider agress to the following:

1. To appoint qualified representatives for training, certification, and authorization as American Red Cross instructors in the Red Cross courses agreed upon in paragraph A.1.

2. To make these representatives available to the Red Cross for such training, retraining, and other events as are needed to gain and maintain levels of skill, knowledge, and understanding for the conduct of Red Cross training and programs.

3. To support the instructors' adherence to American Red Cross policy and procedures.

4. To notify the Red Cross at least _____ week(s) in advance of each scheduled Red Cross training course.

5. To make available for Red Cross course instruction classrooms and other facilities that are conducive to an effective learning environment.

6. To be responsible for the use and prompt return in good condition to the Red Cross of any equipment required in paragraph B.6., added as an appendix to this agreement: to report any equipment in need of servicing, repair, or replacement; and to maintain in good condition all equipment the Authorized Provider owns for this purpose.

7. To use only Red Cross printed or audiovisual materials in the conduct of the classes, except when the Red Cross approves in writing the use of other specific supplemental materials.

8. Unless specifically approved in writing by the Red Cross, to refrain from revising or editing any Red Cross-copyrighted

course materials in whole or in part for teaching any Red Cross courses or for use for any other purpose.

9. To obtain from the Red Cross printed training materials in quantities needed. Neither photocopying or other copying of Red Cross-copyrighted material nor recycling of student workbooks and textbooks from one student to the next is allowed, except under special circumstances in which written permission of the national sector of the Red Cross is obtained in advance.

10. To obtain from the sanctioning Red Cross unit Red Cross–copyrighted films and/or videocassettes in such quantitities as are required. Copying of Red Cross–copyrighted films or videocassettes is not allowed, unless written permission of the Red Cross is obtained in advance.

11. To clarify to all students that they are receiving Red Cross training in accord with Red Cross standards.

12. To provide full and complete course records, listing all students enrolled in each class, to the Red Cross within one week of completion of each class.

13. To designate an individual to be the primary contact with the Red Cross on an operational basis.

14. To remit to the Red Cross the fees invoiced, at the prices noted on the attached price list, within 30 days of receipt of invoice.

Agreed to this ____ day of ____ , 19____.

Authorized Provider

Signature: _____

Name and Title: _____

_____

American Red Cross _____
(Chapter name)

Signature: _____

Name and Title: _____

Course Record and Course Record Addendum

The completion and submission of the *Course Record* (Form 6418) and the *Course Record Addendum* (Form 6418A) to the local Red Cross field unit is one of the instructor responsibilities that **MUST BE** completed at the end of the course. *Course Record* forms provide information validating that a course was held and documenting that course requirements were met and proper procedures were followed. *Course Record* forms also help the Red Cross track and measure its instructional efforts. They are used to monitor instructor, co-instructor, and instructor aide activities; to document and verify the participation and certification of students; and

to reauthorize instructors and co-instructors. On occasion the *Course Record* may be used as a legal document, thus it is extremely important that all portions of the form be properly completed.

For these reasons, every Lifeguarding Instructor should be familiar with the *Course Record* (Form 6418) and *Course Record Addendum* (Form 6418A). A copy of the *Course Record* and the *Course Record Addendum* and instructions for completing them appear on the following pages. Copies of these forms are available from your local Red Cross field unit.

COURSE RECORD

PAGE _____ OF _____ PAGES

COURSE WAS CONDUCTED AT _____
(name of Red Cross unit, organization, etc.)

ADDRESS _____
(street)

_____
(city) (state) (zip)

INSTRUCTOR _____
(last name) (first) (middle)

ADDRESS _____
(street)

_____
(city) (state) (zip)

PHONE NUMBER (____) _____ If new address or phone number, please check ☐

UNIT OF AUTHORIZATION _____
(name of chapter/station/national sector unit)

ADDRESS _____
(city) (state) (zip)

CO-INSTRUCTOR _____
(last name) (first) (middle)

ADDRESS _____
(street)

_____
(city) (state) (zip)

PHONE NUMBER (____) _____ If new address or phone number, please check ☐

UNIT OF AUTHORIZATION (if different from instructor's) _____
(name of chapter/station/national sector unit)

ADDRESS _____
(city) (state) (zip)

SPONSORING RED CROSS UNIT _____

_____

COURSE NAME _____

_____

COURSE CODE _____

DATE COURSE BEGAN _____

DATE COURSE ENDED _____

LENGTH OF COURSE (in hours) _____

NUMBER ENROLLED _____

NUMBER PASSED _____

NUMBER FAILED _____

NUMBER INCOMPLETE _____

CHECK ONE:

☐ INSTRUCTOR WILL PICK UP CERTIFICATES

☐ SEND CERTIFICATES TO INSTRUCTOR

☐ SEND CERTIFICATES TO ORGANIZATION

☐ CERTIFICATES ISSUED ON SITE

INSTRUCTOR'S COMMENTS:

NAME(S) OF OTHER CO-INSTRUCTOR(S), ASSISTING INSTRUCTOR(S), OR AIDE(S)	INDICATE CO-INSTRUCTOR, ASSISTING INSTRUCTOR, OR AIDE	UNIT OF AUTHORIZATION/ AGENCY AFFILIATION	HOURS INVOLVED

I certify that this course has been conducted in accordance with requirements and procedures of the American Red Cross. *Note:* Co-instructor must sign if named above.

(Instructor's signature) _____ (Co-instructor's signature) _____

PARTICIPANT INFORMATION Please print firmly or type the following information. The data will provide the Red Cross with information on the population we serve. Use one of the following letters to indicate your ethnic origin in the space under "EO": (W) white, (B) black, (H) Hispanic, (AP) Asian/Pacific Islander, (AI) American Indian/Alaska Native. Indicate your Red Cross status with a ✓ under "PD" or "VOL." indicate with a ✓ under "DSHR" if you are currently a national DSHR System member.

COURSE GRADE	NAME		MAILING ADDRESS				EO	PD	VOL	DSHR	INSTRUCTOR'S COMMENTS
	LAST		STREET								
	FIRST	MI	CITY	STATE	ZIP				PHONE NO.		
	LAST		STREET								
	FIRST	MI	CITY	STATE	ZIP	( )			PHONE NO.		
	LAST		STREET								
	FIRST	MI	CITY	STATE	ZIP	( )			PHONE NO.		
	LAST		STREET								
	FIRST	MI	CITY	STATE	ZIP	( )			PHONE NO.		
	LAST		STREET								
	FIRST	MI	CITY	STATE	ZIP	( )			PHONE NO.		

SPONSORING RED CROSS UNIT'S COPY

American Red Cross Form 6418 (Rev. 10–91)

NOTES TO THE INSTRUCTOR (COURSE RECORD)

The *Course Record* (American Red Cross Form 6418) and *Course Record Addendum* (Form 6418A) are the forms on which course attendance and course grades are officially recorded. These forms also serve as source documents for issuance of certificates and documentation of teaching activity for monthly or annual statistical reports. On occasion, the *Course Record* may be used as a legal document. Therefore, it is imperative that all portions be properly completed and signed. If a participant is reluctant to provide personal demographic data, submit, at the least, his or her legal name and the course grade.

When you complete the *Course Record,* please—
- Print firmly or type.
- Return appropriate copies of this form within 10 working days to the following locations:
  - Return original (white) to the sponsoring Red Cross unit.
  - Return first copy (yellow) to your unit of authorization (if different from sponsoring unit).
  - Return second copy (pink) to the school, workplace, or community organization where the course was conducted.
  - Retain the last copy (goldenrod) for your personal records.
- Attach a sheet of paper to the sponsoring unit's copy for additional comments regarding the course, supplies, facilities, participants, additional co-instructors or aides, and so forth.
- Refer to the *Disaster Training System* (ARC 3065) for instructions on using this form to report Disaster Services courses.
- Refer to the *HIV/AIDS Instructor's Manual* (Stock No. 329572) for instructions on using this form to report HIV/AIDS Education courses.
- Refer to the "Local Unit Guide for Human Resources Decentralized Training" for instructions on using this form to report Human Resources courses. (Available from Human Resources, Training and Instructional Systems, national headquarters.)

Instructions for completing the form are given below:

Course Was Conducted At. Enter the name of the school, workplace, community organization, or Red Cross unit where the course was conducted.

Sponsoring Red Cross Unit. Enter the name of the Red Cross chapter, station, or national sector unit that is responsible for issuing course completion certificates for this training.

Course Code. Enter the number of the course. For Health and Safety, this number can be obtained either from the back of the course certificate or from your sponsoring unit.

Dates Course Began and Ended. Enter month, day, and year.

Unit of Authorization. Enter the Red Cross chapter, station, or national sector unit that maintains your instructor records and is responsible for reauthorizing you as an instructor.

Instructor's Comments (Body of Form). Record any important overall information about the course, for example, comments about the course materials/supplies and facility; problems with equipment, course materials, or facility; plans to complete the course for participants who receive an INCOMPLETE; and so forth. HIV/AIDS instructors should refer to the *HIV/AIDS Instructor's Manual* for additional information.

Course Grade. Enter a grade of PASS (P), FAIL (F), or INCOMPLETE (I) for each participant. For Health and Safety instructors, criteria for grading are outlined in your instructor's manual. For HIV/AIDS presentations, if participants' names are recorded, N/A is listed for the course grade.

Ethnic Origin (EO). Enter one of the following letters to indicate a participant's ethnic origin: (W) white, (B) black, (H) Hispanic, (AP) Asian/Pacific Islander, (AI) American Indian/Alaska Native.

PD/VOL. Indicate with a check participant's Red Cross status. THIS BLOCK DOES NOT HAVE TO BE FILLED IN FOR HEALTH AND SAFETY COURSES.

DSHR (For Disaster-Related Courses Only). Indicate with a check if participants are enrolled in the national Disaster Services Human Resources (DSHR) System.

Instructor's Comments (Participant Information). Record, after a participant's name, any important information about the participant, for example, interest in becoming an instructor, reason for incomplete or failure, and so forth.

COURSE RECORD ADDENDUM

COURSE NAME AND COURSE CODE _____

NAME OF INSTRUCTOR _____

NAME OF CO-INSTRUCTOR _____

DATE COURSE BEGAN _____ DATE COURSE ENDED _____

FOR DISASTER COURSES ONLY

SPONSORING RED CROSS UNIT _____

CITY AND STATE WHERE COURSE WAS HELD _____

SIGNATURE OF INSTRUCTOR _____

SIGNATURE OF CO-INSTRUCTOR _____

PARTICIPANT INFORMATION Please print firmly or type the following information. The data will provide the Red Cross with information on the population we serve. Use one of the following letters to indicate your ethnic origin in the space under "EO": **(W)** white, **(B)** black, **(H)** Hispanic, **(AP)** Asian/Pacific Islander, **(AI)** American Indian/Alaska Native. Indicate your Red Cross status with a ✓ under "PD" or "VOL." indicate with a ✓ under "DSHR" if you are currently a national DSHR System member.

COURSE GRADE	NAME	MAILING ADDRESS	EO	PD	VOL	DSHR	INSTRUCTOR'S COMMENTS
	LAST	STREET					
	FIRST MI	CITY STATE ZIP ( ) PHONE NO.					
	LAST	STREET					
	FIRST MI	CITY STATE ZIP ( ) PHONE NO.					
	LAST	STREET					
	FIRST MI	CITY STATE ZIP ( ) PHONE NO.					
	LAST	STREET					
	FIRST MI	CITY STATE ZIP ( ) PHONE NO.					
	LAST	STREET					
	FIRST MI	CITY STATE ZIP ( ) PHONE NO.					
	LAST	STREET					
	FIRST MI	CITY STATE ZIP ( ) PHONE NO.					
	LAST	STREET					
	FIRST MI	CITY STATE ZIP ( ) PHONE NO.					
	LAST	STREET					
	FIRST MI	CITY STATE ZIP ( ) PHONE NO.					
	LAST	STREET					
	FIRST MI	CITY STATE ZIP ( ) PHONE NO.					
	LAST	STREET					
	FIRST MI	CITY STATE ZIP ( ) PHONE NO.					
	LAST	STREET					
	FIRST MI	CITY STATE ZIP ( ) PHONE NO.					
	LAST	STREET					
	FIRST MI	CITY STATE ZIP ( ) PHONE NO.					
	LAST	STREET					
	FIRST MI	CITY STATE ZIP ( ) PHONE NO.					
	LAST	STREET					
	FIRST MI	CITY STATE ZIP ( ) PHONE NO.					

SPONSORING RED CROSS UNIT'S COPY

American Red Cross Form 6418A (Rev. 10–91)

NOTES TO THE INSTRUCTOR (COURSE RECORD ADDENDUM)

For all services except Disaster Services, the *Course Record Addendum* (Form 6418A) is to be used only as an addition to the *Course Record (Form* 6418). For Disaster Services, use only the *Course Record Addendum to* report courses. On occasion, the *Course Record Addendum* may be used as a legal document. If a participant is reluctant to provide personal demographic data, submit, at the least, his or her legal name and the course grade.

When you complete the *Course Record Addendum,* please—
- Print firmly or type.
- All services except Disaster Services should attach this form to the *Course Record* (Form 6418).
- Return appropriate copies of this form within 10 working days to the following locations:
- Return original (white) to the sponsoring Red Cross unit.
- Return first copy (yellow) to your unit of authorization (if different from sponsoring unit).
- Return second copy (pink) to the school, workplace, or community organization where the course was conducted.
- Retain the last copy (goldenrod) for your personal records.
- Attach a sheet of paper to the sponsoring unit's copy for additional comments regarding the course, supplies, facilities, participants, additional co-instructors or aides, and so forth.
- Refer to the *Disaster Training System* (ARC 3065) for instructions on using this form to report Disaster Services courses.
- Refer to the *HIV/AIDS Instructor's Manual* (Stock No. 329572) for instructions on using this form to report HIV/AIDS Education courses.
- Refer to the "Local Unit Guide for Human Resources Decentralized Training" for instructions on using this form to report Human Resources courses. (Available from Human Resources, Training and Instructional Systems, national headquarters.)

Instructions for completing the form are given below:

Course Codes. Enter the number of the course. For Health and Safety, this number can be obtained either from the back of the course certificate or from your sponsoring unit. For Disaster Services, refer to the course fact sheet.

Sponsoring Red Cross Unit. Enter the name of the Red Cross chapter, station, or national sector unit that is responsible for issuing course completion certificates for this training.

Dates Course Began and Ended. Enter month, day, and year.

Course Grade. Enter a grade of PASS (P), FAIL (F), or INCOMPLETE (I) for each participant. For Health and Safety instructors, criteria for grading are outlined in your instructor's manual. For HIV/AIDS presentations, if participants' names are recorded, N/A is listed for the course grade.

Ethnic Origin (EO). Enter one of the following letters to indicate a participant's ethnic origin: (W) white, (B) black, (H) Hispanic, (AP) Asian/Pacific Islander, (AI) American Indian/Alaska Native.

PD/VOL. Indicate with a check participant's Red Cross status. THIS BLOCK DOES NOT HAVE TO BE FILLED IN FOR HEALTH AND SAFETY COURSES.

DSHR (For Disaster-Related Courses Only). Indicate with a check if participants are enrolled in the national Disaster Services Human Resources (DSHR) System.

Instructor's Comments (Participant Information). Record, after a participant's name, any important information about the participant, for example, interest in becoming an instructor, reason for incomplete or failure, and so forth.

Course Fact Sheets

- Lifeguard Training
- CPR for the Professional Rescuer
- Waterfront Lifeguarding Module
- Waterpark Lifeguarding Module
- Head Lifeguard
- Community Water Safety
- Safety Training for Swim Coaches
- Lifeguarding Instructor
- Head Lifeguard Instructor
- Waterfront Lifeguarding Instructor
- Waterpark Lifeguarding Instructor
- Lifeguarding Instructor Aide

Course: American Red Cross Lifeguard Training

Course Number 3460

Purpose	To teach lifeguards the skills and knowledge needed to prevent and respond to aquatic emergencies
Prerequisites	Minimum age: 15
	Tread water for 2 minutes using legs only. Participants cross their arms across their chest
	Swim 500 yards continuously using each of the following strokes for at least 100 yards: crawl, breaststroke, and sidestroke. The stroke(s) used for the remaining 200 yards are the participants' choice
	Submerge to a minimum depth of 7 feet, retrieve a 10-pound object and return to the surface
Learning Objectives	Understand the value of behaving in a professional manner
	Learn how to recognize specific characteristic behaviors of distressed swimmers, active and passive drowning victims, and near-drowning victims
	Recognize an aquatic emergency, and act promptly and appropriately
	Perform equipment-based skills and techniques used by professional lifeguards
	Perform proper techniques to care for a possible spinal injury
	Learn how to provide first aid and CPR
Length	Suggested 33 hours (plus a 1 1/2 hour precourse session)
Instructor	Taught by a currently authorized American Red Cross Lifeguarding Instructor
Certification Requirements	Successfully complete two written exams with a minimum score of 80 percent
	Successfully complete two final skill scenarios
	Successfully perform all critical skills

(continued)

Certificate Validity	Lifeguard Training (including First Aid) -3 years
	CPR for the Professional Rescuer —1 year
Participant Materials	*Lifeguarding Today* participant's manual (654110)
	CPR for the Professional Rescuer participant's manual (652048)

Course: CPR for the Professional Rescuer

Course Number 3214

Purpose	To teach professional rescuers (those with a duty to respond) the skills needed to respond appropriately to respiratory and cardiac emergencies
Prerequisites	None
Learning Objectives	Learn the role of the professional rescuer in the EMS system
	Learn the role of the professional rescuer in providing emergency care
	Learn how to recognize and respond to respiratory and cardiac emergencies in infants, children, and adults
	Recognize the risk factors that contribute to cardiovascular disease
	Perform specialized skills and techniques used by professional rescuers
Length	Suggested 9 hours
Instructor	Taught by a currently authorized American Red Cross Lifeguarding Instructor, or
	American Red Cross CPR for the Professional Rescuer Instructor, or
	American Red Cross Emergency Response Instructor
Certification Requirements	Successfully complete a written exam with a minimum score of 80 percent
	Successfully perform all skills taught in the course
Certificate Validity	1 year
Participant Material	*CPR for the Professional Rescuer* participant's manual (652048)

Course: **Waterfront Lifeguarding Module**

Course Number 3461M

Purpose	To teach lifeguards the skills and knowledge needed to prevent and respond to emergencies at a waterfront facility
Prerequisites	Current *American Red Cross Lifeguard Training* Certificate (Cert. 653460)
	Current *American Red Cross CPR for the Professional Rescuer* Certificate (Cert. 653214)
Learning Objectives	Describe conditions that affect surveillance at a waterfront
	Describe the skills used in special rescue situations such as missing person procedures, search for a SCUBA diver, and cold water rescue
	Demonstrate specific rescue skills for a waterfront facility
Length	Suggested 5 1/2 hours
Instructor	Taught by a currently authorized American Red Cross Waterfront Lifeguarding Instructor
Certification Requirements	Successfully complete a written exam with a minimum score of 80 percent
	Successfully perform all critical skills
Certificate Validity	None
Participant Materials	*Lifeguarding Today* participant's manual (654110)

Course: Waterpark Lifeguarding Module

Course Number 3462M

Purpose	To teach lifeguards the skills and knowledge needed to prevent and respond to emergencies at a waterpark facility
Prerequisites	Current *American Red Cross Lifeguard Training Certificate* (Cert. 653460) Current *American Red Cross CPR for the Professional Rescuer* Certificate (Cert. 653214)
Learning Objectives	Describe conditions that affect surveillance at a waterpark Understand and be able to explain safety rules and considerations at waterparks Demonstrate specific rescue skills for waterpark facilities
Length	Suggested 5 hours
Instructor	Taught by a currently authorized American Red Cross Waterpark Lifeguarding Instructor
Certification Requirements	Successfully complete a written exam with a minimum score of 80 percent Successfully perform all critical skills
Certificate Validity	None
Participant Materials	*Lifeguarding Today* participant's manual (654110)

Course: Head Lifeguard

Course Number 3463

Purpose	To provide lifeguards career development training that includes injury prevention, selection and training of lifeguards, team-building, interaction with patrons, and emergency-response planning
Prerequisites	Current *American Red Cross Lifeguard Training* certificate (Cert. 653460), or a current lifeguard training certificate from another nationally recognized organization
Learning Objectives	Understand the roles and responsibilities of a head lifeguard pertaining to safety, supervision, and training
	Understand a head lifeguard's role in a facility's chain of command
	Understand a head lifeguard's role of leadership and professionalism
	Understand how to develop a positive relationship with patrons and lifeguarding staff
Length	Suggested 6 hours
Instructor	Taught by a currently authorized American Red Cross Head Lifeguard Instructor
Certification Requirements	Successfully complete a written exam with a minimum score of 80 percent
	Full attendance and participation in the course
Certificate Validity	None
Participant Materials	*Head Lifeguard* participant's manual (Stock No. 654119)

Course: Community Water Safety

Course Number 3464

Purpose	To present information about various aquatic environments and their potential hazards and to inform the general public on how to safely participate in aquatic activities
Prerequisites	None
Learning Objectives	Learn to recognize and prevent aquatic emergencies Understand what to do in an aquatic emergency Understand self-help skills for aquatic emergencies
Length	Suggested minimum 4 hours
Instructor	Taught by a currently authorized American Red Cross Lifeguarding Instructor or Water Safety Instructor
Certification Requirements	Full attendance
Certificate Validity	None
Participant Materials	*Community Water Safety* participant's manual (654112)

Course: American Red Cross Safety Training for Swim Coaches

Course Number 3414

Purpose	To provide training in aquatic safety for competitive swim coaches, athletic trainers, athletes participating in aquatic activities, aquatic exercise trainers, and other individuals involved in aquatic competition or exercise programs
Prerequisites	None
Learning Objectives	List the safety responsibilities of a swim coach
	List the common hazards associated with swimming pools and explain how to eliminate or minimize such hazards
	Recognize a swimmer in distress or drowning situation
	Explain and demonstrate rescue skills essential to swim coaches
	Recognize specific medical conditions that pertain to their swimmers
	Explain and demonstrate spinal injury management skills
Length	Suggested 8 hours
Instructor	Taught by a currently authorized American Red Cross Lifeguarding Instructor or Water Safety Instructor who meets additional requirements for designation to teach Safety Training for Swim Coaches
Certification Requirements	Successfully complete a written exam with a minimum score of 80 percent
	Successfully complete final skills test
Certificate Validity	3 years
Participant Materials	American Red Cross *Safety Training for Swim Coaches Manual* (329449)
	Safety Training for Swim Coaches certificate (Cert. 3414)

Course: Lifeguarding Instructor
Course Number 3460I

Purpose	To train instructor candidates to teach Lifeguard Training (including first aid), CPR for the Professional Rescuer, Lifeguarding Instructor Aide, and Community Water Safety by developing their understanding of how to use the course materials and methods of conducting training sessions and evaluating participants' progress
Prerequisites	Minimum age: 17
	Show evidence of having completed Instructor Candidate Training (ICT) or a current Health and Safety Instructor authorization by showing one of the following:
	■ ICT certificate (C-3007) issued in last 12 months, or
	■ A current Health and Safety instructor authorization (Form 5736) or (C-3005)
	Successfully complete a precourse session, consisting of Lifeguard Training, first aid and CPR for the Professional Rescuer skills and knowledge evaluation
Learning Objectives	Demonstrate characteristics required of an American Red Cross representative and role model
	Be completely familiar with the American Red Cross Lifeguarding program material
	Plan and conduct Lifeguard Training (including first aid), CPR for the Professional Rescuer, Lifeguarding Instructor Aide, and Community Water Safety, and evaluate participants' progress
	Maintain complete and accurate course and attendance records and reports
	Successfully demonstrate specific skills
Length	Suggested 17 hours (plus a 3 1/2-hour precourse session)
Instructor	Taught by a currently authorized American Red Cross Lifeguarding Instructor Trainer

(continued)

Certification Requirements	Successfully complete written exams with a minimum score of 80 percent
	Successfully demonstrate all critical lifeguarding skills
	Successfully complete all practice- teaching assignments
Certificate Validity	Authorization is for two calendar years. All authorizations expire on December 31. Refer to Section II in the *Health and Safety Manual of Administrative Policies and Procedures* (MAPP) (A-3530) for additional information.
Participant Materials	*Lifeguarding Today* participant's manual (654110)
	CPR for the Professional Rescuer participant's manual (652048)
	Lifeguarding Instructor's Manual (654112)
	Instructor Candidate Training participant's manual (329741)

Course: Head Lifeguard Instructor

Course Number 3463I

Purpose	To train instructor candidates to teach the American Red Cross Head Lifeguard program by developing their understanding of how to use course materials and methods of conducting training and evaluating participants' progress
Prerequisites	Current American Red Cross Lifeguarding Instructor authorization
	Successfully complete the precourse session, consisting of a written exam based on the American Red Cross Head Lifeguard course
Learning Objective	Be completely familiar with the American Red Cross Head Lifeguard material
	Plan and conduct the Head Lifeguard course and evaluate participants' progress
	Maintain complete and accurate course and attendance records and reports
Length	Suggested 2 hours and 15 minutes (plus a 45-minute precourse session)
Instructor	Taught by a currently authorized American Red Cross Lifeguarding Instructor Trainer
Certification Requirements	Successfully complete a written exam with a minimum score of 80 percent
	Successfully complete one practice- teaching assignment
Certificate Validity	Authorization is for two calendar years. All authorizations expire on December 31. Refer to Section II in the *Health and Safety Manual of Administrative Policies and Procedures* (MAPP) (A–3530) for additional information
Participant Materials	*Lifeguarding Today* participant's manual (654110)
	Head Lifeguard participant's manual (654119)
	Lifeguarding Instructor's Manual (654112)

Course: Waterfront Lifeguarding Instructor

Course Number 3461I

Purpose	To train instructor candidates to teach the American Red Cross Waterfront Lifeguarding module by developing their understanding of how to use course materials and methods of conducting training and evaluating participants' progress
Prerequisites	Current American Red Cross Lifeguarding Instructor Authorization
	Successfully complete the Precourse Session consisting of a written exam and two skill scenarios based on the American Red Cross Waterfront Lifeguarding module
Learning Objectives	Be completely familiar with the American Red Cross Waterfront Lifeguarding material
	Plan and conduct the Waterfront Lifeguarding module and evaluate participants' progress
	Maintain complete and accurate course and attendance records and reports
	Successfully demonstrate specific skills
Length	Suggested 3 hours (plus a 2-hour precourse session)
Instructor	Taught by a currently authorized American Red Cross Lifeguarding Instructor Trainer
Certification Requirements	Successfully complete a written exam with a minimum score of 80 percent
	Successfully demonstrate all critical Waterfront Lifeguarding skills
	Successfully complete one practice-teaching assignment
Certificate Validity	Authorization is for two calendar years. All authorizations expire December 31. Refer to Section II in the *Health and Safety Manual of Administrative Policies and Procedures* (MAPP) (A–3530) for additional information
Participant Materials	*Lifeguarding Today* participant's manual (654110)
	Lifeguarding Instructor's Manual (654112)

Course: Waterpark Lifeguarding Instructor

Course Number 3462I

Purpose	To train instructor candidates to teach the American Red Cross Waterpark Lifeguarding module by developing their understanding of how to use course materials, and methods of conducting training and evaluating participants' progress
Prerequisites	Current American Red Cross Lifeguarding Instructor Authorization
	Successfully complete the precourse session consisting of a written exam and a skill scenario based on the American Red Cross Waterpark Lifeguarding module
Learning Objectives	Be completely familiar with the American Red Cross Waterpark Lifeguarding material
	Plan and conduct the Waterpark Lifeguarding module and evaluate participants' progress
	Maintain complete and accurate course and attendance records and reports
	Successfully demonstrate specific skills
Length	Suggested 3 hours (plus a 2-hour precourse session)
Instructor	Taught by a currently authorized American Red Cross Lifeguarding Instructor Trainer
Certification Requirements	Successfully complete a written exam with a minimum score of 80 percent
	Successfully demonstrate all critical Waterpark Lifeguarding skills
	Successfully Complete one practice-teaching assignment
Certification Validity	Authorization is for two calendar years. All authorizations expire on December 31. Refer to Section II in the *Health and Safety Manual of Administrative Policies and Procedures* (MAPP) (A-3530) for additional information
Participant Materials	*Lifeguarding Today* participant's manual (654110)
	Lifeguarding Instructor's Manual (654112)

Course: Lifeguarding Instructor Aide

Course Number 3460A

Purpose	To train individuals who wish to assist lifeguarding instructors in conducting American Red Cross Lifeguarding courses, particularly lifeguards who do not meet the minimum age requirements for the Lifeguarding Instructor course but would like to further their lifeguard training
Prerequisites	Current *American Red Cross Lifeguard Training* certificate (Cert. 653460)
	Current *American Red Cross CPR for the Professional Rescuer* certificate (Cert. 653214)
	Exhibit a strong sense of maturity and responsibility
	Demonstrate all skills listed as completion requirements for the American Red Cross Lifeguarding program
Learning Objectives	Understand the roles and responsibilities of a Lifeguarding Instructor Aide, including clerical, instructional, supervisory, and maintenance duties
Length	Suggested minimum 11 1/2 hours
Instructor	Taught by a currently authorized American Red Cross Lifeguarding Instructor
Certification Requirements	Attend and enthusiastically participate in all course sessions
	Demonstrate critical lifeguarding skills
	Complete the Lifeguarding Instructor Aide exam (no grade requirements)
Certificate Validity	None
Participant Materials	*Lifeguarding Today* participant's manual (654110)
	CPR for the Professional Rescuer participant's manual (652048)

The Americans With Disabilities Act — Course Modifications Guide

As of January 26, 1992, the Americans With Disabilities Act bars discrimination against the handicapped in places of public accommodation. Title III of the law bars private entities (schools, banks, restaurants, social service agencies, offices, retail sales establishments, etc.) from discriminating against individuals with disabilities in the provision of their goods and services. Individuals with physical or mental disabilities may not be denied full and equal enjoyment of the goods, services, facilities, advantages, or accommodations offered to the public. A place of public accommodation may not discriminate against its patrons, clients, invitees, or guests on the basis of real or perceived disabilities.

There is every reason to believe that the law will apply to the American Red Cross. Health and Safety services, because of the public course offerings and the availability of certification, could be significantly affected. For this reason, every chapter must examine its ability to provide services to a population with diverse needs. In addition, every Red Cross representative who comes in contact with the public or makes decisions that affect the public should be made aware of the law.

For years, the American Red Cross Health and Safety Operations Unit at national headquarters and local units have dealt with individuals whose needs required special accommodation to meet the specific objectives set forth in our courses. These decisions have been based on a doctrine of fairness to the individual within standards set forth in the courses. The Americans with Disabilities Act will require close examination of course objectives and a good faith effort to accommodate, within reason, all those who seek training.

General Recommendations for Instructors

- Allow full access to anyone seeking admission to a course regardless of real or perceived disabilities.
- Tell participants in every course to participate within the limits of their ability and learn as much as they can. For some people, certification may not be important. For those individuals, focus on helping them to learn as much as possible.
- Certify each participant who can meet course skill and testing objectives.
- Use available resources to assist people with special needs.
- Provide for the safety of all participants and for your own personal safety. Do not provide assistance to a participant beyond the extent to which you feel comfortable.
- Check regularly with the chapter in whose jurisdiction you are teaching to keep abreast of changes in resources and policies.

Course Modification

The course modification section of this appendix is designed to provide you with insights into providing training opportunities to a diverse population. The courses you teach could include a mix of people who have special needs and those who do not. These courses have been designed to give you the flexibility to train participants who have a wide range of needs and still maintain course standards.

People With Reading Difficulties

If you believe that a course includes participants who have reading difficulties, you should discuss the problem with those participants individually and privately without attracting the attention of the rest of the class.

Identifying People With Reading Difficulties

Whenever you teach a course, you should be aware of the possibility that one or more participants may have reading difficulties. You must be prepared to detect any such difficulties and provide those participants with every opportunity to succeed. Through observation, you may be able to detect that an individual has reading problems. Suspect poor reading skills when—

- A participant says that he or she—
  - Knows English as a second language.
  - Forgot his or her glasses.
  - Has not done well in educational settings.
  - Does not do well in testing situations.
- A participant—
  - Seems nervous and apprehensive.
  - Does not follow along or flips pages as the instructor reads.

The participant in a Lifeguard Training course is required to read material other than the written exam. This exam may be given orally. The challenge for an instructor is to identify participants with reading problems before administering the written test.

People With Physical Limitations

These individuals include those who are hearing disabled, legally blind, lack full use of limbs, or have any other disability that prevents them from participating in a course unless it is specially modified.

Hearing Impaired

The videos shown in these courses are closed captioned to assist those who are deaf or hard of hearing. However, the ability to communicate directions is necessary for a participant to fully take part in course activities. An interpreter should be used whenever possible.

Legally Blind

The success of a legally blind participant who wishes certification in a typical video-based course is obviously limited. The need to touch rather than see demonstrations requires that the participant be given an opportunity to listen to the video and then feel the skill being performed. The integration of touch demonstrations into a course taught by one instructor, within the time recommendations, may be impossible. If special arrangements to provide additional resources have not been made prior to the beginning of the course, you should offer the participant an opportunity to take part in the course by listening to the video and gaining familiarity with the manikins and other equipment. But additional time and resources will be needed to provide an opportunity for success.

As soon as possible, arrangements should be made with your local Red Cross unit representative to provide additional time for a legally blind participant to develop skills.

Other Physical Limitations

Participants with a wide range of limitations may wish to participate in a course. These individuals should be allowed full access to the course and fully briefed as to the types of specific skills required for certification. They must select their level of participation. You may adapt skills within the limit of the objectives in each course component and the text that appears on the skill sheets. Only assist the participant within your personal comfort range. **Do not compromise your safety or the safety of a participant.**

Checklist of Equipment and Supplies Needed to Teach Courses in the American Red Cross Lifeguarding Program

Lifeguard Training Course

For the Class

- ❏ Viewing equipment: 1.2" VCR and monitor
- ❏ Extension cord, and grounded plug adapter, if needed
- ❏ Videos—American Red Cross *Lifeguarding Today* (654114)
  American Red Cross *Community First Aid* (652035)
  American Red Cross *CPR for the Professional Rescuer* (252051)*
- ❏ Rescue tubes (one rescue tube per two or three participants)
- ❏ Backboards with a minimum of three straps and a commercial head immobilizer attached (one backboard per five participants)
- ❏ Decontamination supplies: Decontaminating solution, gauze pads, soap and water, baby-bottle brush, basins or buckets, nonsterile disposable gloves, goggles, and any accessories recommended by the manikin manufacturer*
- ❏ Chalkboard, chalk, and eraser, or
- ❏ Newsprint (flip chart) and marker pens plus easel or tape
- ❏ Manikins of each body type (one per two or three participants)*
- ❏ Blankets or mats (one per two or three participants)*
- ❏ Resuscitation masks (one per two or three participants)*
- ❏ Mouthpiece (one per participant)*
- ❏ Bag-valve masks (one per two or three participants)*
- ❏ Triangular bandages (four per two or three participants)

- ❏ Gauze
- ❏ Roller gauze (two 3-inch gauze pads per two or three participants)
- ❏ Rigid splint (magazine, cardboard, or board) (one per two or three participants)
- ❏ A box or envelope in which to collect Participant Course Evaluations

For each Participant

- ❏ Name tag (optional)
- ❏ Pencil and/or pen
- ❏ Written exam A or B and answer sheet (Appendix S)
- ❏ Copy of alternate exam and answer sheet
- ❏ American Red Cross *Lifeguarding Today* participant's manual (654110)
- ❏ American Red *Cross CPR for the Professional Rescuer* participant's manual (652048)*
- ❏ Swimsuit and towel

For the Instructor

- ❏ American Red Cross identification
- ❏ Name tag
- ❏ Course roster
- ❏ Course outline
- ❏ Participant's manuals: American Red Cross *Lifeguarding Today* (654110)
  American Red Cross *CPR for the Professional Rescuer* (652048)*
- ❏ American Red Cross *Lifeguarding Instructor's Manual* (654112)
- ❏ Lifeguarding Skills Checklist (Appendix M)
- ❏ Lifeguarding Critical Skills Chart (Appendix N)
- ❏ Watch or clock
- ❏ Instructor Course Evaluation

- ❏ Answer key for each written exam (Appendix S)
- ❏ Extra manikin parts (faces, lungs, etc.)*
- ❏ Course record (Form 6418 and 6418A)
- ❏ Swimsuit and towel

* Specifically for the CPR for the Professional Rescuer course

Waterfront Lifeguarding Module

For the Class

- ❏ Viewing equipment: 1/2" VCR and monitor
- ❏ Extension cord and grounded plug adapter, if needed
- ❏ Video—American Red Cross *Lifeguarding Today* (654114)
- ❏ Rescue tubes (one rescue tube per two or three participants)
- ❏ Rescue board (one rescue board per five participants)
- ❏ Chalkboard, chalk, and eraser, or
- ❏ Newsprint (flip chart) and marker pens plus easel or tape
- ❏ A box or envelope in which to collect Participant Course Evaluations

For Each Participant

- ❏ Name tag (optional)
- ❏ Pencil and/or pen
- ❏ Participant Course Evaluation form
- ❏ Written exam A or B and answer sheet (Appendix S)
- ❏ Copy of alternate exam and answer sheet
- ❏ American Red Cross *Lifeguarding Today* participant's manual (654110)
- ❏ Swimsuit and towel
- ❏ Mask and fins (if the facility or local unit of the American Red Cross is unable to supply masks and fins for each participant, participants are responsible for providing them)

For the Instructor

- ❏ American Red Cross identification
- ❏ Name tag
- ❏ Course roster
- ❏ Course outline
- ❏ Participant's manual: American Red Cross *Lifeguarding Today* (654110)
- ❏ American Red Cross *Lifeguarding Instructor's Manual* (654112)
- ❏ Lifeguarding Skills Checklist (Appendix M)
- ❏ Lifeguarding Critical Skills Chart (Appendix N)
- ❏ Watch or clock
- ❏ Instructor Course Evaluation
- ❏ Answer key for written exam (Appendix S)
- ❏ *Course Record* (Form 6418 and 6418A)
- ❏ Swimsuit and towel

Waterpark Lifeguarding Module

- ❏ Viewing equipment: 1/2" VCR and monitor
- ❏ Extension cord and grounded plug adapter, if needed
- ❏ Video—American Red Cross *Lifeguarding Today* (654114)
- ❏ Rescue tubes (one rescue tube per two or three participants)
- ❏ Backboards with a minimum of three straps and a commercial head immobilizer attached (one backboard per five participants)
- ❏ Chalkboard, chalk, and eraser, or
- ❏ Newsprint (flip chart) and marker pens plus easel or tape
- ❏ A box or envelope in which to collect Participant Course Evaluations

For Each Participant

- ❏ Name tag (optional)
- ❏ Pencil and/or pen
- ❏ Participant Course Evaluation form
- ❏ Written exam A or B and answer sheet (Appendix S)

- Copy of alternate exam and answer sheet
- American Red Cross *Lifeguarding Today* participant's manual (654110)
- Swimsuit and towel

For the Instructor

- American Red Cross identification
- Name tag
- Course roster
- Course outline
- Participant's manual: American Red Cross *Lifeguarding Today* (654110)
- Lifeguarding Skills Checklist (Appendix M)
- Lifeguarding Critical Skills Chart (Appendix N)
- Watch or clock
- Instructor Course Evaluation
- Answer key for written exam (Appendix S)
- Course Record (Form 6418 and 6418A)
- Swimsuit and towel

Head Lifeguard Course

For the Class

- Chalkboard, chalk, and eraser, or
- Newsprint (flip chart) and marker pens plus easel or tape
- A box or envelope in which to collect Participant Course Evaluations

For Each Participant

- Name tag (optional)
- Pencil and/or pen
- Written Exam A or B and answer sheet (Appendix S)
- Copy of alternate exam and answer sheet
- American Red Cross Head Lifeguard participant's manual (654119)

For the Instructor

- American Red Cross identification
- Name tag

- Course roster
- Course outline
- Participant's manuals: American Red Cross *Head Lifeguard* (654119)
- American Red Cross *Lifeguarding Instructor's Manual* (654112)
- Watch or clock
- Instructor Course Evaluation
- Answer key for written exam (Appendix S)
- Course Record (Form 6418 and 6418A)

Community Water Safety Course

For the Class

- Viewing equipment: 1/2" VCR and monitor
- Extension cord and grounded plug adapter, if needed
- Videos — *Water the Deceptive Power* (329475)
  Home Pool Safety: It Only Takes a Minute (329474)
  (Both these videos are optional)
- Different types of personal flotation devices
- Rescue tubes (one rescue tube per two or three participants)*
- Ring buoy*
- Throw bag*
- Lifejackets (one per three participants)*
- Chalkboard, chalk, and eraser, or
- Newsprint (flip chart) and marker pens plus easel or tape

For Each Participant

- Name tag (optional)
- Pencil and/or pen
- American Red Cross Community Water Safety participant's manual (654122)
- Swimsuit and towel*

For the Instructor

- American Red Cross identification
- Name tag
- Course roster
- Course outline
- Participant's manual: American Red Cross *Community Water Safety* (654112)
- American Red Cross *Lifeguarding Instructor's Manual* (654112)
- American Red Cross *'Til Help Arrives* booklet (652025) (optional)
- Watch or clock
- Instructor Course Evaluation
- Course Record (Form 6418 and 6418A)
- Swimsuit and towel*

* Only if doing water session

Lifeguarding Instructor Aide Course

For the Class

- Viewing equipment: 1/2" VCR and monitor, if needed
- Extension cord and grounded plug adapter, if needed
- Videos recommended—American Red Cross *Lifeguarding Today* (654114) American Red Cross *CPR for the Professional Rescuer* (252051) American Red Cross *Community First Aid* (625035) American Red Cross *Instructor Candidate Training* (329740) or *General Orientation* (321867)
- Rescue tubes (one rescue tube per two or three participants)
- Backboards with a minimum of three straps and a commercial head immobilizer attached (one backboard per five participants)
- Rescue boards (one rescue board per five participants) (only if teaching the Waterfront Lifeguarding module)

- Decontamination supplies: decontaminating solution, gauze pads, soap and water, baby bottle brush, basin or buckets, nonsterile disposable gloves, goggles, and any accessories recommended by the manikin manufacturer
- Chalkboard, chalk, and eraser, or
- Newsprint (flip chart) and marker pens plus easel or tape
- Manikins of each body type (one per two or three participants)
- Blankets or mats (one per two or three participants)
- Resuscitation masks (one per two or three participants)
- Mouthpiece (one per participant)
- Bag-valve masks (one per two or three participants)
- Triangular bandages (four per two or three participants)
- Gauze
- Roller gauze (two 3-inch gauze per two or three participants)
- Rigid splint (magazine, cardboard, or board) (one per two or three participants)
- *American Red Cross Aquatics Catalog* (654129) (one per participant)
- *Aide Certificates* (Cert. 3003) (one per participant)
- A box or envelope in which to collect Participant Course Evaluations

For Each Participant

- Name tag (optional)
- Pencil and/or pen
- Notebook
- Self assessment test
- American Red Cross *Lifeguarding Today* participant's manual (654110)
- American Red Cross *CPR for the Professional Rescuer* (652048)
- Swimsuit and towel

For the Instructor

- [ ] American Red Cross identification
- [ ] Name tag
- [ ] Participant's manuals: American Red Cross *Lifeguarding Today* (654110) American Red Cross *CPR for the Professional Rescuer* (652048)
- [ ] American Red Cross *Lifeguarding Instructor's Manual* (654112)
- [ ] Watch or clock
- [ ] Instructor Course Evaluation
- [ ] *Course Record* (Form 6418 and 6418A)
- [ ] Swimsuit and towel

Recommendations on Manikin Decontamination

Excerpted from "Standards and Guidelines for Cardiopulmonary Resuscitation and Emergency Cardia Care," Journal of the American Medical Association, No. 16 (October 28, 1992); 268;2195–2197. Copyright 1993, American Medical Association. Used with permission

SAFETY DURING CPR TRAINING AND ACTUAL RESCUE

Safety during CPR training and in actual rescue situations in which CPR is provided has gained increased attention. This section addresses both these issues. Adherence to the following recommen-dations should minimize possible complications for instructors and students during CPR training and implementation. The recommendations for manikin decontamination and rescuer safety originally established in 1978 by the Centers for Disease Control[1] were updated in 1983 and again in 1989 by the AHA, the American Red Cross, and the Centers for Disease Control to minimize possible complications during CPR training and in actual emergencies.[2,3]

Disease Transmission During CPR Training

The 1980s brought about a dramatic increase in inquiries about the possible role of CPR training manikins in transmitting disease such as human immunodeficiency virus (HIV), hepatitis B virus (HBV), herpes viruses, and various upper and lower respiratory infections, such as influenza, infectious mononucleosis, and tuberculosis. It is estimated that approximately 70 million people in the United States have had direct contact with manikins during CPR training courses. Use of these manikins has never been documented as being responsible for an outbreak or even an isolated case of bacterial, fungal, or viral disease.[4]

However, under certain circumstances manikin surfaces present a remote risk of disease transmission. Therefore, manikin surfaces should be cleaned and disinfected in a consistent way.

There are two important infection control considerations in CPR training. First, practice on manikins can result in contamination from trainee hands or oral secretions. If manikins are not cleaned properly between each use and after each class, these contaminants may be transmitted. Second, internal parts such as the valve mechanisms and artificial lungs in manikin airways invariably become contaminated during use. If not dismantled and cleaned or replaced after class, they may become sources of contamination for subsequent classes. There is no evidence, however, that manikin valve mechanisms produce aerosols even when air is forcibly expelled during chest compression. In addition, a number of manufacturers produce different types of manikins for training purposes. Since these manikins have unique features, instructors and training agencies rely heavily on the manufacturers' recommendations for manikin use and maintenance, which should be carefully followed.

Neither HBV nor HIV is as resistant to disinfectant chemicals as previously thought[5-7]. Studies have shown that the retroviral agent that causes acquired immune deficiency syndrome (AIDS), HIV, is comparatively delicate and is inactivated in less than 10 minutes at room temperature by a number of disinfectants, including those agents recommended for manikin cleaning[8-9]. It is emphasized that there is no evidence to date that HIV/AIDS is transmitted by casual personal contact, indirect contact with inanimate surfaces, or the airborne route. The recommendations that follow adequately protect against transmission of either virus, as well as bacterial and fungal infections.

Recommendations

The following recommendations should be adhered to when conducting CPR training courses:

1. Purchasers of training manikins should thoroughly follow the manufacturer's recommendations and provisions for sanitary practice. These recommendations generally have FDA review and approval.

2. Students should be told in advance that training sessions will involve close physical contact with manikins used by their fellow students.

3. Students or instructors should postpone CPR training if they are known to be in the active stages of an infectious disease, have reason to believe they have been exposed to an infectious disease, or have dermatologic lesions on their hands, mouths, or circumoral areas.

4. Chronic infections such as HBV and HIV persist over an extended period and can be transmitted even when the carrier is asymptomatic. If an instructor wishes to train someone with a known chronic infection of if the instructor has a known chronic infection, precautions should be taken to protect other participants from exposure. This is best accomplished by providing the infected person with a separate manikin not used by anyone else until it has been cleaned according to recommended end-of-class decontamination procedures. Requests for individual manikins should be honored, within reason. Equitable accommodations for all participants are encouraged. In such instances the infected person should have his or her personal physician review the circumstances carefully and indicate whether participation is appropriate.

5. If more than one CPR manikin is used in a particular training class, students should preferably be assigned in pairs, with each pair having contact with only one manikin. This would lessen the possible contamination of several manikins by one person, therefore limiting possible exposure of other class members.

6. Instructors in CPR should practice good hygiene by washing their hands before handling manikins and avoiding eating during class. Procedures for cleaning and maintaining manikins and accessories (e.g., face shields and resuscitation masks) should also be practiced. Manikins should be inspected routinely for signs of physical deterioration, such as cracks or tears in plastic surfaces, which make careful cleaning difficult or impossible. The manikins' hair or clothing should be washed periodically (perhaps monthly or if obviously soiled).

7. During two-rescuer CPR training, there is no opportunity to disinfect the manikin between students when the switching procedure is practiced. To limit the potential for disease transmission during this exercise, the second student taking over ventilation on the manikin should simulate ventilation instead of blowing into the manikin.

8. During training in the obstructed airway procedure, the student uses his or her finger to sweep finger matter out of the manikin's mouth. This action could contaminate the student's finger with exhaled moisture and saliva from previous students or contaminate the manikin with material from the student's finger. When practicing this procedure, the finger sweep should either be simulated or done on a manikin whose airway was decontaminated before the procedure and will be decontaminated after the procedure.

9. Manikins should be cleaned as soon as possible at the end of each class to avoid drying of contaminants on manikin surfaces. Personnel disassembling and decontaminating the manikins should wear protective latex gloves and wash their hands when finished. Disassemble the manikins as directed by the manufacturer. As indicated, thoroughly wash all external and internal surfaces as well as reusable protective face shields with warm soapy water and brushes. Rinse all surfaces with fresh water. Wet all surfaces with a sodium hypochlorite solution; have at least 500 ppm free available chlorine (1/4 cup liquid household bleach per gallon of tap water) for 10 minutes. This solution must be made fresh for each class and discarded after each use. Rinse with fresh water and immediately dry all external and internal surfaces. Rinsing with alcohol will aid drying of internal surfaces, which will prevent the survival and growth of bacterial or fungal pathogens if the manikins are stored for periods longer than the day of cleaning.

10. If used, the individual protective face shield should be changed each time a different student uses the manikin in a training class. Between use by students and after demonstrations by the instructor, the manikin's face and the inside of its mouth should be wiped vigorously. Use a clean, absorbent material (e.g., 4 x 4 inch gauze pad) wet with either the hypochlorite solution described above or with 70% alcohol (isopropanol or ethanol). The surfaces should remain wet for at least 30 seconds before they are wiped dry with a second piece of clean, absorbent material.

The use of alcohols is recommended in this instance as an alternative, since some persons object to the odor of sodium hypochlorite. Although highly bactericidal, alcohols are not considered broad-spectrum agents, and use of alcohols here is recommended primarily as an aid in mechanical cleaning. In a short contact period, alcohols may not be as effective against pathogens, but in the context of vigorous cleaning with alcohol and absorbent material, little viable microbial contamination of any kind is likely after cleaning.

11. Instructors in CPR should be encouraged not to rely solely on the use of a disinfectant to protect themselves and their students from cross-infection during training. Thorough physical cleaning (scrubbing and wiping) should be emphasized as the first step in an effective decontamination protocol. Microbial contamination is easily removed from smooth, nonporous surfaces with disposable cleaning cloths moistened with a detergent solution. There is no evidence that soaking alone is as effective as soaking accompanied by vigorous scrubbing.

If these recommendations are consistently followed, students in each class should be able to use manikins whose cleanliness equals or exceeds that of properly cleaned eating utensils. A higher level of surface disinfection is not warranted, and the recommended disinfectant chemicals (household bleach or alcohol) are safe, effective, inexpensive, easily obtained, and well tolerated by students, instructors, and manikin surfaces when used properly.

The risk of transmission of any infectious disease by manikin practice appears to be very low. Although millions of people worldwide have used training manikins in the last 25 years, there has never been a documented case of transmission of bacterial, fungal, or viral disease by a CPR training manikin. Thus, in the absence of evidence of infectious disease transmission, the lifesaving potential of CPR should continue to be vigorously emphasized and energetic efforts in support of broad-scale CPR training should be continued.

Disease Transmission During Actual Performance of CPR

The vast majority of CPR performed in the United States is done by health care and public safety personnel, many of whom assist in ventilation of respiratory and cardiac arrest victims about whom they have little or no medical information. A layperson is far less likely to perform CPR than health care providers. The layperson who performs CPR, whether on an adult or pediatric victim, is most likely to do so in the home, where 70% to 80% of respiratory and cardiac arrests occur.[10]

The layperson who responds to an emergency in an unknown victim should be guided by individual moral and ethical values and knowledge of risks that may exist in various rescue situations. It is safest for the rescuer to assume that any emergency situation that involves exposure to certain body fluids has the potential for disease transmission for both the rescuer and victim.

The greatest concern over the risk of disease transmission should be directed to persons who perform CPR frequently, such as health care providers, both in the hospital and in the prehospital environment. Providers of prehospital emergency health care include paramedics, EMTs, law enforcement personnel, firefighters, lifeguards, and others whose job-defined duties require them to perform first-response medical care. The risk of disease transmission from infected persons to providers of prehospital emergency health care should be no higher than that for those providing emergency care in the hospital if appropriate precautions are taken to prevent exposure to blood or other body fluids.

The probability that a rescuer (lay or professional) will become infected with HBV or HIV as a result of performing CPR is minimal.[11] Although transmission of HBV and HIV between health care workers and patients has been documented as a result of blood exchange or penetration of the skin by blood-contaminated instruments,[12] to date, transmission of HBV and HIV infection during mouth-to-mouth resuscitation has not been documented.[13]

Direct mouth-to-mouth resuscitation will likely result in exchange of saliva between the victim and rescuer. However, HBV-positive saliva has not been shown to be infectious even to oral mucous membranes, through contamination of shared musical instruments, or through HBV carriers.[14] In addition, saliva has not been implicated in the transmission of HIV after bites, percutaneous inoculation, or contamination of cuts and open wounds with saliva from HIV-infected patients.[15] The theoretical risk of infection is greater for salivary or aerosol transmission of herpes simplex, Neisseria meningitides, and airborne diseases such as tuberculosis and other respiratory infections. Rare instances of herpes transmission during CPR have been reported.[16]

The emergence of multidrug-resistant tuberculosis[17,18] and the risk of tuberculosis to emergency workers[19] is a cause for concern. In most instances, transmission of tuberculosis requires prolonged close exposure as is likely to occur in households, but transmission to emergency workers can occur during resuscitative efforts by either the airborne route[20] or by direct contact. The magnitude of the risk is uncertain but probably low.

After performing mouth-to-mouth resuscitation on a person suspected of having tuberculosis, the caregiver should be evaluated for tuberculosis using standard approaches based on the care giver's baseline skin tests.[21] Caregivers with negative baseline skin tests should be retested 12 weeks later.

Preventive therapy should be considered for all persons with positive tests and should be started on all converters.[22] In areas where multidrug-resistant tuberculosis is common or after exposure to known multidrug-resistant tuberculosis, the choice of preventive therapeutic agent is uncertain, but some authorities suggest two or more agents.[23]

Performance of mouth-to-mouth resuscitation or invasive procedures can result in the exchange of blood between the victim and rescuer. This is especially true in cases of trauma or if either victim or rescuer has breaks in the skin on or around the lips or soft tissues of the oral cavity mucosa. Thus, a theoretical risk of HBV and HIV transmission during mouth-to-mouth resuscitation exists.

Because of the concern about disease transmission between victim and rescuer, rescuers with a duty to provide CPR should follow the precautions and guidelines established by the Centers for Disease Control[24] and the Occupational Safety and Health Administration. These guidelines include the use of barriers, such as latex gloves, and mechanical ventilation equipment, such as bag-valve-mask and other resuscitation masks with valves capable of diverting expired air from the rescuer. Rescuers who have an infection that may be transmitted by blood or saliva should not perform mouth-to-mouth resuscitation if circumstances allow other immediate or effective methods of ventilation.

The perceived risk of disease transmission during CPR has reduced the willingness of some laypersons to initiate mouth-to-mouth ventilation in unknown victims of cardiac arrest. Public education is vital to alleviate this fear. In addition, if such concern is identified, rescuers should be encouraged to learn mouth-to-mouth barrier device (face mask or face shield) ventilation. If a lone rescuer refuses to initiate mouth-to-mouth ventilation, he or she should at least access the EMS system, open the airway, and perform chest compressions until a rescuer arrives who is willing to provide ventilation or until ventilation can

be initiated by skilled rescuers (arriving EMT/paramedics) with the necessary barrier devices.

Although the efficacy of barrier devices has not been documented conclusively, those with a duty to respond should be instructed during CPR training in the use of masks with one-way valves. Plastic mouth and nose covers with filtered openings are also available and may provide a degree of protection.[25] Masks without one-way valves (including those with S-shaped devices) offer little, if any, protection and should not be considered for routine use. Since intubation obviates the need for mouth-to-mouth resuscitation and is more effective than the use of masks alone, early intubation is encouraged when equipment and trained professionals are available. Resuscitation equipment known or suspected to be contaminated with blood or other body fluids should be discarded or thoroughly cleaned and disinfected after each use.[26] Following these precautions and guidelines should further reduce the risk of disease transmission when providing CPR.

References

1. Recommendations for Decontaminating Manikins Used in Cardiopulmonary Resuscitation: Hepatitis Surveillance, Report 42. Atlanta, GA: Centers for Disease Control; 1978:34–36.

2. Standards and guidelines for cardiopulmonary resuscitation (CPR) and emergency cardiac care (ECC). JAMA. 1986;255:2905–2989.

3. The Emergency Cardiac Care Committee of the American Heart Association: Risk of infection during CPR training and rescue: supplemental guidelines. JAMA. 1989:262:2714–2715.

4. Ibid, fn 3.

5. Favero MS, Bond WW. Sterilization, disinfection and antisepsis in the hospital. In: Balows A, Hausler WJ Jr, Hermann KL,

Eisenberg HD, Shadom HJ, eds. Manual of Clinical Microbiology. 5th ed. Washington, DC: American Society for Microbiology; 1991;183–200.

6. Centers for Disease Control. Acquired immune deficiency syndrome (AIDS); precautions for clinical and laboratory staffs. MMWR. 1982;31:577–580.

7. A hospital wide approach to AIDS: recommendations of the Advisory Committee on Infections within Hospitals. American Hospital Association. Infect Control. 1984;5:242–248.

8. Resnik LK, Veren K, Salahuddin SF, Tondreau S, Markham PD. Stability and inactivation of HTLV-III-LAV under clinical and laboratory environments. JAMA. 1986;255:1187–1891.

9. Spire B, Dormont D, Barre Sinoussi F, Montagnier L, Chermann JC. In activation of lymphadenopathy-associated with heat, gamma rays, and ultraviolet light. Lancet. 1985;1:188–189.

10. Ibid, fn. 2.

11. Centers for Disease Control. Guidelines for prevention of transmission of human immunodeficiency virus and hepatitis B virus to health care and public safety workers. MMWR. 1989;38(suppl 6):1–37.

12. Marcus R. Surveillance of health care workers exposed to blood from patients infected with the human immunodeficiency virus. N Engl J Med. 1988;319:1118–1123.

13. Sande MA. Transmission of AIDS: the case against casual contagion. N Engl J Med. 1986;314:380–382.

14. Ibid, fn. 11.

15. Friedland GH, Saltzman BR, Rogers MF, et al. Lack of transmission of HTLV-III/LAV infection to household contacts of patients with AIDS or AIDS-related complex with oral candidiasis. N Engl J Med. 1986; 314:344–349.

16. Hendricks AA, Shapiro EP. Primary herpes simplex infection following mouth-to-mouth resuscitation. JAMA 1980;243:257–258.

17. Centers for Disease Control. Outbreak of multidrug-resistant-tuberculosis—Texas, California, and Pennsylvania. MMSR. 1990;39:369–372.

18. Centers for Disease Control. Nosocomial transmission of multidrug-resistant tuberculosis among HIV-infected persons—Florida and New York, 1988-1991. MMWR. 1991;40:585–591.

19. Haley CE, McDonald RC, Rossi L, Jones WD Jr., Haley RW, Luby JP. Tuberculosis epidemic among hospital personnel. Infect Control Hosp Epidemiol. 1989;10:204–210.

20. Ibid, fn. 19.

21. Dooley SW Jr, Castro KG, Hutton MD, Mullan RJ, Polder JA, Snider DE Jr. Guidelines for preventing the transmission of tuberculosis in health-care settings with special focus on HIV-related issues. MMWR. 1990;39:1–29.

22. Centers for Disease Control. The use of preventive therapy for tuberculosis infection in the United States: recommendation of the Advisory Committee for Elimination of Tuberculosis. MMWR. 1990;39:9–12.

23. Steinberg JL, Nardell EA, Kass EH. Antibiotic prophylaxis after exposure to antibiotic-resistant Mycobacterium tuberculosis. Rev Infect Dis. 1988;10:1208–1219.

24. Ibid, fn. 11.

25. Recommendation for prevention of HIV transmission in healthcare settings. MMWR. 1987;36(No. 25):1S–18S.

26. Ibid, fn. 25.

Risk of Infection During CPR Training and Rescue: Supplemental Guidelines

The American Heart Association and the American Red Cross used the findings from the 1985 National Conference on Standards and Guidelines for Cardiopulmonary Resuscitation and Emergency Cardiac Care to establish their policy on the risk of infection during cardiopulmonary resuscitation (CPR) training and rescue. Findings that support the safety of CPR training and rescue and appropriate risk reduction strategies are presented as an update to the 1985 article. The Emergency Cardiac Care Committee of the American Heart Association incorporated recent advisories from the Centers for Disease Control as well as other information into guidelines that augment earlier recommendations.

(*JAMA.* 1989;262:2714–2715)

FINDINGS from the 1985 National Conference on Standards and Guidelines for Cardiopulmonary Resuscitation and Emergency Cardiac Care are the basis of the official position of both the American Heart Association and the American Red Cross on risk of infections during cardiopulmonary resuscitation (CPR) training and rescue. These guidelines[1] have been augmented by advisories from the Centers for Disease Control released in 1987[2] and 1988[3] and from the National Institute of Occupational Safety and Health in 1989.[4]

The Emergency Cardiac Care Committee of the American Heart Association considered specific issues related to risk of infection associated with both training and on-site rescue. The American Heart Association and the American Red Cross recommend the following guidelines for adoption.

GUIDELINES FOR RESCUERS WITH KNOWN OR SUSPECTED INFECTIONS

Transmission of hepatitis B virus (HBV) between health care workers and patients has been documented. Instruments and patients' open wounds have been contaminated when health care workers with high concentrations of HBV (much higher than that achieved in human immunodeficiency virus [HIV] infections) in their blood sustained a puncture wound while performing invasive procedures or had weeping lesions or small lacerations on their hands. Transmission of HIV from patients to health care workers has been documented in cases of blood exchange or penetration of the skin by blood-contaminated instruments.[5]

Direct mouth-to-mouth resuscitation will likely result in exchange of saliva between victim and rescuer. Hepatitis B-positive saliva has not been shown to be infectious, however, when applied to oral mucous membranes or through contamination of shared musical instruments or CPR training mannequins used by hepatitis B carriers. In addition, saliva has not been implicated in the transmission of HIV after bites, percutaneous inoculation, or contamination of cuts and open wounds with saliva from HIV-infected patients.[6,7]

Performance of mouth-to-mouth resuscitation or invasive procedures can result in exchange of blood between victim and rescuer if either has had breaks in the skin on or around the lips or soft tissues of the oral

413 ∎

cavity mucosa. Thus, there is a theoretical risk of HBV and HIV transmission during mouth-to-mouth resuscitation.[8] It is important to note that the theoretical risk of infection is greater for salivary or aerosol transmission of herpes simplex and *Neisseria meningitidis* and for transmission of airborne diseases such as tuberculosis and respiratory infections.

• *Regardless of the type of infection, rescuers who have an infection that may be transmitted by blood or saliva or who believe they have been exposed to such an infection should not perform mouth-to-mouth resuscitation if circumstances allow other immediate or effective methods of ventilation, such as use of a bag-valve mask.*

GUIDELINES FOR RESCUERS WITH A DUTY TO PROVIDE CPR

The probability of a rescuer's becoming infected with HBV or HIV as a result of performing CPR is minimal.[4] To date, transmission of HBV or HIV infection during mouth-to-mouth resuscitation has not been documented.[9] However, to minimize the risk of transmitting a variety of diseases, mechanical ventilation or barrier devices should be accessible to those asked to provide CPR in the course of their employment. This includes emergency medical service personnel, firefighters, police, and lifeguards, as well as hospital and clinic health care workers.

Although efficacy in preventing disease transmission has not been demonstrated conclusively, masks with one-way valves and bag-valve devices are available, and those with a duty to respond should be instructed in their use during training. Plastic mouth and nose covers with filtered openings also are available and *may* provide a degree of protection against transfer of oral fluids and aerosols. Masks without one-way valves (including those

with S-shaped mouthpieces) and handkerchiefs offer little, if any, protection and should not be considered for routine use. Intubation obviates the need for mouth-to-mouth resuscitation and is more effective than the use of bag-valve-mask devices. Early intubation should be encouraged when equipment and trained professionals are available.

• *Individuals with a duty to respond are reminded of their moral, ethical, and, in certain situations, legal obligations to provide CPR, especially in the occupational setting.*

GUIDELINES FOR THE LAYPERSON

The layperson who responds in an emergency should be guided by individual moral and ethical values and knowledge of risks that may exist in various rescue situations. It is safest for the rescuer to assume that all emergency situations that involve transfer of certain body fluids have the potential for disease transmission for both rescuer and victim.

Intact skin is the primary defense against transmission of blood-borne diseases during CPR. Transmission of HBV or HIV is more likely if the rescuer has lesions, cuts, or sores in or around the mouth or on the hands and has contact with the victim's blood, vomitus that contains blood, and/or saliva that contains blood. A rescuer who believes he or she has had parenteral or mucous membrane contact with the victim's blood or blood-contaminated body fluids should wash promptly and thoroughly and contact a physician.

• *As a minimum action, in situations perceived as high-risk for disease transmission, the lay rescuer should assess the victim's responsiveness, call for help, position the victim, open the airway, and, in the absence of a pulse, perform chest compressions.[10] However, the rescuer should remember that delayed ventilation could mean death or disablement for an otherwise healthy person, while risk to the rescuer, even with a known HBV/HIV-positive victim, is considered very low.*

CPR TRAINING FOR INFECTED INDIVIDUALS

To date, transmission of HBV infection through use of CPR mannequins by HBV carriers has not been shown. Neither has saliva been implicated in HIV transmission. Because of potential breakdown of oral and circumoral mucosa during practice on a mannequin, however, CPR training poses a theoretical risk to class participants. It is recommended that students and instructors adhere to the guidelines that follow.

Acute Infections or Dermatologic Lesions

Acute respiratory infections such as the common cold run a short course, and most breaks in the skin heal naturally or after medical attention. Therefore, students and instructors should postpone CPR training if they (1) are known to be in the active stage of an infection, (2) have reason to believe they have been exposed to an infectious disease, or (3) have dermatologic lesions on their hands or in oral or circumoral areas.

Chronic Infections

Chronic infections such as HBV and HIV persist over an extended period and can be transmitted even when the carrier is asympto-matic. If an instructor wishes to train or to present course completion cards to an individual with a known chronic infection or if the instructor has a known chronic infection, precautions must be taken to protect other participants from exposure. This is best accomplished by providing the infected individual with a separate mannequin that is not used by anyone else until it has been cleaned according to recommended end-of-class decontamination procedures.

• *An individual who has an acute or chronic infection that may be transmitted by blood or saliva must not participate in CPR training until his or her personal physician has reviewed the circumstances carefully and indicated whether participation is appropriate. Because CPR course participants may not know that they have been exposed to an infection, it is imperative that participants and instructors adhere strictly to established procedures for decontamination of the mannequin.*[11] *In addition, requests for individual mannequins should be honored, within reason. Equitable accommodations for all participants in CPR programs are encouraged.*

EDUCATION FOR THE CHRONICALLY INFECTED RESCUER

Individuals with chronic infections should be educated about potential transmission of infection to victims during CPR. Course participants should be made aware of guidelines for rescuers with known or suspected infections. Health risks to the chronically infected rescuer also should be emphasized. If the rescuer's immune system has been altered by any cause, performance of CPR may pose a greater risk to the rescuer. Contact with a victim who is in the active stage of an infection (eg, influenza, tuberculosis, HBV infection, and other respiratory infections) may jeopardize the health of the rescuer with depressed immune function.

GUIDELINES FOR INDIVIDUALS UNABLE TO COMPLETE A CPR COURSE

It is the position of the American Heart Association and the American Red Cross that all reasonable accommodations should be made to provide CPR training to anyone who desires it. It is understood, however, that not everyone will be able to meet the standards required for completion of a CPR course. Such individuals include, but are not limited to, those with physical disabilities that prevent acute ventilation of a mannequin or patient, those unable to perform adequate chest compressions, and those with chronic infections. This may create a dilemma for an individual whose job requires CPR course completion.

Whether an infected worker can care for patients adequately and safely must be determined on an individual basis. The worker's personal physician should make this decision in conjunction with the employing agency and its medical advisers.

• *It is not the role of the American Heart Association or the American Red Cross to lower their course completion standards to accommodate, for purposes of employment, individuals unable to meet these standards. This is an issue that must be resolved by the employer and the employee; thus, the employer must decide whether to waive the CPR course completion requirement. The more important issue for someone who is unable to complete the desired course is whether he or she is able to work in a situation that requires administration of CPR.*

Approved by the Steering Committee of the American Heart Association.

References

1. Standards and guidelines for cardiopulmonary resuscitation and emergency cardiac care. *JAMA.* 1986;255:2905–3044.
2. Centers for Disease Control. Recommendations for prevention of HIV transmission in health-care settings. *MMWR.* 1987;36 (suppl 2):1S–18S.
3. Centers for Disease Control. Update: universal precautions for prevention of transmission of human immunodeficiency virus, hepatitis B virus, and other blood-borne pathogens in health-care settings. *MMWR.* 1988;37:377–382, 387–388.
4. Centers for Disease Control. Guidelines for prevention of transmission of human immunodeficiency virus and hepatitis B virus to health-care and public safety workers. *MMWR.* 1989;38(suppl 6):1–37.
5. Marcus R, the CDC Cooperative Needlestick Surveillance Group. Surveillance of health care workers exposed to blood from patients infected with human immunodeficiency virus. *N Engl J Med.* 1988;319:1118–1123.
6. Fox PC, Wolff A, Yeh CK, Atkinson JC, Baum BJ. Saliva inhibits HIV-1 infectivity. *J Am Dent Assoc.* 1988;116:635–637.
7. Friedland GH, Saltzman BR, Rogers MF, Lesser ML, Mayers MM, Klein RS. Lack of transmission of HTLV III/LAV infection to household contacts of patients with AIDS or AIDS-related complex with oral candidiasis. *N Engl J Med.* 1986; 314: 344–349.
8. Piazza M, Chirianni A, Picciotto L, Guadagnino V, Orlando R, Cataldo PT. Passionate kissing and microlesions of the oral mucosa: possible role in AIDS transmission. *JAMA.* 1989;261:244–245.
9. Sande MA. Transmission of AIDS: the case against casual contagion. *N Engl J Med.* 1986;314:380–382.
10. Lesser R, Bircher N, Safar P, Stezoski W. Sternal compression before ventilation in cardiopulmonary resuscitation (CPR). *J World Assoc Emerg Disaster Med.* 1985;1(suppl 1):239–241.

11. Centers for Disease Control. *Understanding AIDS: A Message From the Surgeon General.* Washington, DC: US Dept of Health and Human Services; 1988.

Appendix I

Sample Letter to Lifeguard Training Participants

On the following page is a sample letter. It can be used to confirm registration and give participants important information about the Lifeguard Training course. If you are teaching the Waterfront or Waterpark modules, Community Water Safety, or Head Lifeguard and wish to send this letter to participants, you will need to modify the contents accordingly.

Date

Dear Course Participant,

Thank you for enrolling in an American Red Cross Lifeguard Training course. The time and place of the class meetings are listed below.

Course Name (specify): _____

Date(s): _____

Time: _____

Place: _____

Directions (if needed): _____

_____

_____

In this course, you will learn about the duties and responsibilities of a lifeguard and how to carry them out in a professional manner. You will also learn a number of lifeguarding techniques, such as how to use surveillance techniques; how to use rescue equipment to help rescue a distressed swimmer, an active drowning victim, and a passive drowning victim; and how to manage a suspected spinal injury victim.

These practices require strenuous activity. If you have a medical condition or disability that might prevent you from taking part in the practice sessions, or if you have any questions at all about your ability to participate fully in the Lifeguard Training course, you should discuss it with the appropriate person at your local chapter or unit before you start the course.

To enroll in a Lifeguard Training course, you must be at least 15 years old. There will also be a precourse session, in which you will be required to pass a skills test. The skills you will perform are as follows:

■ Tread water for 2 minutes, with arms across chest (legs only), in a minimum water depth of 7 feet.

■ Swim 500 yards continuously using each of the following strokes for at least 100 yards each: crawl, breaststroke, and sidestroke. The stroke (s) you use for the remaining 200 yards are your choice.

■ Surface dive, retrieve, and return to the surface a 10 pound object from a water depth of at least 7 feet.

Upon successful completion of the American Red Cross Lifeguard Training course, you will receive an American Red Cross Lifeguard Training certificate. The Lifeguard Training certificate, which includes First Aid skills, is valid for 3 years. Along with the Lifeguard Training certificate you will also receive a certificate in CPR for the Professional Rescuer, which is valid for 1 year.

Sincerely,

(Name)
Lifeguarding Instructor

Facility Layout #1

Facility: 6 lane, 25 yard swimming pool with diving area in the deep end.

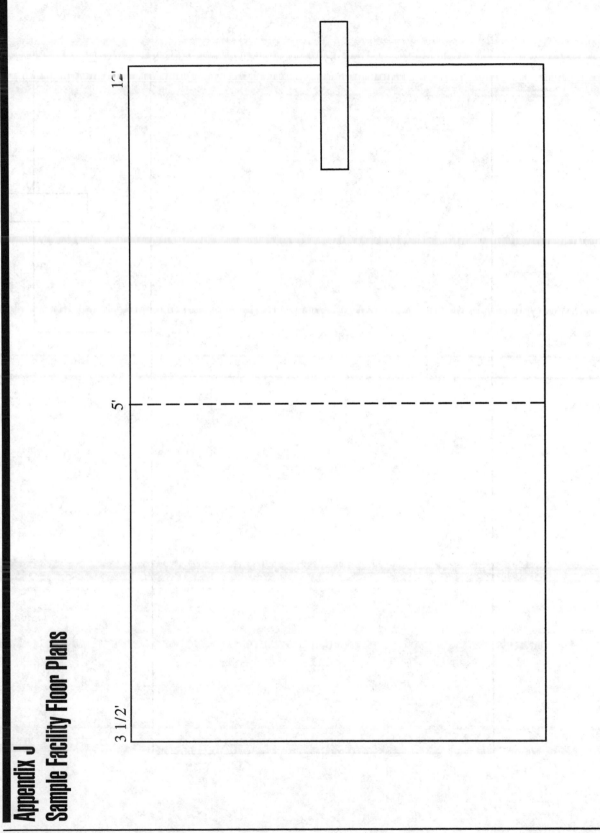

Facility Layout #2

Facility: "L" shaped pool—25 yards long with a diving well.

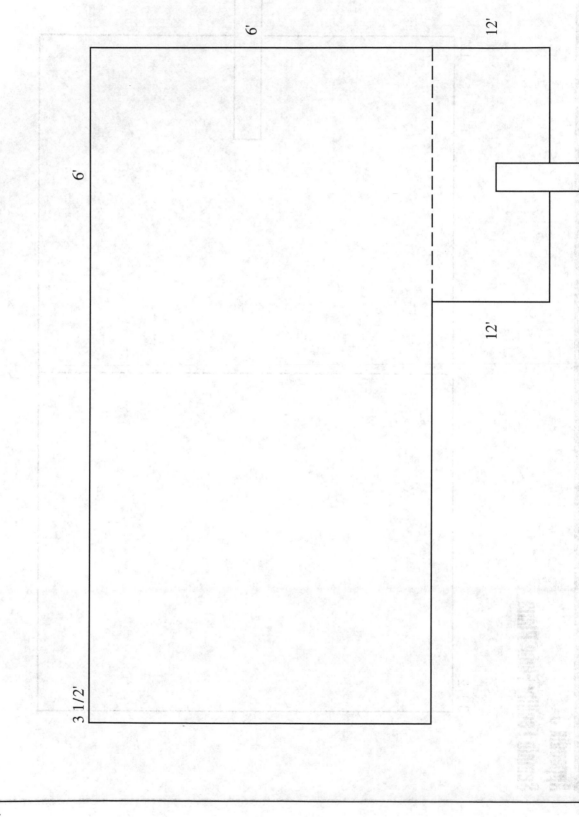

Facility Layout #3

Facility: "Z" shaped pool — 25 yards long with a diving well and a wading pool.

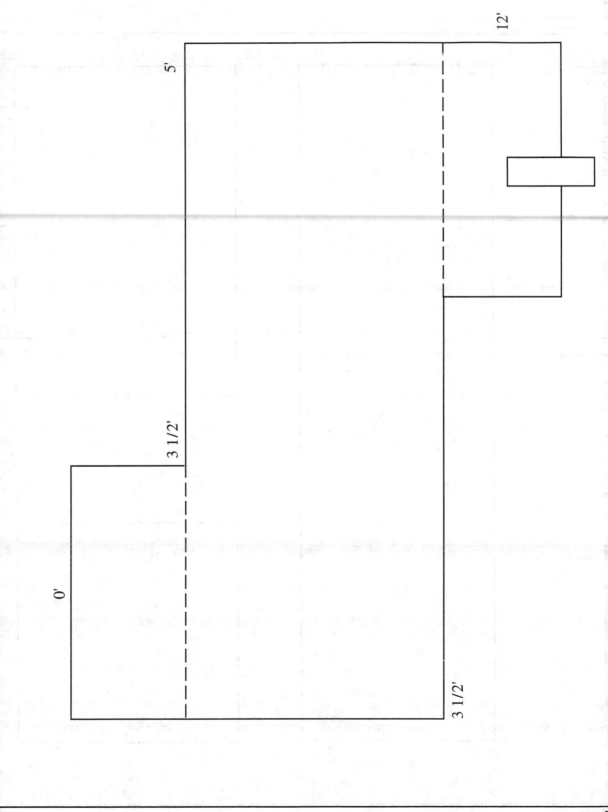

Facility: Multipool Facility—8 lane 50 meter pool—diving well—wading pool

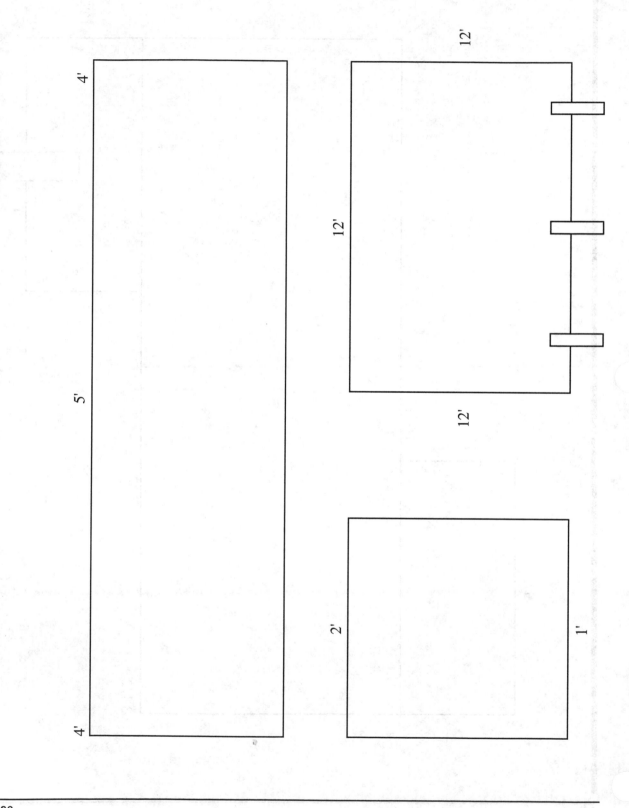

Sample Facility Safety Checklist

	Yes	No	Action Taken	Date of Safety Check	Action Needed
Deck					
Safety equipment in good repair					
Rescue tubes and straps in good repair					
Backboards with head immobilizers and straps readily accessible					
First aid station clean; first aid equipment and supplies accessible and well stocked					
Telephones working properly					
Deck not slippery and in good repair					
Deck clear of patrons' belongings					
All equipment used by patrons stored properly if not in use					
Lifeguard stands clean and in good repair					
Clear of standing water					
Clear of glass objects					
Pool					
Ladders secured properly					
Ladder handles clean and rust free					
Steps not slippery and in good repair					
Ramp not slippery and in good repair					
Drain covers secured properly					
Drain covers clean					
Suction at drains not excessive					
Lifelines and buoys in order					
Water clarity satisfactory					
Water color satisfactory					
Pool free of debris					
Gutters clean					

(Continued)

	Yes	No	Action Taken	Date of Safety Check	Action Needed
Pool (cont'd)					
Water temperature in pool satisfactory					
Water temperature in spa satisfactory					
Recreational Equipment and Play Structures					
Ladders to diving boards not slippery and in good repair					
Rails at diving boards clean and in good repair					
Diving boards clean and not slippery					
Diving apparatus in good repair					
Movable fulcrums locked in forward position					
Removable starting blocks stored properly					
Access to permanent starting blocks restricted					
Play structures clean, in good repair, and not slippery					
Nonmoving parts on play structures secure					
Joints on play structures move freely					
Removable play structures placed at an appropriate distance from the deck and from other structures					
Removable play structures tethered properly; attachment points secure, hooks and connections in good condition with no sharp edges, tethers not worn or frayed					
Seams on play structures have no gaps or leaks					
Inflatable play structures have the correct air pressure					
"Flow-through" inflatable play structures have pump attached securely, located in a safe place, and plugged into the appropriate electrical circuit					
Removable play structures stored properly					

(Continued)

	Yes	No	Action Taken	Date of Safety Check	Action Needed
Recreational Equipment and Play Structures (cont'd)					
Water slides smooth and in good repair					
Water flows properly on slides					
Landing pads under slides in good condition, securely fastened, and with no gaps to cause tripping					
Removable slides placed over water that is deep enough					
Equipment such as kickboards stored properly when not in use					
Chemical Storage Area					
Chemicals stored properly					
Door labeled properly					
Signs legible and in good condition					
Doors locked					
No suspicious odors					
Showers, Locker Rooms, and Rest Rooms					
All areas clean and free of algae					
Floor clean and not slippery					
Shows in good repair (no drips)					
Liquid soap available					
Drains clean					
Wastebaskets empty					
Drinking fountains and sinks clean and in good working order					
Signs in good repair and properly displayed					
Walls clean and free of markings					
Toilets and urinals clean					
Mirrors clean and unbroken					

(Continued)

	Yes	No	Action Taken	Date of Safety Check	Action Needed
Showers, Locker Rooms, and Rest Rooms (cont'd)					
No unpleasant odors					
Toilet tissue available					
Paper towels available					
Doors and windows working properly (including locks)					
No broken pins on locker keys					
All articles removed from lockers daily					
Collapsible shower seats in upright position					
Locker benches clean					
Clear of glass objects					

Appendix L
Participant Progress Log

Name of Participant	Positioning a Victim, Primary Survey	Rescue Breathing, Adult, Child	Abdominal Thrusts, Unconscious Adult, Child	Abdominal Thrusts, Conscious Adult, Child	Checking a Child or Infant, Unconscious	Rescue Breathing, Infant	Back Blows and Chest Thrusts, Unconscious Infant	CPR, Adult	CPR, Child	CPR, Infant	Using a Resuscitation Mask	Using a Bag-Valve Mask	Two-Rescuer CPR, Beginning Together	Two-Rescuer CPR, Changing Positions
SKILLS														
1.														
2.														
3.														
4.														
5.														
6.														
7.														
8.														
9.														
10.														
11.														
12.														

Appendix M

Lifeguarding Skills Checklist

American Red Cross
Lifeguarding Skills Checklist

		Names									
Entries	Stride Jump With Rescue Tube										
	Compact Jump With Rescue Tube										
	Enter the Water										
Approaches	Front Crawl Approach With Rescue Tube										
	Breaststroke Approach With Rescue Tube										
	Feet-First Surface Dive										
	Approach the Victim										
Rescues	Extension Assist From the Deck										
	Swimming Extension Rescue										
	Passive-Victim Rear Rescue										
	Active-Victim Rear Rescue										
	Multiple Victim Rescue										
	Submerged-Victim Rescue										
Lifts	One-Person Lift										
	Two-Person Lift										
Spinal Injury Management	Head & Chin Support (Including deep-water faceup)										
	Head & Chin Support — Submerged Victim										
	Head Splint (shallow water)										
	Head Splint (deep water)										
	Shallow-Water Backboarding										
	Deep-Water Backboarding										
First Aid	Controlling Bleeding										
	Immobilizing Muscle, Bone & Joint Injury										
Final Skills Scenarios	Scenario 1—Active Victim										
	Scenario 2—Submerged Passive Victim										

Unshaded Areas = Specific Skills

Shaded Areas = Critical Skills

Lifeguarding Skills Checklist

		Names								
Waterfront Lifeguarding Module	Run and Swim Entry									
	Walking Assist									
	Beach Drag									
	Head-First Surface Dive									
	Rescue Board—Launch and Approach									
	Rescue Board—Distressed Victim									
	Rescue Board—Unconscious Victim									
Waterpark Lifeguarding Module	Compact Jump With Rescue Tube									
	Run and Swim Entry									
	Walking Assist									
	Front and Back Carry									
	Beach Drag									
	Simple Assist									
	Spinal Injury Management—Winding River									
	Spinal Injury Management—Catch Pool									
	Spinal Injury Management—Speed Slide									
Precourse Session	500-Yard Swim									
	Submerge 7 feet, Retrieve 10-pound object, and return									
	Tread Water for 2 minutes—legs only									

Unshaded Areas = Specific Skills

Shaded Areas = Critical Skills

Appendix N
Lifeguarding Critical Skills Chart

Skill	Start of Skill	End of Skill	Objective	Critical Skill
Stride Jump with Rescue Tube	On the deck	In the water	Enter into water at least 5 feet deep, controlling the rescue tube.	No
Compact Jump with Rescue Tube	On the deck or a permanent elevated structure, such as a lifeguard chair	In the water	Enter into water at least 5 feet deep, controlling the rescue tube.	No
Front Crawl Approach with Rescue Tube	In the water	In the water 15 yards from the starting point	Safely and effectively swim towards the victim while maintaining control of the rescue tube.	No
Breaststroke Approach with Rescue Tube	In the water	In the water 15 yards from the starting point	Safely and effectively swim towards the victim while maintaining control of the rescue tube.	No
Feet-First Surface Dive	On the surface of water at least 7 feet deep	Submerged underwater to a level equal to that of the victim's	Submerged underwater, feet- or legs- first, to a depth equal to that of the victim's.	No
Extension Assist from the Deck	On the deck	On the deck	Safely and effectively extend the rescue tube to the victim while holding the strap.	No
Swimming Extension Assist	On the surface of water at least 7 feet deep	On the surface of the water at least 7 feet deep	Safely and effectively extend the rescue tube to the victim.	No
Active Victim Rear Rescue	On the surface of water at least 7 feet deep	On the surface of the water and moving to safety	Approach the victim from the rear, control the victim with the rescue tube, and move the victim to safety while keeping the victim's airway above water.	Yes
Passive Victim Rescue	On the surface of water at least 7 feet deep	On the surface of the water and moving to safety	Approach the victim from the rear, control the victim with the rescue tube, and move the victim to safety while keeping the victim's airway above water	Yes

Skill	Start of Skill	End of Skill	Objective	Critical Skill
Multiple Victim Rescue	On the surface of water at least 7 feet deep	On the surface of the water and moving to safety	Approach one victim from the rear, control one victim with the rescue tube, and move both victims to safety while keeping both victims' airways above water.	Yes
Submerged Victim Rescue	On the surface of water at least 7 feet deep	At the surface of the water and moving to safety	Submerge to the victim, bring the victim to the surface, control the victim with the rescue tube, and move the victim to safety while keeping the victim's airway above water.	Yes
Two-Person Lift	On the surface of water at least 7 feet deep	On the deck	Safely and effectively remove the victim from the water.	Yes
One-Person Lift	On the surface of water at least 7 feet deep	On the deck	Safely and effectively remove the victim from the water.	Yes
Head and Chin Support — Shallow Water	On the surface of water not greater than 5 feet deep	At a position of safety where effective backboarding procedures can be performed	Maintain in-line stabilization, and move the victim to safety while keeping the victim's airway above water.	Yes
Head and Chin Support — Deep Water	On the surface of water at least 7 feet deep	At a position of safety where effective backboarding procedures can be performed	Maintain in-line stabilization, and move the victim to safety while keeping the victim's airway above water.	Yes
Head and Chin Support —Submerged Victim	Submerged underwater at least 7 feet deep	At a position of safety where effective backboarding procedures can be performed	Maintain in-line stabilization, and move the victim to safety while keeping the victim's airway above water.	Yes
Head Splint — Shallow Water	On the surface of water not greater than 5 feet deep	At a position of safety where effective backboarding procedures can be performed	Maintain in-line stabilization, and move the victim to safety while keeping the victim's airway above water.	Yes
Head Splint — Deep Water	On the surface of water at least 7 feet deep	At a position of safety where effective backboarding procedures can be performed	Maintain in-line stabilization, and move the victim to safety while keeping the victim's airway above water.	Yes

Skill	Start of Skill	End of Skill	Objective	Critical Skill
Shallow Water Backboarding	On the surface of water not greater than 5 feet deep	On the deck	Immobilize the victim on the backboard while ensuring in-line stabilization of the head, neck, and back, and remove the victim safely and effectively from the water.	Yes
Deep Water Backboarding	On the surface of water at least 7 feet deep	On the deck	Immobilize the victim on the backboard while ensuring in-line stabilization of the head, neck, and back, and remove the victim safely and effectively from the water	Yes
Bleeding Control	Identify the need to control and bandage a bleeding wound on a victim	Bleeding is controlled and bandage securely applied	Effectively control bleeding.	Yes
Splinting	Identify the need to immobilize an injured area on a victim	Injured area securely immobilized	Effectively immobilize the injured area.	Yes

Waterfront Lifeguarding Critical Skills Chart

Skill	Start of Skill	End of Skill	Objective	Critical Skill
Run and Swim Entry	From the beach	In the water	With the rescue tube attached to the rescuer, enter the water safely and effectively, and swim towards the victim.	Yes
Walking Assist	In water not greater than 5 feet deep	On the beach	Safely and effectively assist a conscious victim from the water.	No
Beach Drag	In water not greater than 5 feet deep	On the beach	Safely and effectively remove the victim from the water.	Yes
Head-First Surface Dive	On the surface of water at least 7 feet deep	Submerged underwater to a level equal to that of the victim's	Submerge underwater, feet- or legs- first, to a depth equal to that of the victim's.	No
Rescue Board — Launch and Approach	From the beach	In the water 15 yards from the starting point	Safely and effectively enter the water with the rescue board and approach the victim while maintaining control of the rescue board.	Yes
Rescue Board — Distressed Victim	On the surface of water at least 7 feet deep	On the surface of the water and moving to safety	Approach the victim, control and assist the victim onto the rescue board, and move the victim to safety while keeping the victim's airway above water.	Yes
Rescue Board — Unconscious Victim	On the surface of water at least 7 feet deep	On the surface of the water and moving to safety	Approach the victim, control and place the victim onto the rescue board, and move the victim to safety while keeping the victim's airway above water.	Yes

Waterpark Lifeguarding Training Critical Skills Chart

Skill	Start of Skill	End of Skill	Objective	Critical Skill
Compact Jump with Rescue Tube	On the deck or a permanent elevated structure, such as a lifeguard chair	In the water	Enter into water at least 5 feet deep, controlling the rescue tube.	No
Run and Swim Entry	From the beach	In the water	With the rescue tube attached to the rescuer, enter the water safely and effectively, and swim towards the victim.	Yes
Walking Assist	In water not greater than 5 feet deep	On the beach	Safely and effectively assist a conscious victim from the water.	No
Front and Back Carry	In water not greater than 5 feet deep	On the beach	Safely and effectively remove the victim from the water.	Yes
Beach Drag	In water not greater than 5 feet deep	On the beach	Safely and effectively remove the victim from the water.	Yes
Simple Assist	On the surface of water at least 7 feet deep	On the surface of the water and moving to safety	While controlling the rescue tube between the rescuer and a distressed victim, assist the victim to safety.	Yes
Spinal Injury Management — Winding Rivers	On the surface of water not greater than 5 feet deep	At a position of safety where effective backboarding procedures can be performed	Maintain in-line stabilization, and move the victim to safety while keeping the victim's airway above water.	Yes
Spinal Injury Management — Catch Pools	On the surface of water not greater than 5 feet deep	At a position of safety where effective backboarding procedures can be performed	Maintain in-line stabilization, and move the victim to safety while keeping the victim's airway above water.	Yes
Spinal Injury Management — Speed Slides	In the speed side runout	On the deck	Immobilize the victim on the backboard while ensuring in-line stabilization of the head, neck, and back, and remove the victim safely and effectively from the water.	Yes

Appendix O

Sample Incident Report Form

Date of Report: _____ Date of Incident: _____

Time of Incident: _____ A.M. ☐ P.M. ☐

Facility Information

Facility: _____ Phone # (___) _____

Address: _____ City _____ State _____ Zip _____

Personal Data — Injured Party

Name: _____ Age: _____ Gender: Male ☐ Female ☐

Address: _____ City _____ State _____ Zip _____

Phone Number(s): Home (___) _____ Work (___) _____

Family Contact (Name and Phone #): _____ (___) _____

Incident Data

Location of Incident: _____

_____

Description of Incident: _____

_____

_____

Was an injury sustained?   Yes ☐   No ☐

If yes, describe the type of inury sustained: _____

_____

_____

Witnesses

1. Name: _____ Phone #: (___) _____

   Address: _____ City _____ State _____ Zip _____

2. Name: _____ Phone #: (___) _____

   Address: _____ City _____ State _____ Zip _____

Care Provided

Did victim refuse medical attention by staff?   Yes ☐   No ☐

Was care provided by facility staff: Yes ☐   No ☐

Name of person that provided care: _____

Describe in detail care given: _____

_____

_____

_____

_____

Was EMS called? Yes ☐   No ☐   If yes, by whom? _____

Time EMS called: _____   A.M. ☐   P.M. ☐

Was the victim transported to an emergency facility? Yes ☐   No ☐

If yes, where?_____   If no, person returned to activity? Yes ☐ No ☐

_____
Victim's signature (Parent's/Guardian's if victim is a minor):

Facility Data

Number of lifeguards on duty at time of incident: _____

Number of patrons in facility at time of incident: _____

Weather condition at time of incident: _____

Water condition at time of incident: _____

Deck condition at time of incident: _____

Name(s) of lifeguard(s) involved in incident: _____

_____

Report Prepared by:

Name (please print) _____   Position: _____

Signature: _____

Appendix P

Review and Challenge Courses

Guidelines for Conducting the American Red Cross CPR for Professional Rescuers Review Course and Challenge

Review Courses and Challenges

Review courses and challenges are opportunities for people to update their certificates for the course they wish to review without completing an entire course. Individuals who hold a current American Red Cross *CPR for the Professional Rescuer* certificate (certificate #653214) may either enter into the Review Course or Challenge as often as they like as long as their certificate remains current.

Individuals who do **not** hold a current American Red Cross *CPR for the Professional Rescuer* certificate may participate in a challenge **one time only.** If non-certificate holders do not pass the challenge, then they should be referred to their local American Red Cross unit for information on taking the full course. They should not be allowed to attempt the Challenge format again. Non-certificate holders may **not** participate in the Review course option. To teach any review course or conduct a challenge, the instructor must be currently authorized as an American Red Cross Instructor of the course being updated. The instructor should use the same teaching tools in this manual that he or she would use in teaching the regular course.

A review outline is provided in this appendix. Each participant should have the opportunity to view video segments, practice and perform skills for evaluation, and complete the written examination for the course being reviewed. Because this course component depends on the video presentation for instruction, the length of the review is reduced, primarily by the shorter skill check time required and the deletion of lecture and discussions.

A list of completion requirements for the course Challenge is also presented. The list consists of skill segments and written examinations that should be included in the challenge. The Challenge is intended as an opportunity for a person to demonstrate skills and be evaluated. Those taking part in the Challenge should be tested for their ability to perform the skill, not take part in the instructor-led practice sessions or be coached. As an instructor, you should provide the participant with signals of the victim's condition and the participant should provide proper care. The length of the Challenge is dependent on the skill level of the participant.

Review Course

To be eligible, the participant must—
- Posses a current *American Red Cross CPR for the Professional Rescuer* certificate (Stock No. 653214) or
- An *American Red Cross Emergency Response* certificate (Stock No. 653216) or
- An equivalent American Heart Association CPR certificate (issued within one year)

CPR for the Professional Rescuer Review Course Outline
Length: Approximately 7 hours

Lecture	Introduction to Course
Video	*The Professional Rescuer*
Video	*Human Body Systems*
Video	*Primary Survey*
Skill	Primary Survey
Video	*Rescue Breathing*
Skill	Rescue Breathing

Video	*Clearing an Obstructed Airway—Adult and Child*
Skill	Airway Obstruction—Unconscious Adult/Child
Skill	Airway Obstruction—Conscious Adult/Child
Video	*Clearing an Obstructed Airway—Infant*
Skill	Airway Obstruction—Unconscious Infant
Video	*Using a Resuscitation Mask*
Skill	Using a Resuscitation Mask
Video	*Using a Bag-Valve Mask*
Skill	Using a Bag-Valve Mask
Video	*Recognizing a Heart Attack*
Video	*Adult CPR*
Skill	Adult CPR
Video	*Child CPR*
Skill	Child CPR
Video	*Infant CPR*
Skill	Infant CPR
Video	*Two-Rescuer CPR*
Skill	Two Rescuers Beginning CPR Together Two Rescuers: Changing Positions
Read/Write	Written Examination

CPR for the Professional Rescuer Challenge

Skill	Primary Survey
Skill	Rescue Breathing
Skill	Clearing an Obstructed Airway (adult and child, unconscious and conscious)
Skill	Clearing an Obstructed Airway (unconscious infant)
Skill	Using a Resuscitation Mask
Skill	Using a Bag-Valve Mask
Skill	Adult CPR

Skill	Child CPR
Skill	Infant CPR
Skill	Two-Rescuer CPR (beginning together, changing positions
Read/Write	Written Examination

Guidelines for Conducting the Lifeguard Training Review

The American Red Cross Lifeguard Training Review has two formats:
(1) a challenge format and (2) a review course format that is an abbreviated version of the original course. For either format, the instructor must be a currently authorized American Red Cross Lifeguarding Instructor. Individuals who hold a current American Red Cross *Lifeguard Training* certificate (Cert. 653460) and *CPR for the Professional Rescuer* certificate (Cert. 653214)* may enter into the review training, either the Review Course or Challenge as often as they like as long as their certificates remain current. Before taking the Review Course or Challenge, the participant must perform the following skills in a satisfactory manner:

1. Swim 500 yards continuously using each of the following strokes for at least 100 yards each: crawl stroke, breaststroke, and sidestroke. The stroke (s) used for the remaining 200 yards are the participant's choice. There is no time requirement for this skill.
2. Submerge to a minimum depth of 7 feet, retrieve a 10–pound object, and return with it to the surface. There is no time requirement for this skill.
3. Tread water for 2 minutes, using legs only. Participants cross their arms across their chest and place their hands under their armpits.

Challenge Format

The purpose is to provide individuals the opportunity to prove their competencies in specific knowledge and skills. All responsibility for preparedness for the Challenge rests solely on the participants. The instructor's responsibility is to assess and verify the participant's competency. Individuals who **do not** hold a current American Red Cross *Lifeguard Training* certificate and *CPR for the Professional Rescuer* certificate may participate in a challenge **one time only.** If non–certificate holders do not pass the Challenge, then they should be referred to their local American Red Cross unit for information on taking the full course. They should not be allowed to attempt the Challenge again.

In order to challenge the Lifeguard Training course, the participant must also perform the following:

■ Pass the 50–question Lifeguard Training written exam (A or B) from Appendix S in the *Lifeguarding Instructor's Manual,* with a score of 80 percent or higher.
■ Demonstrate properly the following scenarios:
  1. The rescuer finds a victim with severe bleeding on the left lower arm and signs of a possible fracture of the right lower arm. Control bleeding on the victim's left arm and splint the victim's right arm.
  2. Ease into deep water. Swim to a face–down victim who has a suspected spinal injury. Effectively rescue the victim. Return the victim to safety.
■ Pass all scenarios listed in lesson 11 in the instructor's manual.

Evaluation of the scenarios are based upon the Lifeguarding Critical Skills Chart (Appendix N) in the American Red Cross *Lifeguarding Instructor's Manual.*

Review Course Format

The purpose is to provide individuals with an opportunity to review the material within a formal structure. The responsibility for preparing for the final tests is shared by the instructor and the participant. Individuals who do not hold a current American Red Cross *Lifeguard Training* certificate and *CPR for the Professional Rescuer* certificate may not participate in the Review course option.

The outline in these guidelines is to be used in conjunction with the lesson plans in this manual.

Length

The Review course format takes approximately 8 hours for 6 persons to complete.

Testing

The participant must—
■ Pass the 50–question Lifeguard Training written exam (A or B) from Appendix S in the *Lifeguarding Instructor's Manual,* with a score of 80 percent or higher.
■ Successfully complete the skills tests as described in Lesson 11 of the American Red Cross Lifeguarding Instructor's Manual.

Recordkeeping — Challenge Format and Review Course Format

Prepare *Course Record* (Form 6418) and *Course Record Addendum* (Form 6418A) and indicate Lifeguard Training Review (Course Code 3416R) for submission to your Red Cross Unit.

* The Lifeguard Training Review Challenge/ Course Format does not include the CPR for the Professional Rescuer review. See guidelines for conducting the American Red Cross CPR for the Professional Rescuer Review Course and Challenge later in this Appendix.

447 ■

Session 1	Approximate Time
Welcome	5 minutes
Discuss course requirements	10 minutes
Review professional aspects of Lifeguarding	15 minutes
Skills Screening	90 minutes
Conduct a review of the critical skills (see the Lifeguarding Skills Checklist, Appendix M)	60 minutes
Session 1, Total Time	**3 hours**

Session 2	Approximate Time
Patron Surveillance (includes video segment)	30 minutes
First Aid Skills (includes video segment) • Controlling bleeding • Immobilizing muscle, bone, and joint injuries	45 minutes
Spinal Injury Management (includes video segment) • In-line stabilization techniques (shallow and deep water) • Using a backboard (shallow and deep water)	105 minutes
Session 2, Total Time	**3 hours**

Session 3	Approximate Time
Administer the Lifeguard Training written test	60 minutes
Administer the final kills scenarios	60 minutes
Session 3, Total Time	**2 hours**

Appendix Q

Sample Participant Course Evaluation Form

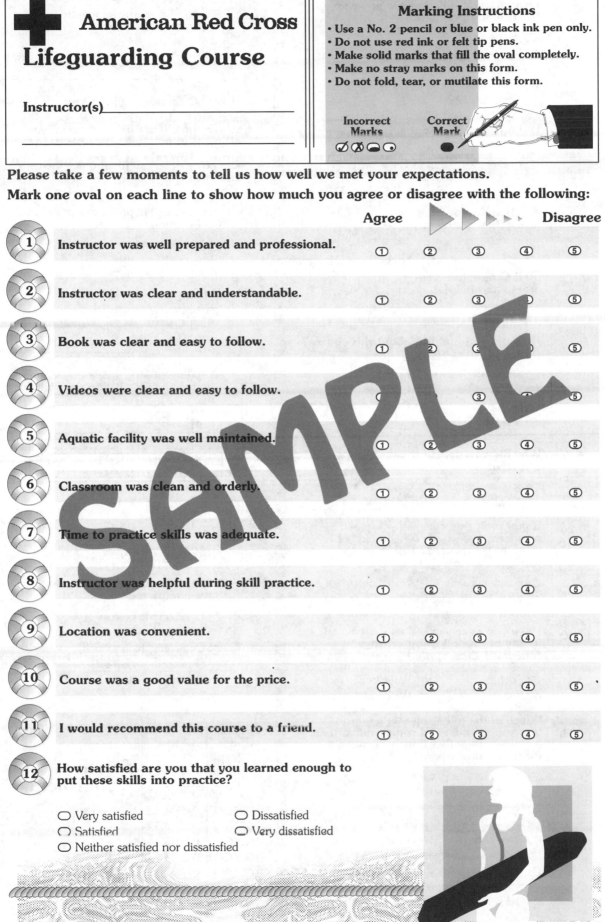

American Red Cross
Lifeguarding Course

Instructor(s) _____

_____

Marking Instructions
- Use a No. 2 pencil or blue or black ink pen only.
- Do not use red ink or felt tip pens.
- Make solid marks that fill the oval completely.
- Make no stray marks on this form.
- Do not fold, tear, or mutilate this form.

Incorrect Marks   Correct Mark

Please take a few moments to tell us how well we met your expectations.

Mark one oval on each line to show how much you agree or disagree with the following:

Agree ▶ ▶ ▶ ▶ Disagree

1. Instructor was well prepared and professional.   ① ② ③ ④ ⑤

2. Instructor was clear and understandable.   ① ② ③ ④ ⑤

3. Book was clear and easy to follow.   ① ② ③ ⑤

4. Videos were clear and easy to follow.   ① ③ ④ ⑤

5. Aquatic facility was well maintained.   ① ② ③ ④ ⑤

6. Classroom was clean and orderly.   ① ② ③ ④ ⑤

7. Time to practice skills was adequate.   ① ② ③ ④ ⑤

8. Instructor was helpful during skill practice.   ① ② ③ ④ ⑤

9. Location was convenient.   ① ② ③ ④ ⑤

10. Course was a good value for the price.   ① ② ③ ④ ⑤

11. I would recommend this course to a friend.   ① ② ③ ④ ⑤

12. How satisfied are you that you learned enough to put these skills into practice?

○ Very satisfied   ○ Dissatisfied
○ Satisfied   ○ Very dissatisfied
○ Neither satisfied nor dissatisfied

Mark Reflex® by NCS EM-156700:321 AAS06 Printed in U.S.A.

13 Overall, how satisfied are you with the training provided?

- ○ Very satisfied
- ○ Satisfied
- ○ Neither satisfied nor dissatisfied
- ○ Dissatisfied
- ○ Very dissatisfied

14 Did you register for this course yourself?

- ○ Yes ▶ ▶ ▶ Go to Question 15.
- ○ No ▶ ▶ ▶ Skip to Question 17.

Agree ▶ ▶ Disagree

15 Registration process was efficient and easy. ① ② ③ ④ ⑤

Agree ▶ ▶ Disagree

16 Red Cross staff was polite and helpful. ① ② ③ ④ ⑤

17 How did you find out about this course? *(Mark all that apply.)*

- ○ Employer
- ○ Poster
- ○ Newspaper
- ○ Radio or TV
- ○ Friend or neighbor
- ○ Local Red Cross unit
- ○ Other ▶ How? _____

18 Why did you decide to take this course? *(Mark one.)*

- ○ Job requirement
- ○ Another reason   Why? _____

19 If you took this course for a job requirement, where do you expect to work as a lifeguard? *(Mark one.)*

- ○ Pool
- ○ Beach (Ocean)
- ○ Waterfront (Lake)
- ○ Waterpark
- ○ Don't know/Not sure

20 Have you ever worked as a lifeguard in any of the following settings? *(Mark all that apply.)*

- ○ Pool
- ○ Beach (Ocean)
- ○ Waterfront (Lake)
- ○ Waterpark

21 Which of the following was a reason that you selected this course rather than a course at another time or location? *(Mark all that apply.)*

- ○ Employer arranged for course.
- ○ Location was convenient.
- ○ Needed course as soon as possible.
- ○ Day of the week was convenient.
- ○ Time of day was convenient.
- ○ Price was more reasonable than other choices.
- ○ Sponsoring agency has a good reputation.
- ○ Someone recommended this course.
- ○ Did not know of any other courses.
- ○ Other ▶ What? _____

22 Do you have any suggestions for improving this course?

_____

_____

A Few Questions About You

The American Red Cross is committed to serving clients from all racial and ethnic groups. To help us verify that clients from all backgrounds are well served, please tell us about your race and ethnicity.

23 Are you of Hispanic origin or background?

- ○ Yes   ○ No

24 Do you consider yourself:

- ○ White   ○ Asian
- ○ Black   ○ Other ▶ What?

_____

25 Do you regularly speak any language other than English with your family?

- ○ Yes   ○ No

26

Age										
⓪	①	②	③	④	⑤	⑥	⑦	⑧	⑨
⓪	①	②	③	④	⑤	⑥	⑦	⑧	⑨

27 Gender:

- ○ Male   ○ Female

28 What is the highest grade that you have completed?

- ○ Eighth grade or less
- ○ Some high school
- ○ Completed high school
- ○ Some college courses
- ○ Completed college
- ○ Graduate school

Chapter Code				Instructor Code			
⓪	⓪	⓪	⓪	⓪	⓪	⓪	⓪
①	①	①	①	①	①	①	①
②	②	②	②	②	②	②	②
③	③	③	③	③	③	③	③
④	④	④	④	④	④	④	④
⑤	⑤	⑤	⑤	⑤	⑤	⑤	⑤
⑥	⑥	⑥	⑥	⑥	⑥	⑥	⑥
⑦	⑦	⑦	⑦	⑦	⑦	⑦	⑦
⑧	⑧	⑧	⑧	⑧	⑧	⑧	⑧
⑨	⑨	⑨	⑨	⑨	⑨	⑨	⑨

Thank you for your help.

Lifeguarding Instructor Self-Assessment

Lifeguarding Instructors: Using the assessment categories (1, 2, 3, and 4) described below, rate yourself as well as you can on each of the following instructor skills.

> 1 — Fully successful
> 2 — Successful
> 3 — Adequate
> 4 — Needs improvement
> N/A — Not applicable

1	2	3	4	N/A	Instruction
					1. Planning and managing physical environment (safety, audiovisual aids, equipment, excess noise, distraction, etc.)
					2. Designing effective block plans and lesson plans.
					3. Adjusting block plans and/or lesson plans for the next class as necessary.
					4. Managing time—allowing enough time for practice, review and evaluation; beginning and ending class on time.
					5. Using appropriate opening and closing activities.
					6. Explaining and presenting material from *Lifeguarding Today* or other American Red Cross books.
					7. Conducting effective practice sessions.
					8. Assessing participant's progress and skill proficiency.
					9. Keeping participants actively involved throughout the lessons.
					10. Conducting effective discussions.
					11. Being sensitive to cultural diversity and individuals with disabilities and other conditions.
					12. Bridging effectively—moving from one topic or skill practice to another.
					13. Utilizing other instructors and instructor aides effectively.
					14. Being aware of your personal image—qualities that add or detract from your other instructor skills.

Appendix S

Written Exams, Answer Sheets and Answer Keys

- Lifeguard Training Exams A and B, Answer Sheets
- CPR for the Professional Rescuer Exams A and B, Answer Sheets
- Waterfront Lifeguarding Exams A and B
  (Answer Sheets for Waterfront Exams follow Waterpark Exams)
- Waterpark Lifeguarding Exams A and B, Answer Sheets
  (Answer Sheets for Waterfront and Waterpark Exams)
- Head Lifeguard Exams A and B, Answer Sheets

American Red Cross Lifeguard Training

Exam A

IMPORTANT: Read all instructions before beginning this exam.

INSTRUCTIONS: Mark all answers in pencil on the separate answer sheet. **Do not write on this exam.** The questions on this exam are multiple choice. Read each question slowly and carefully. Then choose the best answer and fill in that circle on the answer sheet. If you wish to change an answer, erase your first answer completely. Return this exam with your answer sheet to your instructor when you are finished.

EXAMPLE

ANSWER SHEET

xx. (a) (b) (c) ●

xx. As an American Red Cross Lifeguard Training Instructor, your responsibilities include—

a. Representing the American Red Cross in a positive manner.

b. Creating a nonthreatening environment that encourages participants to meet course objectives.

c. Remaining alert to your own cultural and ethnic stereotypes and being creative and flexible in presenting material in an effective and culturally sensitive manner.

d. All of the above.

1. Which of the following is **not** the purpose of a staff debriefing after an incident?

   a. To get a well-rounded picture of what occurred.

   b. To evaluate the effectiveness of existing emergency plans.

   c. To assign blame or criticize.

   d. To generate material for a thorough report of the incident.

2. Before providing care for a victim at the scene of an emergency, check to see that the scene is safe. This may include—

   a. Determining that there is no immediate threat of fire.

   b. Avoiding areas of chemical spills, unless you have proper equipment and training.

   c. Making sure that power is turned off if a person is in contact with a live source of electricity.

   d. All of the above.

3. Which of the following is **not** necessary to create a team whose members work well together.

   a. Shared commitment

   b. Clear safety goals

   c. Effective Communication

   d. Close social involvement between lifeguards and staff

4. To which region of the spine do spinal injuries in diving incidents primarily occur?

   a. Thoracic (upper back)

   b. Cervical (neck)

   c. Lumbar (lower back)

   d. None of the above

5. A lifeguard should clear the pool when—

   a. The lifeguard stand gets wet during a rainstorm.

   b. The deck becomes wet and slippery as a result of rain.

   c. There is an emergency in a single guard facility.

   d. Storm clouds are seen at a distance.

6. Which of the following is **not** an example of the lifeguards' role during an emergency?
   a. Make certain that the zone of responsibility is covered.
   b. To assist the rescuing lifeguard or otherwise give first aid.
   c. To inspect all safety and rescue equipment on a daily basis and to repair or replace such equipment as needed.
   d. To decide if the victim's condition requires calling EMS and to make sure the call is made.

7. In a multiple-victim situation in deep water, the best safety arrangement is—
   a. Two lifeguards without rescue tubes.
   b. One lifeguard working alone without a rescue tube.
   c. One lifeguard for each victim, with one rescue tube per lifeguard.
   d. One lifeguard working alone with a rescue tube.

8. A lifeguard's primary responsibilities include—
   a. Preventing injuries by minimizing or eliminating hazardous situations or behaviors.
   b. Recognizing and responding quickly and effectively to all emergency situations.
   c. Enforcing all rules and regulations of the facility.
   d. All of the above.

9. The harmful effects of the sun's ultraviolet rays can be reduced by—
   a. Wearing light colored clothing and head protection.
   b. Not using a sunscreen.
   c. Not wearing sunglasses.
   d. Staying in the water

10. After an incident in which the facility was closed—
    a. It can reopen immediately.
    b. Patrons must leave the facility.
    c. It should not be reopened until all required staff and equipment are available.
    d. The facility must stay closed for the rest of the day.

11. Lifeguards should deal with hazardous areas at their facility by—
    a. Keeping hazardous areas secret so patrons won't be alarmed.
    b. Whistling every time anyone goes near a hazardous area.
    c. Not being concerned about hazardous areas because they are trained to handle emergencies.
    d. Identifying hazardous areas, keeping patrons away from them, and attempting to correct them.

12. The swimming extension rescue, the active victim rear rescue, and the passive victim rear rescue are all rescue skills used for—
    a. Multiple victims.
    b. Submerged victims.
    c. Spinal injury victims.
    d. Victims at or near the surface.

13. When a patron asks you about a rule while you are engaged in surveillance, you should—
    a. Devote your full attention to the patron.
    b. Briefly explain the rule while maintaining your surveillance.
    c. Tell patron to ask another lifeguard who is also on duty.
    d. Ignore the patron because of your responsibilities.

14. Information given in an incident report should **not include** which of the following?

    a. Rescue, assistance, or aid given.

    b. Personal opinions and assumptions about what happened.

    c. Narrative statements by witnesses.

    d. a and b

15. Which of the following describes the sequence a lifeguard should take when responding to an emergency?

    a. Recognize emergency, alert others, rescue victim, call EMS if necessary.

    b. Recognize emergency, call EMS, alert other lifeguards, rescue victim, notify management.

    c. Alert others, recognize victim's characteristics, ensure the scene is safe, rescue victim, call EMS

    d. Applying rubbing alcohol.

16. Which pair of injuries is the most serious?

    a. Broken arms and legs.

    b. Headache and cramp.

    c. Near drowning/drowning and spinal injury.

    d. Heat and cold related injuries.

17. The ability to cover another lifeguard's area of responsibility in the event of an emergency is known as—

    a. Zone coverage

    b. Backup coverage

    c. Media coverage

    d. Total coverage

18. Which of the following promotes an atmosphere of safety in the facility?

    a. All of the below

    b. Lifeguards who reinforce facility rules

    c. Lifeguards who gain confidence of patrons

    d. Lifeguards who look professional

19. The primary purpose of rules is to—
    a. Make guarding the facility more difficult.
    b. Provide for the safety of the patrons while allowing them to enjoy themselves.
    c. Have everyone do the same activity in the water.
    d. Give the lifeguards reasons to remove people from the facility.

20. Which of the following best describes the correct sequences for any rescue?
    a. 1. Activate emergency action plan
       2. Perform appropriate rescue
       3. Provide emergency care as needed
       4. Remove victim from water
    b. 1. Activate emergency action plan
       2. Perform appropriate rescue
       3. Move victim to safety
       4. Provide emergency care as needed
    c. 1. Enter the water
       2. Activate emergency action plan
       3 Perform appropriate rescue
       4. Move victim to safety
    d. 1. Position victim face up
       2. Provide in-line stabilization
       3. Activate emergency action plan
       4. Check for consciousness and breathing
       5. Immobilize on a backboard
       6. Remove from water

21. Which of the following is a characteristic of an active drowning victim?
    a. Struggles to keep the face above the water in an effort to breathe.
    b. Arms extended to the sides and pressing down for support. NO supporting kick.
    c. Calls and waves for help.
    d. A vertical body position in the water.

22. You notice a person in the water whose body is diagonal and who is able to breathe and wave. The arms and legs are moving to keep the person's head above water, but there is no forward progress. This person is probably—
    a. An active drowning victim.
    b. A passive drowning victim.
    c. A distressed swimmer.
    d. A spinal injury victim.

23. The most important function of a professional lifeguard is to—
    a. Protect lives.
    b. Engage in public relations of the facility
    c. Perform as many maintenance tasks as possible.
    d. Keep the facility clean.

24. Which technique(s) would you use for a victim of a suspected spinal injury found facedown near the surface of water that is 5 feet deep?
    a. Head and chin support
    b. Head splint technique
    c. a or b
    d. Hip and shoulder technique

25. Which of the following sequences best describes an emergency action plan for suspected spinal injury?

a. 1. Activate emergency action plan
   2. Position victim face up
   3. Check for consciousness and breathing
   4. Move to shallow water
   5. Provide in-line stabilization
   6. Immobilize victim on a backboard

b. 1. Provide in-line stabilization
   2. Check for consciousness and breathing
   3. Activate emergency action plan
   4. Move to shallow water
   5. Immobilize victim on a backboard
   6. Remove from water

c. 1. Activate emergency action plan
   2. Provide in-line stabilization
   3. Position victim face up
   4. Check for consciousness and breathing
   5. Move to shallow water
   6. Immobilize victim on a backboard

d. 1. Position victim face up
   2. Provide in-line stabilization
   3. Activate emergency action plan
   4. Check for consciousness and breathing
   5. Immobilize on a backboard
   6. Remove from water

26. The purpose of dressings and bandages is to—
    a. Reduce the victim's pain.
    b. Reduce internal bleeding.
    c. Make it easier to take the victim to the hospital.
    d. Help control bleeding and prevent infection.

27. What should you do for a victim of heat exhaustion?
    a. Force the victim to quickly drink a lot of water.
    b. Get the victim out of the heat and into a cooler place.
    c. Put more layers of clothing on the victim as a protection against the heat.
    d. All of the above.

28. Which is the first step in caring for bleeding wounds?
    a. Apply direct pressure with a clean or sterile dressing.
    b. Apply pressure at a pressure point.
    c. Add bulky dressings to reinforce blood-soaked bandages.
    d. Care for shock.

29. Your first step in controlling severe bleeding should be to—
    a. Apply a pressure bandage.
    b. Apply direct pressure against the wound.
    c. Apply pressure to a pressure point.
    d. Elevate the wound above the level of the heart.

30. How can you reduce the risk of disease transmission when caring for open, bleeding wounds?
    a. Wash your hands before and immediately after giving care.
    b. Avoid direct contact with blood.
    c. Use protective barriers such as gloves or plastic wrap.
    d. All of the above.

31. What should be your first concern at a scene where a person has been seriously burned?
    a. Cooling the burned area
    b. Checking the victim's breathing and pulse
    c. Calling your local emergency phone number
    d. Checking the scene for safety

32. You find a person at the bottom of the stairs. He appears to have fallen and seems badly hurt. After sending someone for help, you would—
    a. Position the victim on his back with the head slightly elevated.
    b. Roll the victim onto his stomach, keeping the head and back in a straight line.
    c. Roll the victim onto one side.
    d. Hold the victim's head to keep it from moving.

33. When caring for a victim who is having a seizure, you should—
    a. Try to hold the person still.
    b. Always keep the victim lying on his or her stomach.
    c. Place a spoon between the person's teeth.
    d. Remove nearby objects that might cause injury.

34. Two children collide in the hall. Although there is no visible bleeding, the upper left leg of one child is very red and swelling fast. This type of wound is a—
    a. Cut.
    b. Bruise.
    c. Puncture.
    d. Scrape.

35. A woman has fallen and injured her ankle. She says she heard something snap. She looks pale and is sweating. What should you do?

    a. Care for the injury as if it were serious.

    b. Have the victim try to walk with the injured ankle.

    c. Apply heat and elevate the injury.

    d. Apply a dressing and loosely bandage.

36. Which should be part of your care for a severely bleeding open wound?

    a. Allow the wound to bleed to minimize infection.

    b. Remove any blood-soaked dressings.

    c. Use a tourniquet to stop all blood flow.

    d. Apply direct pressure and elevate the injured area (if no broken bones).

37. Most injuries are due to situations that—

    a. You have no control over or could not have been prevented.

    b. Involve five or more people.

    c. You have some control over or could have been prevented.

    d. Involve water sports.

38. A lifeguard who is diabetic is drowsy and seems confused. He is not sure if he took his insulin that day. What should you do?

    a. Suggest he rest for an hour or so.

    b. Tell him to go take his insulin.

    c. Give him some sugar.

    d. a and b.

39 Why should you cover burns with a clean or sterile dressing?

    a. To cool the burned area

    b. To keep the burned area warm

    c. To identify the burned area

    d. To prevent infection

40. Which is a critical, life-threatening burn?

    a. A sunburn on the upper back

    b. A burn with a few open blisters

    c. A blistered burn covering most of the face

    d. A burn that has no open blisters

41. A victim has a large piece of glass sticking out of her leg. You should—

    a. Place a dressing over the entire area and bandage.

    b. Leave the glass in her leg and control bleeding around the glass.

    c. Remove the glass and then control bleeding.

    d. a and b.

42. A lifeguard has just splashed a chemical on his face. After sending someone to call for an ambulance, you would—

    a. Cover the burned area.

    b. Have the victim stay calm until the ambulance arrives.

    c. Flush the burned area with water until the ambulance arrives.

    d. Immediately drive the victim to the hospital.

43. Splint an injury to a muscle, bone, or joint only when—

    a. You see a deformed area.

    b. You have to move or transport the victim.

    c. You have splinting materials available.

    d. The victim is in pain.

44. A child running in the locker room has fallen and hit his stomach. He has just vomited and now appears to be coughing up blood. He is breathing very quickly, and his pulse is fast and weak. What is most likely wrong?
    a. He is having a seizure.
    b. He is having a heart attack.
    c. He has internal bleeding.
    d. He is having a diabetic emergency.

45. What should you do if you think a victim has serious internal bleeding?
    a. Apply heat to the injured area.
    b. Give fluids to drink to replace blood loss.
    c. Place the victim in a sitting position.
    d. Call your local emergency phone number for help.

46. A victim has lost a lot of blood through a deep cut in his leg. He is breathing fast and seems pale and restless. He is probably—
    a. Having a stroke.
    b. In shock.
    c. Having a heart attack.
    d. Choking.

47. You have tried to control a victim's bleeding with direct pressure and elevation, but bleeding does not stop. Where would you apply pressure to slow the flow of blood to a wound on the forearm?
    a. Inside of the arm midway between the shoulder and elbow
    b. Outside of the arm midway between the shoulder and elbow
    c. On the inside of the elbow
    d. Any of the above will slow the flow of blood

48. You suspect that a person has been poisoned. She is conscious. Your first call should be to—
    a. The hospital emergency department.
    b. The victim's physician.
    c. The Poison Control Center or your local emergency phone number.
    d. The local pharmacy.

49. In general, a splint should be—
    a. Tied with cravats over the injured area.
    b. Loose, so that the victim can still move the injured limb.
    c. Snug, but not so tight that it slows circulation.
    d. None of the above.

50. When caring for a victim with hypothermia, you should—
    a. Give coffee if fully conscious.
    b. Rewarm the body as quickly as possible.
    c. Rewarm the body gradually.
    d. All of the above.

Name _____   Date _____

DIRECTIONS: Fill in the correct answer for each question.

1. (a) (b) (c) (d)   26. (a) (b) (c) (d)
2. (a) (b) (c) (d)   27. (a) (b) (c) (d)
3. (a) (b) (c) (d)   28. (a) (b) (c) (d)
4. (a) (b) (c) (d)   29. (a) (b) (c) (d)
5. (a) (b) (c) (d)   30. (a) (b) (c) (d)
6. (a) (b) (c) (d)   31. (a) (b) (c) (d)
7. (a) (b) (c) (d)   32. (a) (b) (c) (d)
8. (a) (b) (c) (d)   33. (a) (b) (c) (d)
9. (a) (b) (c) (d)   34. (a) (b) (c) (d)
10. (a) (b) (c) (d)   35. (a) (b) (c) (d)
11. (a) (b) (c) (d)   36. (a) (b) (c) (d)
12. (a) (b) (c) (d)   37. (a) (b) (c) (d)
13. (a) (b) (c) (d)   38. (a) (b) (c) (d)
14. (a) (b) (c) (d)   39. (a) (b) (c) (d)
15. (a) (b) (c) (d)   40. (a) (b) (c) (d)
16. (a) (b) (c) (d)   41. (a) (b) (c) (d)
17. (a) (b) (c) (d)   42. (a) (b) (c) (d)
18. (a) (b) (c) (d)   43. (a) (b) (c) (d)
19. (a) (b) (c) (d)   44. (a) (b) (c) (d)
20. (a) (b) (c) (d)   45. (a) (b) (c) (d)
21. (a) (b) (c) (d)   46. (a) (b) (c) (d)
22. (a) (b) (c) (d)   47. (a) (b) (c) (d)
23. (a) (b) (c) (d)   48. (a) (b) (c) (d)
24. (a) (b) (c) (d)   49. (a) (b) (c) (d)
25. (a) (b) (c) (d)   50. (a) (b) (c) (d)

You may wish to go back and check your answers to be sure that you matched the right answer with the right question.

American Red Cross Lifeguard Training

IMPORTANT. Read all instructions before beginning this exam.

INSTRUCTIONS: Mark all answers in pencil on the separate answer sheet. **Do not write on this exam.** The questions on this exam are multiple choice. Read each question slowly and carefully. Then choose the best answer and fill in that circle on the answer sheet. If you wish to change an answer, erase your first answer completely. Return this exam with your answer sheet to your instructor when you are finished.

EXAMPLE

ANSWER SHEET

xx （a）（b）（c）●

---

xx. Why does the American Red Cross teach this course?

   a. To help people stay calm in emergencies

   b. To help people make appropriate decisions when they confront an emergency

   c. To help people in an emergency keep a victim's injuries from getting worse until EMS arrives

   d. All of the above

1. A lifeguard should clear the pool when—

    a. The lifeguard stand gets wet during a rainstorm.

    b. The deck becomes wet and slippery as a result of rain.

    c. There is an emergency in a single guard facility.

    d. Storm clouds are seen at a distance.

2. Before providing care for a victim at the scene of an emergency, check to see that the scene is safe. This may include—

    a. Determining that there is no immediate threat of fire.

    b. Avoiding areas of chemical spills, unless you have proper equipment and training.

    c. Making sure that power is turned off if a person is in contact with a live source of electricity.

    d. All of the above.

3. Which of the following is **NOT** necessary to create a team whose members work well together.

    a. Shared commitment

    b. Clear safety goals

    c. Effective communication

    d. Close social involvement between lifeguards and staff

4. The harmful effects of the sun's ultraviolet rays can be reduced by—

    a. Wearing light-colored clothing and head protection.

    b. Not using a sunscreen.

    c. Not wearing sunglasses.

    d. Staying in the water.

5. Which of the following is NOT an example of the lifeguards' role during an emergency?

   a. To make certain that the zone of responsibility is covered

   b. To assist the rescuing lifeguard or otherwise give first aid

   c. To inspect all safety and rescue equipment on a daily basis and to repair or replace such equipment as needed

   d. To decide if the victim's condition requires calling EMS and to make sure the call is made

6. In a multiple-victim situation in deep water, the best safety arrangement is—

   a. Two lifeguards without rescue tubes.

   b. One lifeguard working alone without a rescue tube.

   c. One lifeguard for each victim, with one rescue tube per lifeguard.

   d. One lifeguard working alone with a rescue tube.

7. Which pair of injuries is the most serious?

   a. Broken arms and legs

   b. Headache and cramp

   c. Near drowning/drowning and spinal injury

   d. Heat and cold related injuries

8. Which of the following describes the sequence a lifeguard should take when responding to an emergency?

   a. Recognize emergency, alert others, rescue victim, call EMS if necessary.

   b. Recognize emergency, call EMS, alert other lifeguards, rescue victim, notify management.

   c. Alert others, recognize victim's characteristics, ensure the scene is safe, rescue victim, call EMS.

   d. Applying rubbing alcohol.

9. Lifeguards should deal with hazardous areas at their facility by—

    a. Keeping hazardous areas secret so patrons won't be alarmed.

    b. Whistling every time anyone goes near a hazardous area.

    c. Not being concerned about hazardous areas because they are trained to handle emergencies.

    d. Identifying hazardous areas, keeping patrons away from them, and attempting to correct them.

10. To which region of the spine do spinal injuries in diving incidents primarily occur?

    a. Thoracic (upper back)

    b. Cervical (neck)

    c. Lumbar (lower back)

    d. None of the above

11. After an incident in which the facility was closed

    a. It can reopen immediately.

    b. Patrons must leave the facility.

    c. It should not be reopened until all required staff and equipment are available.

    d. The facility must stay closed for the rest of the day.

12. You notice a person in the water whose body is diagonal and who is able to breathe and wave. The arms and legs are moving to keep the person's head above water, but there is no forward progress. This person is probably—

    a. An active drowning victim.

    b. A passive drowning victim.

    c. A distressed swimmer.

    d. A spinal injury victim.

13. The swimming extension rescue, the active victim rear rescue, and the passive victim rear rescue are all rescue skills used for—

    a. Multiple victims.

    b. Submerged victims.

    c. Spinal injury victims.

    d. Victims at or near the surface.

14. When a patron asks you about a rule while you are engaged in surveillance, you should—

    a. Devote your full attention to the patron.

    b. Briefly explain the rule while maintaining your surveillance.

    c. Tell patron to ask another lifeguard who is also on duty.

    d. Ignore the patron because of your responsibilities.

15. A lifeguard's primary responsibilities include—

    a. Preventing injuries by minimizing or eliminating hazardous situations or behaviors.

    b. Recognizing and responding quickly and effectively to all emergency situations.

    c. Enforcing all rules and regulations of the facility.

    d. All of the above.

16. Which of the following is NOT the purpose of a staff debriefing after an incident?

    a. To get a well-rounded picture of what occurred

    b. To evaluate the effectiveness of existing emergency plans

    c. To generate material for a thorough report of the incident

    d. To assign blame or criticize

17. Which techniques would you use for a victim of a suspected spinal injury found facedown near the surface of water that is 5 feet deep?

    a. Head and chin support

    b. Head splint technique

    c. a or b

    d. Hip and shoulder technique

18. The primary purpose of rules is to—

    a. Make guarding the facility more difficult.

    b. Give the lifeguards reasons to remove people from the facility.

    c. Have everyone do the same activity in the water.

    d. Provide for the safety of the patrons while allowing them to enjoy themselves.

19. The ability to cover another lifeguard's area of responsibility in the event of an emergency is known as—

    a. Zone coverage.

    b. Total coverage.

    c. Media coverage.

    d. Backup coverage.

20. Which of the following sequences best describes an emergency action plan for suspected spinal injury?

    a. 1. Activate emergency action plan.

        2. Position victim face up.

        3. Check for consciousness and breathing.

        4. Move to shallow water.

        5. Provide in-line stabilization.

        6. Immobilize victim on a backboard.

    b. 1. Provide in-line stabilization.

        2. Check for consciousness and breathing.

        3. Activate emergency action plan.

        4. Move to shallow water.

        5. Immobilize victim on a backboard.

        6. Remove from water.

    c. 1. Activate emergency action plan.

        2. Provide in-line stabilization.

        3. Position victim face up.

        4. Check for consciousness and breathing.

        5. Move to shallow water.

        6. Immobilize victim on a backboard.

    d. 1. Position victim face up.

        2. Provide in-line stabilization.

        3. Activate emergency action plan.

        4. Check for consciousness and breathing.

        5. Immobilize on a backboard.

        6. Remove from water.

21. Which of the following is a characteristic of an active drowning victim?

    a. Struggles to keep the face above the water in an effort to breathe

    b. Calls and waves for help

    c. Arms extended to the sides pressing down for support. NO supporting kick

    d. A vertical body position in the water

22. The most important function of a professional lifeguard is to —

    a. Perform as many maintenance tasks as possible.

    b. Engage in public relations for the facility.

    c. Protect lives.

    d. Keep the facility clean.

23. Information given in an incident report should **not** include which of the following?

    a. Rescue, assistance, or aid given.

    b. Narrative statements by witnesses.

    c. Personal opinions and assumptions about what happened.

    d. a and b

24. Which of the following promotes an atmosphere of safety in the facility?

    a. All of the below

    b. Lifeguards who reinforce facility rules

    c. Lifeguards who gain confidence of patrons

    d. Lifeguards who look professional

25. Which of the following best describes the correct sequences for any rescue?

   a. 1. Activate emergency action plan.

      2. Perform appropriate rescue.

      3. Move victim to safety.

      4. Provide emergency care as needed.

   b. 1. Activate emergency action plan.

      2. Perform appropriate rescue.

      3. Provide emergency care as needed.

      4. Remove victim from water.

   c. 1. Enter the water.

      2. Activate emergency action plan.

      3 Perform appropriate rescue.

      4. Move victim to safety.

   d. 1. Position victim face up.

      2. Provide in-line stabilization.

      3. Activate emergency action plan.

      4. Check for consciousness and breathing.

      5. Immobilize on a backboard.

      6. Remove from water.

26. How can you reduce the risk of disease transmission when caring for open, bleeding wounds?

   a. Wash your hands before and immediately after giving care.

   b. Avoid direct contact with blood.

   c. Use protective barriers such as gloves or plastic wrap.

   d. All of the above.

27. Most injuries are due to situations that—

    a. You have no control over or could not have been prevented.

    b. Involve five or more people.

    c. You have some control over or could have been prevented.

    d. Involve water sports.

28. A lifeguard who is diabetic is drowsy and seems confused. He is not sure if he took his insulin that day. What should you do?

    a. Suggest he rest for an hour or so.

    b. Tell him to go take his insulin.

    c. Give him some sugar.

    d. a and b.

29. Which is the **first** step in caring for bleeding wounds?

    a. Apply direct pressure with a clean or sterile dressing.

    b. Apply pressure at a pressure point.

    c. Add bulky dressings to reinforce blood-soaked bandages.

    d. Care for shock.

30. The purpose of dressings and bandages is to—

    a. Help control bleeding and prevent infection.

    b. Reduce internal bleeding.

    c. Make it easier to take the victim to the hospital.

    d. Reduce the victim's pain.

31. You have tried to control a victim's bleeding with direct pressure and elevation, but bleeding does not stop. Where would you apply pressure to slow the flow of blood to a wound on the forearm?

    a. Inside of the arm midway between the shoulder and elbow

    b. Outside of the arm midway between the shoulder and elbow

    c. On the inside of the elbow

    d. Any of the above will slow the flow of blood

32. Your first step in controlling severe bleeding should be to—

    a. Apply a pressure bandage.

    b. Apply direct pressure against the wound.

    c. Apply pressure to a pressure point.

    d. Elevate the wound above the level of the heart.

33. Two children collide in the hall. Although there is no visible bleeding, the upper left leg of one child is very red and swelling fast. This type of wound is a—

    a. Cut.

    b. Bruise.

    c. Puncture.

    d. Scrape.

34. Which should be part of your care for a severely bleeding open wound?

    a. Allow the wound to bleed to minimize infection.

    b. Remove any blood-soaked dressings.

    c. Use a tourniquet to stop all blood flow.

    d. Apply direct pressure and elevate the injured area (if no broken bones).

35. A woman has fallen and injured her ankle. She says she heard something snap. She looks pale and is sweating. What should you do?

    a. Care for the injury as if it were serious.

    b. Have the victim try to walk with the injured ankle.

    c. Apply heat and elevate the injury.

    d. Apply a dressing and loosely bandage.

36. Which is a critical, life-threatening burn?

    a. A sunburn on the upper back

    b. A blistered burn covering most of the face

    c. A burn with a few open blisters

    d. A burn that has no open blisters

37. What should be your first concern at a scene where a person has been seriously burned?

    a. Cooling the burned area

    b. Checking the victim's breathing and pulse

    c. Calling your local emergency phone number

    d. Checking the scene for safety

38. A victim has a large piece of glass sticking out of her leg. You should—

    a. Leave the glass in her leg and control bleeding around the glass.

    b. Place a dressing over the entire area and bandage.

    c. Remove the glass and then control bleeding.

    d. a and b.

39. What should you do if you think a victim has serious internal bleeding?

    a. Apply heat to the injured area.

    b. Give fluids to drink to replace blood loss.

    c. Place the victim in a sitting position.

    d. Call your local emergency phone number for help.

40. Why should you cover burns with a clean or sterile dressing?

    a. To cool the burned area

    b. To keep the burned area warm

    c. To identify the burned area

    d. To prevent infection

41. You find a person at the bottom of the stairs. He appears to have fallen and seems badly hurt. After sending someone for help, you would—

    a. Position the victim on his back with the head slightly elevated.

    b. Roll the victim onto his stomach, keeping the head and back in a straight line.

    c. Roll the victim onto one side.

    d. Hold the victim's head to keep it from moving.

42. A lifeguard has just splashed a chemical on his face. After sending someone to call for an ambulance, you would—

    a. Cover the burned area.

    b. Have the victim stay calm until the ambulance arrives.

    c. Flush the burned area with water until the ambulance arrives.

    d. Immediately drive the victim to the hospital.

43. When caring for a victim who is having a seizure, you should—

    a. Try to hold the person still.

    b. Always keep the victim lying on his or her stomach.

    c. Place a spoon between the person's teeth.

    d. Remove nearby objects that might cause injury.

44. Splint an injury to a muscle, bone, or joint only when—

    a. You see a deformed area.

    b. The victim is in pain.

    c. You have splinting materials available.

    d. You have to move or transport the victim.

45. A child running in the locker room has fallen and hit his stomach. He has just vomited and now appears to be coughing up blood. He is breathing very quickly, and his pulse is fast and weak. What is most likely wrong?

    a. He is having a seizure.

    b. He is having a heart attack.

    c. He has internal bleeding.

    d. He is having a diabetic emergency.

46. You suspect that a person has been poisoned. She is conscious. Your first call should be to—

    a. The hospital emergency department.

    b. The victim's physician.

    c. The Poison Control Center or your local emergency phone number.

    d. The local pharmacy.

47. In general, a splint should be—

    a. Tied with cravats over the injured area.

    b. Loose, so that the victim can still move the injured limb.

    c. Snug, but not so tight that it slows circulation.

    d. None of the above.

48. A victim has lost a lot of blood through a deep cut in his leg. He is breathing fast and seems pale and restless. He is probably—

    a. Having a stroke.

    b. In shock.

    c. Having a heart attack.

    d. Choking.

49. When caring for a victim with hypothermia, you should—

    a. Rewarm the body gradually.

    b. Rewarm the body as quickly as possible.

    c. Give coffee if fully conscious.

    d. All of the above.

50. What should you do for a victim of heat exhaustion?

    a. Force the victim to quickly drink a lot of water.

    b. Get the victim out of the heat and into a cooler place.

    c. Put more layers of clothing on the victim as a protection against the heat.

    d. All of the above.

ANSWER SHEET: AMERICAN RED CROSS LIFEGUARD TRAINING   EXAM B

Name _____ Date _____

DIRECTIONS: Fill in the correct answer for each question.

1. ⓐ ⓑ ⓒ ⓓ	26. ⓐ ⓑ ⓒ ⓓ
2. ⓐ ⓑ ⓒ ⓓ	27. ⓐ ⓑ ⓒ ⓓ
3. ⓐ ⓑ ⓒ ⓓ	28. ⓐ ⓑ ⓒ ⓓ
4. ⓐ ⓑ ⓒ ⓓ	29. ⓐ ⓑ ⓒ ⓓ
5. ⓐ ⓑ ⓒ ⓓ	30. ⓐ ⓑ ⓒ ⓓ
6. ⓐ ⓑ ⓒ ⓓ	31. ⓐ ⓑ ⓒ ⓓ
7. ⓐ ⓑ ⓒ ⓓ	32. ⓐ ⓑ ⓒ ⓓ
8. ⓐ ⓑ ⓒ ⓓ	33. ⓐ ⓑ ⓒ ⓓ
9. ⓐ ⓑ ⓒ ⓓ	34. ⓐ ⓑ ⓒ ⓓ
10. ⓐ ⓑ ⓒ ⓓ	35. ⓐ ⓑ ⓒ ⓓ
11. ⓐ ⓑ ⓒ ⓓ	36. ⓐ ⓑ ⓒ ⓓ
12. ⓐ ⓑ ⓒ ⓓ	37. ⓐ ⓑ ⓒ ⓓ
13. ⓐ ⓑ ⓒ ⓓ	38. ⓐ ⓑ ⓒ ⓓ
14. ⓐ ⓑ ⓒ ⓓ	39. ⓐ ⓑ ⓒ ⓓ
15. ⓐ ⓑ ⓒ ⓓ	40. ⓐ ⓑ ⓒ ⓓ
16. ⓐ ⓑ ⓒ ⓓ	41. ⓐ ⓑ ⓒ ⓓ
17. ⓐ ⓑ ⓒ ⓓ	42. ⓐ ⓑ ⓒ ⓓ
18. ⓐ ⓑ ⓒ ⓓ	43. ⓐ ⓑ ⓒ ⓓ
19. ⓐ ⓑ ⓒ ⓓ	44. ⓐ ⓑ ⓒ ⓓ
20. ⓐ ⓑ ⓒ ⓓ	45. ⓐ ⓑ ⓒ ⓓ
21. ⓐ ⓑ ⓒ ⓓ	46. ⓐ ⓑ ⓒ ⓓ
22. ⓐ ⓑ ⓒ ⓓ	47. ⓐ ⓑ ⓒ ⓓ
23. ⓐ ⓑ ⓒ ⓓ	48. ⓐ ⓑ ⓒ ⓓ
24. ⓐ ⓑ ⓒ ⓓ	49. ⓐ ⓑ ⓒ ⓓ
25. ⓐ ⓑ ⓒ ⓓ	50. ⓐ ⓑ ⓒ ⓓ

You may wish to go back and check your answers to be sure that you matched the right answer with the right question.

American Red Cross CPR for the Professional Rescuer

Exam A

IMPORTANT: Read all instructions before beginning this exam.

INSTRUCTIONS: Mark all answers in pencil on the separate answer sheet. **Do not write on this exam.** The questions on this exam are multiple choice. Read each question slowly and carefully. Then choose the best answer and fill in that circle on the answer sheet. If you wish to change an answer, erase your first answer completely. Return this exam with your answer sheet to your instructor when you are finished.

EXAMPLE

ANSWER SHEET

xx. (a) (b) (c) ●

xx.   Why does the American Red Cross teach this course?

  a.   To help people stay calm in emergencies

  b.   To help people make appropriate decisions when they confront an emergency

  c.   To help people in an emergency keep a victim's injuries from getting worse until EMS arrives

  d.   All of the above

1. Which person in the EMS system has the role of recognizing that an emergency exists, deciding to act, activating the EMS system, and providing first aid care?
   a. Paramedic
   b. Emergency medical technician
   c. Fire fighter
   d. Citizen responder

2. Which person in the EMS system provides the transition between care provided by the citizen responder and that provided by more advanced medical personnel?
   a. EMS dispatcher
   b. First responder
   c. Emergency medical technician
   d. Paramedic

3. The two body systems that work together to provide oxygen for the cells of the body are—
   a. Musculoskeletal and integumentary.
   b. Respiratory and circulatory.
   c. Integumentary and respiratory.
   d. Circulatory and musculoskeletal.

4. Pathogens enter the body through—
   a. Bites by an infected animal or insect.
   b. Inhaling infected droplets in the air.
   c. Direct contact with an infected person's body fluids.
   d. All of the above.

5. Which of these emergency action principles should you implement first at the scene of an emergency?
   a. Do a secondary survey.
   b. Do a primary survey.
   c. Survey the scene.
   d. Call more advanced medical personnel for help.

6. A victim who can answer your question, "Are you O.K.?"—

   a. Is conscious.

   b. Is breathing.

   c. Has a pulse.

   d. All of the above

7. Why should you do a primary survey in every emergency situation?

   a. Because it will protect you from legal liability

   b. Because it identifies conditions that are an immediate threat to life

   c. Because it identifies conditions that could become life-threatening if not cared for

   d. Because it enables you to protect the victim and bystanders from dangers at the scene

8. In what order are the four elements of a primary survey assessed (first to last)?

   a. Consciousness, airway, breathing, circulation

   b. Airway, breathing, circulation, consciousness

   c. Breathing, airway, circulation, consciousness

   d. Circulation, consciousness, airway, breathing

9. In which circumstances should you move a victim before providing care?

   a. There is danger from fire, poisonous fumes, or an unstable structure.

   b. The victim is complaining of pain.

   c. It is impossible to splint fractures or bandage wounds without moving the victim.

   d. The victim is in a position in which more advanced medical personnel will have difficulty giving care.

10. For which of the following individuals should you immediately summon more advanced medical personnel?
    a. A 22-year-old who has had a fever and vomited twice during the night
    b. A 60-year-old experiencing severe knee pain after a morning run
    c. A 40-year-old complaining that he has felt nauseated, sweaty, and short of breath for at least an hour
    d. An 8-year-old who was hit on the leg by a baseball and now has a large bruise

11. Which should you do to keep the airway open when giving rescue breaths if you do not suspect a head injury?
    a. Lift the chin.
    b. Tilt the head back and lift the chin.
    c. Tilt the head back and lift the neck.
    d. Roll the victim onto one side.

12. Which is a sign/symptom of respiratory distress?
    a. Pale or bluish skin
    b. Tingling in the hands
    c. Constriction of the pupils
    d. a and b

13. What are you accomplishing when you provide rescue breathing to a victim?
    a. Artificially circulating oxygenated blood to the body cells
    b. Supplementing the air the victim is already breathing
    c. Supplying the victim with oxygen necessary for survival
    d. All of the above

14. During which step will you determine if a victim requires rescue breathing?
    a. Secondary survey
    b. Survey of the scene
    c. Primary survey
    d. Preparation for transport

15. What must you do to determine if a victim requires rescue breathing?
    a. Check for a pulse in the neck.
    b. Look, listen, and feel for breathing.
    c. Check for bluish or grayish skin color.
    d. Look at the pupils to check for dilation.

16. When you give rescue breaths, how much air should you breathe into the victim?
    a. Enough to make the stomach rise
    b. Enough to make the chest rise
    c. Enough to feel resistance
    d. Enough to fill the victim's cheeks

17. How can you minimize the amount of air forced into a victim's stomach during rescue breathing?
    a. Breathe slowly into the victim when delivering breaths.
    b. Don't pause between breaths unless absolutely necessary.
    c. Press on the victim's stomach while delivering breaths.
    d. Breathe as hard as you can into the victim.

18. When performing rescue breathing, what should you do after giving the first 2 breaths?
    a. Reposition the head.
    b. Check for a pulse.
    c. Check for consciousness.
    d. Repeat the 2 breaths.

19. If your first 2 breaths do not cause the victim's chest to rise, what should you do?
    a. Call for more advanced medical professionals.
    b. Do a finger sweep of the victim's mouth.
    c. Give 2 more breaths with more force.
    d. Retilt the head and try to give breaths again.

20. What should you do for a conscious adult or child who is choking and cannot cough, speak, or breathe?
    a. Give two full breaths.
    b. Do a finger sweep.
    c. Give abdominal thrusts.
    d. Lower the victim to the floor and open the airway.

21. Where should you position your hands when giving abdominal thrusts to a conscious adult or child?
    a. In the middle of the abdomen just above the navel
    b. On the center of the chest
    c. In the middle of the abdomen well below the navel
    d. None of the above

22. After giving abdominal thrusts to an unconscious adult with an obstructed airway, you should—
    a. Give 2 slow breaths and then do a finger sweep.
    b. Check for a pulse, give 2 slow breaths, and then do a finger sweep.
    c. Do a finger sweep and then check for a pulse.
    d. Do a finger sweep and then give 2 slow breaths.

23. What should you do for a conscious infant who is choking and cannot cry, cough, or breathe?
    a. Give 5 back blows and then 5 chest thrusts.
    b. Give abdominal thrusts.
    c. Give back blows until the victim starts to cough or becomes unconscious.
    d. Any of the above is acceptable.

24. How often should you give rescue breaths to an infant or child who is not breathing but does have a pulse?
    a. Once every second
    b. Once every 3 seconds
    c. Once every 5 seconds
    d. Once every 10 seconds

25. Advantages of using breathing devices include—
    a. Reducing the possibility of disease transmission.
    b. Helping to perform rescue breathing.
    c. Reducing the amount of oxygen in a victim's bloodstream.
    d. a and b.

26. When using a resuscitation mask, the best way to maintain an open airway is to —
    a. Tilt the person's head back.
    b. Lift the jaw upward with both hands.
    c. Keep the person's mouth open, using your thumbs.
    d. All of the above

27. How does a bag-valve mask differ from a resuscitation mask?
    a. It does not help prevent disease transmission.
    b. It is usually more effective when used by two rescuers.
    c. It can be used for victims in respiratory arrest.
    d. a and c

28. Criteria for an effective resuscitation mask include—
    a. A one-way exhalation valve.
    b. An inlet for delivery of supplemental oxygen.
    c. Working well in conditions of extreme heat and cold.
    d. All of the above

29. Which is a disadvantage of the bag-valve mask?
    a. It does not form a tight seal on a victim's face.
    b. It takes regular practice to stay proficient.
    c. It is not readily available to all professional rescuers.
    d. b and c

30. Which is the leading cause of death for adults in the United States?
    a. Stroke
    b. Cancer
    c. Cardiovascular disease
    d. Unintentional injuries

31. The most prominent sign/symptom of a heart attack is—
    a. Persistent chest pain.
    b. Difficulty breathing.
    c. Jaw and left arm pain.
    d. Nausea and sweating.

32. Which action is the most important in caring for a victim complaining of shortness of breath and pressure in the chest?
    a. Providing CPR
    b. Calling for more advanced medical personnel immediately
    c. Asking family members about the victim's health
    d. Calling the victim's personal physician

33. In which position should you place a victim who may be experiencing a heart attack?
    a. Lying on the left side
    b. Sitting or semisitting
    c. The most comfortable position for the victim
    d. Lying on the back with legs elevated

34. Which is the primary sign of cardiac arrest?
    a. No breathing
    b. Dilation of the pupils
    c. Absence of blood pressure
    d. Absence of a pulse

35. The purpose of cardiopulmonary resuscitation (CPR) is to—
    a. Restart heartbeat and breathing in a victim of cardiac arrest
    b. Prevent clinical death from occurring in a victim of cardiac arrest.
    c. Keep the brain supplied with oxygen until the heart can be restarted.
    d. All of the above

36. When two rescuers giving CPR change positions, they—
    a. Do not change sides.
    b. Quickly change sides.
    c. Omit part of a cycle.
    d. a and c.

37. Once you have started CPR, when should you check to determine whether the victim has a pulse?
    a. After the first 2 minutes (8 cycles) and every 2 minutes thereafter
    b. After the first minute (4 cycles) and every few minutes thereafter
    c. After each minute (4 cycles) of continuous CPR
    d. None of the above

38. During two-rescuer CPR, the person giving the breaths should—
    a. Count aloud to keep the person giving the compressions at the proper rate.
    b. Call for a stop in the compressions after every minute to check for a return of pulse.
    c. Periodically check the effectiveness of the compressions by checking the carotid pulse.
    d. All of the above.

39. When two rescuers are available to begin CPR at the same time, the first rescuer should—
    a. Check the victim's breathing while the second rescuer checks the pulse.
    b. Begin rescue breathing and chest compressions while the second rescuer completes a secondary survey.
    c. Check the victim's breathing and pulse while the second rescuer does a head-tilt and chin-lift.
    d. Do a primary survey while the second rescuer locates the correct position for chest compressions.

40. When a second rescuer arrives while CPR is being given, the second rescuer should immediately—
    a. Replace the first rescuer and continue CPR.
    b. Determine whether more advanced medical personnel have been summoned.
    c. Assist the first rescuer by taking over responsibility for ventilations.
    d. Join the CPR effort by taking over compressions at the end of a cycle of compressions and ventilations.

41. One cycle of CPR for an adult includes—
    a. 30 compressions and 5 breaths.
    b. 10 compressions and 2 breaths.
    c. 15 compressions and 2 breaths.
    d. 15 compressions and 5 breaths.

42. One cycle of CPR for an infant or a child includes—
    a. 5 compressions and 1 breath.
    b. 5 compressions and 2 breaths.
    c. 15 compressions and 2 breaths.
    d. 10 compressions and 1 breath.

43. Where should your hands be when compressing an infant's chest during CPR?
    a. One hand on the chin and one hand on the chest
    b. One hand on the forehead and 2 or 3 fingers on the center of the chest
    c. One hand on the forehead and one hand on the chest
    d. One hand on the chin and 2 or 3 fingers on the center of the chest

44. To deliver chest compressions to a child, you would use the—
    a. Heel of one hand.
    b. Pads of two fingers.
    c. Heel of two hands.
    d. Pads of three fingers.

45. What should you do if a victim's breathing and heartbeat return while you are giving CPR?
    a. Have a bystander transport you and the victim to the nearest hospital.
    b. Continue rescue breathing while waiting for advanced medical personnel to arrive.
    c. Keep the airway open and monitor vital signs.
    d. Complete a secondary survey before calling more advanced medical personnel for assistance.

46. Chest compressions for a near-drowning victim—
    a. Should be given while the victim is in the water.
    b. Are not effective unless the victim is on a hard, firm surface.
    c. Should be given along with rescue breathing.
    d. b and c.

47. For a victim of hypothermia, you should—
    a. Remove any wet clothing.
    b. Warm the victim gradually and handle gently.
    c. Check for a pulse for at least 45 seconds.
    d. All of the above.

48. When transporting a person without a pulse down a stairway—
    a. Give CPR, then move the victim and resume CPR within 30 seconds.
    b. Give rescue breathing at once but no compressions until the victim is off the stairs.
    c. Get the victim off the stairs before giving CPR.
    d. Give CPR on the stairs until more advanced medical help arrives.

49. You are summoned to a scene where a lineman has received a severe electric shock and is still on the pole. Your first action is—
    a. To bring him down from the pole immediately.
    b. To make sure he is not in contact with the power source and it is safe for you to help.
    c. To give him rescue breathing while he is still on the pole.
    d. To check his pulse.

50. When a victim of an automobile accident is still in the car, you remove the victim—
    a. If the victim is conscious.
    b. If you suspect a head or spine injury.
    c. If the victim asks to be moved.
    d. If you must to provide care.

Name _____   Date _____

1.	ⓐ ⓑ ⓒ ⓓ			26.	ⓐ ⓑ ⓒ ⓓ		
2.	ⓐ ⓑ ⓒ ⓓ			27.	ⓐ ⓑ ⓒ ⓓ		
3.	ⓐ ⓑ ⓒ ⓓ			28.	ⓐ ⓑ ⓒ ⓓ		
4.	ⓐ ⓑ ⓒ ⓓ			29.	ⓐ ⓑ ⓒ ⓓ		
5.	ⓐ ⓑ ⓒ ⓓ			30.	ⓐ ⓑ ⓒ ⓓ		
6.	ⓐ ⓑ ⓒ ⓓ			31.	ⓐ ⓑ ⓒ ⓓ		
7.	ⓐ ⓑ ⓒ ⓓ			32.	ⓐ ⓑ ⓒ ⓓ		
8.	ⓐ ⓑ ⓒ ⓓ			33.	ⓐ ⓑ ⓒ ⓓ		
9.	ⓐ ⓑ ⓒ ⓓ			34.	ⓐ ⓑ ⓒ ⓓ		
10.	ⓐ ⓑ ⓒ ⓓ			35.	ⓐ ⓑ ⓒ ⓓ		
11.	ⓐ ⓑ ⓒ ⓓ			36.	ⓐ ⓑ ⓒ ⓓ		
12.	ⓐ ⓑ ⓒ ⓓ			37.	ⓐ ⓑ ⓒ ⓓ		
13.	ⓐ ⓑ ⓒ ⓓ			38.	ⓐ ⓑ ⓒ ⓓ		
14.	ⓐ ⓑ ⓒ ⓓ			39.	ⓐ ⓑ ⓒ ⓓ		
15.	ⓐ ⓑ ⓒ ⓓ			40.	ⓐ ⓑ ⓒ ⓓ		
16.	ⓐ ⓑ ⓒ ⓓ			41.	ⓐ ⓑ ⓒ ⓓ		
17.	ⓐ ⓑ ⓒ ⓓ			42.	ⓐ ⓑ ⓒ ⓓ		
18.	ⓐ ⓑ ⓒ ⓓ			43.	ⓐ ⓑ ⓒ ⓓ		
19.	ⓐ ⓑ ⓒ ⓓ			44.	ⓐ ⓑ ⓒ ⓓ		
20.	ⓐ ⓑ ⓒ ⓓ			45.	ⓐ ⓑ ⓒ ⓓ		
21.	ⓐ ⓑ ⓒ ⓓ			46.	ⓐ ⓑ ⓒ ⓓ		
22.	ⓐ ⓑ ⓒ ⓓ			47.	ⓐ ⓑ ⓒ ⓓ		
23.	ⓐ ⓑ ⓒ ⓓ			48.	ⓐ ⓑ ⓒ ⓓ		
24.	ⓐ ⓑ ⓒ ⓓ			49.	ⓐ ⓑ ⓒ ⓓ		
25.	ⓐ ⓑ ⓒ ⓓ			50.	ⓐ ⓑ ⓒ ⓓ		

You may wish to go back and check your answers to be sure that you matched the right answer with the right question.

American Red Cross CPR for the Professional Rescuer

Exam B

IMPORTANT: Read all instructions before beginning this exam.

INSTRUCTIONS: Mark all answers in pencil on the separate answer sheet. **Do not write on this exam.** The questions on this exam are multiple choice. Read each question slowly and carefully. Then choose the best answer and fill in that circle on the answer sheet. If you wish to change an answer, erase your first answer completely. Return this exam with your answer sheet to your instructor when you are finished.

EXAMPLE

ANSWER SHEET

xx. (a) (b) (c) ●

xx. Why does the American Red Cross teach this course?
   a. To help people stay calm in emergencies
   b. To help people make appropriate decisions when they confront an cmergency
   c. To help people in an emergency keep a victim's injuries from getting worse until EMS arrives
   d. All of the above

1. Laws that protect people who willingly give emergency care without accepting anything in return are called—
   a. Citizen Responder laws.
   b. Hold Harmless laws.
   c. Good Samaritan laws.
   d. Medical Immunity laws.

2. Which person in the EMS system has the role of recognizing that an emergency exists, deciding to act, activating the EMS system, and providing first aid care?
   a. Paramedic
   b. Emergency medical technician
   c. Fire fighter
   d. Citizen responder

3. Which body system has the heart, blood, and blood vessels as major components?
   a. Respiratory
   b. Nervous
   c. Circulatory
   d. Integumentary

4. Which body system regulates all body functions?
   a. Respiratory
   b. Circulatory
   c. Integumentary
   d. Nervous

5. How should you determine if a victim is conscious?
   a. Slap the victim's face and ask, "Are you awake?"
   b. Gently tap the victim and ask, "Are you O.K.?"
   c. Pinch the victim's shoulder and ask, "Does this hurt?"
   d. None of the above

6. Before beginning a primary survey, you should first—
   a. Position the victim so that you can open the airway.
   b. Survey the scene.
   c. Check for consciousness.
   d. Call more advanced medical professionals for help.

7. Why should you do a primary survey in every emergency situation?
   a. Because it will protect you from legal liability
   b. Because it identifies conditions that are an immediate threat to life
   c. Because it identifies conditions that could become life-threatening if not cared for
   d. Because it will enable you to protect the victim and bystanders from dangers at the scene

8. In which circumstances should you move a victim before providing care?
   a. There is danger from fire, poisonous fumes, or an unstable structure.
   b. The victim is complaining of pain.
   c. It is impossible to splint fractures or bandage wounds without moving the victim.
   d. The victim is in a position in which more advanced medical personnel will have difficulty giving care.

9. In which order are the four elements of a primary survey assessed (first to last)?
   a. Consciousness, circulation, breathing, airway
   b. Breathing, circulation, airway, consciousness
   c. Consciousness, airway, breathing, circulation
   d. Circulation, airway, breathing, consciousness

10. For which of the following individuals should you immediately summon more advanced medical personnel?
    a. A 22-year-old who has had a fever and vomited twice during the night
    b. A 60-year-old experiencing severe knee pain after a morning run
    c. A 40-year-old complaining that he has felt nauseated, sweaty, and short of breath for at least an hour
    d. An 8-year-old who was hit on the leg by a baseball and now has a large bruise

11. The most common type of breathing emergency is—
    a. Respiratory distress.
    b. Respiratory arrest.
    c. Hyperventilation.
    d. Anaphylactic shock.

12. In which position should you usually place a victim of respiratory distress?
    a. A sitting position
    b. Flat on the back
    c. On one side with head down
    d. Head raised on a pillow

13. Rescue breathing is the proper emergency care for—
    a. Respiratory distress.
    b. Cardiac arrest.
    c. Airway obstruction.
    d. Respiratory arrest.

14. How often should you give rescue breaths to an infant or child who is not breathing but does have a pulse?
    a. Once every 3 seconds
    b. Once every 4 seconds
    c. Once every 6 seconds
    d. Once every 10 seconds

15. When you give rescue breaths, how much air should you breathe into the victim?
    a. Enough to make the stomach rise
    b. Enough to make the chest rise
    c. Enough to feel resistance
    d. Enough to fill the victim's cheeks

16. What should you do for a conscious adult or child who is choking and cannot cough, speak, or breathe?
    a. Give two full breaths.
    b. Do a finger sweep.
    c. Give abdominal thrusts.
    d. Lower the victim to the floor and open the airway.

17. One sign of respiratory distress is—
    a. Pain in the abdomen.
    b. Dilation of the pupils.
    c. Feeling dizzy or lightheaded.
    d. a and b.

18. Which should you do to keep the airway open when giving rescue breaths if you do not suspect a head injury?
    a. Lift the chin.
    b. Tilt the head back and lift the chin.
    c. Tilt the head back and lift the neck.
    d. Roll the victim onto one side.

19. What must you do to determine if a victim requires rescue breathing?
    a. Look, listen, and feel for breathing.
    b. Check for a pulse in the neck.
    c. Check for pale or sweaty skin.
    d. Look at the pupils to check for constriction.

20. If your first 2 breaths do not cause the victim's chest to rise, what should you do?
    a. Call for more advanced medical professionals.
    b. Do a finger sweep of the victim's mouth.
    c. Give 2 more breaths with more force.
    d. Retilt the head and try to give breaths again.

21. After giving abdominal thrusts to an unconscious adult with an obstructed airway, you should—
    a. Begin CPR.
    b. Check for a pulse, give 2 slow breaths, and then do a finger sweep.
    c. Give 2 slow breaths and then do a finger sweep.
    d. Do a finger sweep and then give 2 slow breaths.

22. How can you minimize the amount of air forced into a victim's stomach during rescue breathing?
    a. Breathe slowly into the victim when delivering breaths.
    b. Don't pause between breaths unless absolutely necessary.
    c. Press on the victim's stomach while delivering breaths.
    d. Breathe as hard as you can into the victim.

23. What should you do for a conscious infant who is choking and cannot cry, cough, or breathe?
    a. Give 5 back blows and then 5 chest thrusts.
    b. Give abdominal thrusts.
    c. Give back blows until the victim starts to cough or becomes unconscious.
    d. Any of the above.

24. Where should you position your hands when giving abdominal thrusts to a conscious adult or child?
    a. In the middle of the abdomen just above the navel
    b. On the center of the chest
    c. In the middle of the abdomen well below the navel
    d. None of the above

25. Which is a disadvantage of the bag-valve mask?

    a. It does not form a tight seal on a victim's face.

    b. It takes regular practice to stay proficient.

    c. It is not readily available to all professional rescuers.

    d. b and c.

26. When using a resuscitation mask, the best way to maintain an open airway is to—

    a. Tilt the person's head back.

    b. Lift the jaw upward with both hands.

    c. Keep the person's mouth open, using your thumbs.

    d. All of the above.

27. How does a bag-valve mask differ from a resuscitation mask?

    a. It does not help prevent disease transmission.

    b. It is usually more effective when used by two rescuers.

    c. It can be used for victims in respiratory arrest.

    d. a and c.

28. Criteria for an effective resuscitation mask include—

    a. A one-way exhalation valve.

    b. An inlet for delivery of supplemental oxygen.

    c. Working well in conditions of extreme heat and cold.

    d. All of the above.

29. Which of the following is an advantage of using a resuscitation mask to provide artificial ventilation?

    a. It reduces the volume of air needed to expand the victim's lungs.

    b. It prevents airway obstruction from occurring when facial injuries are involved.

    c. It reduces the risk of disease transmission between the rescuer and victim.

    d. All of the above.

30. Which is the most common cause of cardiac arrest?
    a. Electrocution
    b. Drowning/suffocation
    c. Cardiovascular disease
    d. Drug overdose/poisoning

31. If CPR is not started, how long after cardiac arrest will the brain begin to die?
    a. Immediately
    b. 2–4 minutes
    c. 4–6 minutes
    d. 8–10 minutes

32. Which of these risk factors for heart disease can be controlled?
    a. High blood pressure
    b. Family history of heart disease
    c. Smoking
    d. a and c

33. One cycle of CPR for an adult includes—
    a. 30 compressions and 5 breaths.
    b. 15 compressions and 2 breaths.
    c. 10 compressions and 2 breaths.
    d. 5 compressions and 1 breath.

34. During two-rescuer CPR, the person giving the breaths should—
    a. Count aloud to keep the person giving the compressions at the proper rate.
    b. Call for a stop in the compressions after every minute to check for a return of pulse.
    c. Periodically check the effectiveness of the compressions by checking the carotid pulse.
    d. All of the above.

35. Where should your hands be when compressing an infant's chest during CPR?
    a. One hand on the chin and one hand on the chest
    b. One hand on the forehead and 2 or 3 fingers on the center of the chest
    c. One hand on the forehead and one hand on the chest
    d. One hand on the chin and 2 or 3 fingers on the center of the chest

36. One cycle of CPR for an infant or a child includes—
    a. 5 compressions and 1 breath.
    b. 5 compressions and 2 breaths.
    c. 15 compressions and 1 breath.
    d. 15 compressions and 2 breaths.

37. When two rescuers giving CPR change positions, they—
    a. Do not change sides.
    b. Quickly change sides.
    c. Omit part of a cycle.
    d. a and c.

38. When two rescuers are available to begin CPR at the same time, the first rescuer should—
    a. Check the victim's breathing while the second rescuer checks the pulse.
    b. Begin rescue breathing and chest compressions while the second rescuer completes a secondary survey.
    c. Check the victim's breathing and pulse while the second rescuer does the head-tilt and chin-lift.
    d. Do a primary survey while the second rescuer locates the correct position for chest compressions.

39. Which is the primary sign of cardiac arrest?
    a. No breathing
    b. Absence of a pulse
    c. Skin which is pale or bluish in color
    d. Absence of blood pressure

40. Once you have started CPR, when should you check to determine whether the victim has a pulse?
    a. After the first 2 minutes (8 cycles) and every 2 minutes thereafter
    b. After the first minute (4 cycles) and every few minutes thereafter
    c. After each minute (4 cycles) of continuous CPR
    d. None of the above

41. The purpose of cardiopulmonary resuscitation (CPR) is to—
    a. Restart heartbeat and breathing in a victim of cardiac arrest.
    b. Prevent clinical death from occurring in a victim of cardiac arrest.
    c. Keep the brain supplied with oxygen until the heart can be restarted.
    d. All of the above.

42. Which is the leading cause of death for adults in the United States?
    a. Unintentional injuries
    b. Cardiovascular disease
    c. Pneumonia
    d. Cancer

43. When a second rescuer arrives while CPR is being given, the second rescuer should immediately —
    a. Do a primary survey.
    b. Replace the first rescuer and continue CPR.
    c. Join the CPR effort by taking over compressions at the end of a cycle of compressions and ventilations.
    d. Determine whether advanced medical personnel have been summoned.

44. The most prominent sign/symptom of a heart attack is —
    a. A pulse which is faster or slower than normal.
    b. Persistent chest pain.
    c. Difficulty breathing.
    d. Nausea and sweating.

45. Which action is the most important in caring for a victim complaining of shortness of breath and pressure in the chest?
    a. Providing CPR
    b. Having the victim lie down while you check his/her breathing and pulse
    c. Calling for more advanced medical personnel immediately
    d. Calling the victim's personal physician

46. When a victim of an automobile accident is still in the car, you remove the victim —
    a. If the victim is conscious.
    b. If you must to provide care.
    c. If the victim asks to be moved.
    d. If you suspect a head or spine injury.

47. You are summoned to a scene where a lineman has received a severe electric shock and is still on the pole. Your first action is—
   a. To bring him down from the pole immediately.
   b. To give him rescue breathing while he is still on the pole.
   c. To check his pulse.
   d. To make sure he is not in contact with the power source and it is safe for you to help.

48. When transporting a person without a pulse down a stairway—
   a. Give CPR, then move the victim and resume CPR within 30 seconds.
   b. Give rescue breathing at once but no compressions until the victim is off the stairs.
   c. Get the victim off the stairs before giving CPR.
   d. Give CPR on the stairs until more advanced medical help arrives.

49. Chest compressions for a near-drowning victim—
   a. Are not effective unless the victim is on a hard, firm surface.
   b. Should be given while the victim is in the water.
   c. Should be given along with rescue breathing.
   d. a and c.

50. For a victim of hypothermia, you should—
   a. Remove any wet clothing.
   b. Warm the victim gradually and handle gently.
   c. Check for a pulse for as long as 45 seconds.
   d. All of the above.

Name _____ Date _____

1.	(a)	(b)	(c)	(d)		26.	(a)	(b)	(c)	(d)
2.	(a)	(b)	(c)	(d)		27.	(a)	(b)	(c)	(d)
3.	(a)	(b)	(c)	(d)		28.	(a)	(b)	(c)	(d)
4.	(a)	(b)	(c)	(d)		29.	(a)	(b)	(c)	(d)
5.	(a)	(b)	(c)	(d)		30.	(a)	(b)	(c)	(d)
6.	(a)	(b)	(c)	(d)		31.	(a)	(b)	(c)	(d)
7.	(a)	(b)	(c)	(d)		32.	(a)	(b)	(c)	(d)
8.	(a)	(b)	(c)	(d)		33.	(a)	(b)	(c)	(d)
9.	(a)	(b)	(c)	(d)		34.	(a)	(b)	(c)	(d)
10.	(a)	(b)	(c)	(d)		35.	(a)	(b)	(c)	(d)
11.	(a)	(b)	(c)	(d)		36.	(a)	(b)	(c)	(d)
12.	(a)	(b)	(c)	(d)		37.	(a)	(b)	(c)	(d)
13.	(a)	(b)	(c)	(d)		38.	(a)	(b)	(c)	(d)
14.	(a)	(b)	(c)	(d)		39.	(a)	(b)	(c)	(d)
15.	(a)	(b)	(c)	(d)		40.	(a)	(b)	(c)	(d)
16.	(a)	(b)	(c)	(d)		41.	(a)	(b)	(c)	(d)
17.	(a)	(b)	(c)	(d)		42.	(a)	(b)	(c)	(d)
18.	(a)	(b)	(c)	(d)		43.	(a)	(b)	(c)	(d)
19.	(a)	(b)	(c)	(d)		44.	(a)	(b)	(c)	(d)
20.	(a)	(b)	(c)	(d)		45.	(a)	(b)	(c)	(d)
21.	(a)	(b)	(c)	(d)		46.	(a)	(b)	(c)	(d)
22.	(a)	(b)	(c)	(d)		47.	(a)	(b)	(c)	(d)
23.	(a)	(b)	(c)	(d)		48.	(a)	(b)	(c)	(d)
24.	(a)	(b)	(c)	(d)		49.	(a)	(b)	(c)	(d)
25.	(a)	(b)	(c)	(d)		50.	(a)	(b)	(c)	(d)

You may wish to go back and check your answers to be sure that you matched the right answer with the right question.

American Red Cross Waterfront Lifeguarding Module

Exam A

IMPORTANT: Read all instructions before beginning this exam.

INSTRUCTIONS: Mark all answers in pencil on the separate answer sheet. **Do not write on this exam.** The questions on this exam are multiple choice. Read each question slowly and carefully. Then choose the best answer and fill in that circle on the answer sheet. If you wish to change an answer, erase your first answer completely. Return this exam with your answer sheet to your instructor when you are finished.

EXAMPLE

ANSWER SHEET

xx. (a) (b) (c) ●

xx. As an American Red Cross Waterfront Lifeguarding Instructor, your responsibilities include—

a. Representing the American Red Cross in a positive manner.

b. Creating a nonthreatening environment that encourages participants to meet course objectives.

c. Remaining alert to your own cultural and ethnic stereotypes and being creative and flexible in presenting material in an effective and culturally sensitive manner.

d. All of the above.

1. Which of the following statements about a waterfront facility is true?
   a. Training at a waterfront setting prepares you for the environment where you will be working.
   b. Skills relating to pools do not apply to waterfronts.
   c. You would be able to do surf lifeguarding after completing the Waterfront module.
   d. Open water can be a lake, reservoir, or canal.

2. Hazardous conditions at a waterfront facility—
   a. Change infrequently.
   b. Require occasional safety checks.
   c. Do not require facility surveillance to be adapted.
   d. Are unique to each waterfront.

3. Physical characteristics and structures in and around the water are shown on—
   a. An area map.
   b. A waterfront map.
   c. A contour map.
   d. A depth map.

4. When using fins—
   a. It doesn't matter which size blade you choose.
   b. Use your legs and arms to swim under water.
   c. Use a modified flutter kick.
   d. Smaller fins are faster but require more strength.

5. Your lifeguard station—
   a. May need to be moved throughout the day.
   b. Should be tall enough to prevent patrons from asking you questions while you are on surveillance duty.
   c. Should enable you to see 100 feet out.
   d. Will always be combined with another station to provide two-guard zone coverage.

6. Which of the following is a true statement about the use of rescue craft?
   a. You would use a v-hull rowboat in calm areas.
   b. You would patrol the outer edge of the swimming area.
   c. Rescue craft are manned by one lifeguard.
   d. Only rowboats are used as rescue craft.

7. The buddy system—
   a. Combines a weak and a strong swimmer so that the weak swimmer is watched.
   b. Is not frequently used.
   c. Can have two or three swimmers form a group.
   d. Adds another buddy to a group of 10.

8. If a tag on a buddy board is found in the "in" section after the water is cleared, what should you do?
   a. Call EMS personnel immediately.
   b. Perform an in-water search immediately.
   c. Perform the buddy check one or two more times.
   d. Do not worry; a camper forgot to move the tag to the "out" side.

9. In an emergency action plan for a waterfront—
   a. Lifeguards do not have primary responsibility for managing the emergency.
   b. Only lifeguards are included in the plan.
   c. There are fewer steps than in a plan for a pool facility.
   d. Backup coverage should be predetermined based on the positions of lifeguard stands.

10. Which entry would you use from a gradually sloping shoreline?
    a. Compact jump
    b. Run-and-swim entry
    c. Stride jump
    d. Run-and-jump entry

11. Which is **not** a step in a walking assist?
    a. Stand behind the victim and grasp him or her under the armpits.
    b. Maintain a firm grasp, and help the victim walk out of the water.
    c. Place one of the victim's arms around your neck and across your shoulder.
    d. Grasp the wrist of the arm that is across your shoulder, and wrap your free arm around the victim's back or waist to provide support.

12. On a sloping beach, to remove an unconscious victim who is very heavy and unable to walk from the water, use the—
    a. Beach drag.
    b. Unconscious victim assist.
    c. Passive victim rear rescue.
    d. Walking assist.

13. When using a rescue board—
    a. Always paddle lying down.
    b. Do not get on it until you are in chest-deep water.
    c. Climb on just behind the middle.
    d. Oil it regularly to keep it from drying out.

14. To provide spinal injury management in water with waves or a current—
    a. Be aware that a dock or raft may increase waves.
    b. Point the victim's head away from the current once the victim is face up.
    c. Do not modify how you would provide care.
    d. Align the victim's body with the current.

15. When using a rescue board to rescue a distressed swimmer, approach the victim from—
    a. The front.
    b. The back.
    c. Below.
    d. The side.

16. Sudden entry into cold water can cause which of the following reactions?
    a. Rapid breathing only if the victim's face is under water
    b. Quick decrease in heart rate
    c. Hypothermia, which will not lead to unconsciousness
    d. A gasp reflex

17. When using a rescue board to rescue a distressed swimmer, grasp the victim's—
    a. Leg.
    b. Arm.
    c. Wrist.
    d. Shoulder.

18. Which effects of cold water may increase the chance of survival?
    a. Body temperature does not drop quickly.
    b. Water taken in will not go to the stomach.
    c. The older the victim, the better the chance of survival.
    d. Any oxygen left in the blood is diverted to the brain and heart to maintain minimal function.

19. To rescue a distressed swimmer when using a rescue craft—
    a. Extend an oar to the victim.
    b. Never let the victim get close enough to grasp your hand.
    c. Pull the victim to the front of the craft.
    d. Always bring the victim onto the rescue craft.

20. When using motorized water craft—
    a. Approach the victim from upwind and upstream.
    b. Approach the victim from downwind and downstream.
    c. Shut off the engine one boat length from the victim.
    d. Shut off the engine 10 boat lengths away from the victim.

21. To keep track of a drowning victim who has submerged when another lifeguard is available, take a—
    a. Cross bearing.
    b. Sighting.
    c. Double sighting.
    d. Cross sighting.

22. Which of the following statements is true regarding a missing person procedure?
    a. Have two people in charge of the entire search at all times.
    b. You may use volunteers to search some water areas.
    c. Volunteers should only assist outside of the water.
    d. The person who made the missing person report should wait by the waterfront to identify the person as soon as the victim is brought out of the water.

23. To search shallow-water areas—
    a. Searchers should form in a "V" pattern.
    b. The tallest person should be in water no more than waist deep.
    c. Searchers should pause to sweep the bottom with their hands every 5 feet because of poor water clarity.
    d. Adult volunteers and non-lifeguarding staff members can take part in this search.

24. When searching deep-water areas—
    a. Searchers dive and resurface no more than 5 times.
    b. Lifeguards should be no more than 3 arm lengths apart.
    c. If the water is murky, searchers search the bottom by sweeping their hands back and forth.
    d. At least two lifeguards should serve as lookouts in case a searcher gets in trouble or the missing person is found.

25. When performing a cold-water rescue—
    a. Your body will not react like the victim's since you are active and the victim is passive.
    b. Use a rescue craft with a towline attached.
    c. Do not attempt the rescue without assistance.
    d. You do not need rescue equipment.

American Red Cross Waterfront Lifeguarding Module

Exam B

IMPORTANT: Read all instructions before beginning this exam.

INSTRUCTIONS: Mark all answers in pencil on the separate answer sheet. **Do not write on this exam.** The questions on this exam are multiple choice. Read each question slowly and carefully. Then choose the best answer and fill in that circle on the answer sheet. If you wish to change an answer, erase your first answer completely. Return this exam with your answer sheet to your instructor when you are finished.

EXAMPLE

ANSWER SHEET

xx. (a) (b) (c) ●

xx. As an American Red Cross Waterfront Lifeguarding Instructor, your responsibilities include—

a. Representing the American Red Cross in a positive manner.

b. Creating a nonthreatening environment that encourages participants to meet course objectives.

c. Remaining alert to your own cultural and ethnic stereotypes and being creative and flexible in presenting material in an effective and culturally sensitive manner.

d. All of the above.

1. Your lifeguard station—
   a. May need to be moved throughout the day.
   b. Should be tall enough to prevent patrons from asking you questions while you are on surveillance duty.
   c. Should enable you to see 100 feet out.
   d. Will always be combined with another station to provide two-guard zone coverage.

2. The buddy system—
   a. Combines a weak and a strong swimmer so that the weak swimmer is watched.
   b. Is not frequently used.
   c. Can have two or three swimmers form a group.
   d. Adds another buddy to a group of 10.

3. Physical characteristics and structures in and around the water are shown on—
   a. An area map.
   b. A contour map.
   c. A waterfront map.
   d. A depth map.

4. To provide spinal injury management in water with waves or a current—
   a. Align the victim's body with the current.
   b. Point the victim's head away from the current once the victim is face up.
   c. Do not modify how you would provide care.
   d. Be aware that a dock or raft may increase waves.

5. Which of the following is a true statement about the use of rescue craft?
   a. You would use a v-hull rowboat in calm areas.
   b. You would patrol the outer edge of the swimming area.
   c. Rescue craft are manned by one lifeguard.
   d. Only rowboats are used as rescue craft.

6. When using fins—
   a. It doesn't matter which size blade you choose.
   b. Use your legs and arms to swim under water.
   c. Use a modified flutter kick.
   d. Smaller fins are faster but require more strength.

7. Which of the following statements about a waterfront facility is true?
   a. Training at a waterfront setting prepares you for the environment where you will be working.
   b. Skills relating to pools do not apply to waterfronts.
   c. You would be able to do surf lifeguarding after completing the Waterfront module.
   d. Open water can be a lake, reservoir, or canal.

8. Which is **not** a step in a walking assist?
   a. Stand behind the victim and grasp him or her under the armpits.
   b. Maintain a firm grasp, and help the victim walk out of the water.
   c. Place one of the victim's arms around your neck and across your shoulder.
   d. Grasp the wrist of the arm that is across your shoulder, and wrap your free arm around the victim's back or waist to provide support.

9. Which effects of cold water may increase the chance of survival?
   a. Body temperature does not drop quickly.
   b. Any oxygen left in the blood is diverted to the brain and heart to maintain minimal function.
   c. The older the victim, the better the chance of survival.
   d. Water taken in will not go to the stomach.

10. If a tag on a buddy board is found in the "in" section after the water is cleared, what should you do?

    a. Call EMS personnel immediately.

    b. Perform an in-water search immediately.

    c. Perform the buddy check one or two more times.

    d. Do not worry; a camper forgot to move the tag to the "out" side.

11. Which entry would you use from a gradually sloping shoreline?

    a. Compact jump

    b. Run-and-swim entry

    c. Stride jump

    d. Run-and-jump entry

12. On a sloping beach, to remove an unconscious victim who is very heavy and unable to walk from the water, use the—

    a. Beach drag.

    b. Unconscious victim assist.

    c. Passive victim rear rescue.

    d. Walking assist.

13. When using a rescue board—

    a. Always paddle lying down.

    b. Do not get on it until you are in chest-deep water.

    c. Climb on just behind the middle.

    d. Oil it regularly to keep it from drying out.

14. Hazardous conditions at a waterfront facility—

    a. Change infrequently.

    b. Do not require occasional safety checks.

    c. Do not require facility surveillance to be adapted.

    d. Are unique to each waterfront.

15. In an emergency action plan for a waterfront—
    a. Lifeguards do not have primary responsibility for managing the emergency.
    b. Only lifeguards are included in the plan.
    c. There are fewer steps than in a plan for a pool facility.
    d. Backup coverage should be predetermined based on the positions of lifeguard stands.

16. When searching deep-water areas—
    a. Searchers dive and resurface no more than 5 times.
    b. If the water is murky, searchers search the bottom by sweeping their hands back and forth.
    c. Lifeguards should be no more than 3 arm lengths apart.
    d. At least two lifeguards should serve as lookouts in case a searcher gets in trouble or the missing person is found.

17. To keep track of a drowning victim who has submerged when another lifeguard is available, take a—
    a. Cross bearing.
    b. Sighting.
    c. Double sighting.
    d. Cross sighting.

18. When using a rescue board to rescue a distressed swimmer, approach the victim from—
    a. The front.
    b. The side.
    c. Below.
    d. The back.

19. Sudden entry into cold water can cause which of the following reactions?
    a. Rapid breathing only if the victim's face is under water
    b. A gasp reflex
    c. Hypothermia, which will not lead to unconsciousness
    d. Quick decrease in heart rate

20. When using motorized water craft—
    a. Approach the victim from upwind and upstream.
    b. Approach the victim from downwind and downstream.
    c. Shut off the engine one boat length from the victim.
    d. Shut off the engine 10 boat lengths away from the victim.

21. When using a rescue board to rescue a distressed swimmer, grasp the victim's—
    a. Leg.
    b. Arm.
    c. Wrist.
    d. Shoulder.

22. To rescue a distressed swimmer when using a rescue craft—
    a. Extend an oar to the victim.
    b. Never let the victim get close enough to grasp your hand.
    c. Pull the victim to the front of the craft.
    d. Always bring the victim onto the rescue craft.

23. Which of the following statements is true regarding a missing person procedure?
    a. Have two people in charge of the entire search at all times.
    b. Volunteers should only assist outside of the water.
    c. You may use volunteers to search some water areas.
    d. The person who made the missing person report should wait by the waterfront to identify the person as soon as the victim is brought out of the water.

24. To search shallow-water areas—
    a. Searchers should form in a "V" pattern.
    b. The tallest person should be in water no more than waist deep.
    c. Adult volunteers and non-lifeguarding staff members can take part in this search.
    d. Searchers should pause to sweep the bottom with their hands every 5 feet because of poor water clarity.

25. When performing a cold-water rescue—
    a. Your body will not react like the victim's since you are active and the victim is passive.
    b. Use a rescue craft with a towline attached.
    c. Do not attempt the rescue without assistance.
    d. You do not need rescue equipment.

American Red Cross Waterpark Lifeguarding Module

Exam A

IMPORTANT: Read all instructions before beginning this exam.

INSTRUCTIONS: Mark all answers in pencil on the separate answer sheet. **Do not write on this exam.** The questions on this exam are multiple choice. Read each question slowly and carefully. Then choose the best answer and fill in that circle on the answer sheet. If you wish to change an answer, erase your first answer completely. Return this exam with your answer sheet to your instructor when you are finished.

EXAMPLE

ANSWER SHEET

xx.   (a)   (b)   (c)   ●

xx. As an American Red Cross Waterpark Lifeguarding Instructor, your responsibilities include—

a. Representing the American Red Cross in a positive manner.

b. Creating a nonthreatening environment that encourages participants to meet course objectives.

c. Remaining alert to your cultural and ethnic stereotypes and being creative and flexible in presenting material in an effective and culturally sensitive manner.

d. All of the above.

1. Which of the following perceptions that a patron would have about a waterpark is correct?
   a. You can get caught off balance from the turbulence in some attractions.
   b. All attractions at a waterpark are appropriate for all patrons.
   c. Just like an amusement park, a waterpark has a roller coaster.
   d. Because of the unfamiliar environment, patrons will be sure to take extra time to read all rules and regulations.

2. How should a lifeguard prevent rules from being broken?
   a. Throw patrons out of the facility if they get overexcited.
   b. Don't worry as long they're having fun.
   c. Handle rule enforcement in a fair and friendly manner.
   d. Do not allow a family to split up, since children may be unsupervised.

3. To ensure patrons learn the facility's rules and regulations—
   a. You could post lots of signs so that patrons will read at least some of them.
   b. You could use a taped message to state the rules.
   c. You should never use more than one language on a sign.
   d. You should not list more than five rules or a patron will get confused.

4. A small pool at the end of a slide where patrons enter water deep enough to cushion their landing is called—
   a. A catch pool.
   b. A landing pool.
   c. A wading pool.
   d. A plunge pool.

5. Which of the following statements is true about performing a safety check?
   a. If you cannot correct a problem before the facility is scheduled to open, call EMS.
   b. Take test rides on all attractions.
   c. Perform one safety check monthly.
   d. Check light signals, the public address systems, telephones, and two-way radios weekly.

6. Which of the following is **not** a factor that affects lifeguard rotations?
   a. Location of stations
   b. Number of patrons
   c. Position of sun
   d. Whether the station is in or out of water

7. Which is the method of starting patrons safely on a ride?
   a. Ride interval
   b. Stationing
   c. Ride monitor
   d. Dispatch

8. Which of the following is a recommendation for guarding winding rivers?
   a. Patrons should not stack up tubes.
   b. Patrons can ride on tubes or go down wearing a life jacket.
   c. At least two patrons should be in a tube at all times.
   d. Children are prohibited from winding rivers.

9. What should a lifeguard do when dispatching riders at a water slide?
   a. Dispatch riders more quickly if the line gets too long.
   b. Dispatch lighter riders more slowly than heavier riders.
   c. Allow patrons to bring equipment onto the water slide.
   d. Hose the slide regularly to keep it fast.

10. How deep is the water in a runout in a speed slide?

    a. 1 foot

    b. 6 inches

    c. 2 inches

    d. 2 feet

11. The recommended riding position for a speed slide is—

    a. Lying headfirst on the back.

    b. Lying on the back with legs crossed.

    c. Lying on the stomach with feet first.

    d. Lying on the stomach with arms flat at the sides.

12. Which of the following is a guideline for speed slides?

    a. Use a signal if the lifeguard at the top cannot see the lifeguard at the bottom.

    b. Wear a life jacket to support you in the catch pool.

    c. Wear eyeglasses under goggles if needed to be able to see.

    d. Wear water shoes.

13. A slide with a nearly vertical drop that gives riders the sensation of falling is a—

    a. Vertical slide.

    b. Drop slide.

    c. Free-fall slide.

    d. Speed slide.

14. A head wall at a wave pool is primarily—

    a. An observation deck.

    b. A place where patrons can jump in.

    c. A place to store equipment.

    d. A house for the system that creates the waves.

15. Where would you **not** need a rescue tube to perform your job responsibilities?
    a. At a shallow-water attraction
    b. At a deep-water attraction
    c. In or beside a catch pool
    d. At the top of a slide

16. Which of the following is an example of an assist?
    a. Telling a patron the time
    b. Helping a patron out of a raft
    c. Using a compact jump to enter deep water
    d. Using the run-and-swim entry on a gradual slope

17. Spinal injury—
    a. Can occur from rough horseplay in inner tubes.
    b. Is frequent in winding rivers.
    c. Is easier to manage in moving water.
    d. Cannot be managed with a backboard.

18. Which do you need to consider when performing spinal injury management in a catch pool?
    a. The water in a catch pool moves with less force than in a winding river.
    b. An eddy is created when water flows opposite the main current.
    c. The surface of an eddy cannot be still.
    d. The flow of water should never be stopped in a catch pool.

19. Which is the calmest area of a catch pool?
    a. At the center when there are several slides
    b. At the center when there is one slide
    c. At the edge when there is one slide
    d. On the opposite end of the slides if there are several slides

20. What should a lifeguard do if there is a spinal injury on a speed slide?
    a. Turn the water on higher so that it will support the victim.
    b. Have additional rescuers kneel along the outside of the slide.
    c. Do not use a backboard; space will be too tight.
    d. Apply in-line stabilization outside the slide.

21. To perform a simple assist—
    a. Do not use a rescue tube.
    b. Grasp the victim with both hands under the armpits to help the victim to his or her feet.
    c. Grasp the victim with both hands under the armpits if the victim is under water.
    d. Have the rescue tube at your side.

22. For a front-and-back carry, grasp the victim—
    a. By the wrists and under the knees.
    b. Under the elbows and by the ankles.
    c. By the wrists and the ankles.
    d. Under the elbows and under the knees.

23. What is a common guideline for a water slide?
    a. Running, standing, kneeling, rotating, or tumbling are allowed on the slides.
    b. People may dive into catch pools.
    c. Patrons must be a certain height to ride water slides.
    d. Swimsuits or shorts with metal rivets, buttons, or fasteners are allowed on the water slides.

24. What is another name for a waterpark facility?

    a. A waterfront facility

    b. An expanded pool facility

    c. A multi-attraction aquatic facility

    d. A play structure facility

25. Nationwide, how many patrons visit waterparks annually?

    a. Hundreds

    b. Thousands

    c. Millions

    d. Hundreds of thousands

American Red Cross Waterpark Lifeguarding Module

Exam R

IMPORTANT: Read all instructions before beginning this exam.

INSTRUCTIONS: Mark all answers in pencil on the separate answer sheet. **Do not write on this exam.** The questions on this exam are multiple choice. Read each question slowly and carefully. Then choose the best answer and fill in that circle on the answer sheet. If you wish to change an answer, erase your first answer completely. Return this exam with your answer sheet to your instructor when you are finished.

EXAMPLE

ANSWER SHEET

xx. (a) (b) (c) ●

xx As an American Red Cross Waterpark Lifeguarding Instructor, your responsibilities include—

a. Representing the American Red Cross in a positive manner.

b. Creating a nonthreatening environment that encourages participants to meet course objectives.

c. Remaining alert to your cultural and ethnic stereotypes and being creative and flexible in presenting material in an effective and culturally sensitive manner.

d. All of the above.

1. Which do you need to consider when performing spinal injury management in a catch pool?
   a. The water in a catch pool moves with less force than in a winding river.
   b. The flow of water should never be stopped in a catch pool.
   c. The surface of an eddy cannot be still.
   d. An eddy is created when water flows opposite the main current.

2. Which of the following is **not** a factor that affects lifeguard rotations?
   a. Location of stations
   b. Number of patrons
   c. Whether the station is in or out of water
   d. Position of sun

3. How should a lifeguard prevent rules from being broken?
   a. Throw patrons out of the facility if they get overexcited.
   b. Don't worry as long they're having fun.
   c. Handle rule enforcement in a fair and friendly manner.
   d. Do not allow a family to split up, since children may be unsupervised.

4. Which of the following perceptions that a patron would have about a waterpark is correct?
   a. Just like an amusement park, a waterpark has a roller coaster.
   b. All attractions at a waterpark are appropriate for all patrons.
   c. You can get caught off balance from the turbulence in some attractions.
   d. Because of the unfamiliar environment, patrons will be sure to take extra time to read all rules and regulations.

5. A small pool at the end of a slide where patrons enter water deep enough to cushion their landing is called—
   a. A catch pool.
   b. A landing pool.
   c. A wading pool.
   d. A plunge pool.

6. Which of the following statements is true about performing a safety check?
   a. If you cannot correct a problem before the facility is scheduled to open, call EMS.
   b. Take test rides on all attractions.
   c. Perform one safety check monthly.
   d. Check light signals, the public address systems, tele- phones, and two-way radios weekly.

7 Which of the following is an example of an assist?
   a. Telling a patron the time
   b. Using the run-and-swim entry on a gradual slope
   c. Helping a patron out of a raft
   d. Using a compact jump to enter deep water

8. Which is the calmest area of a catch pool?
   a. At the center when there are several slides
   b. At the edge when there is one slide
   c. At the center when there is one slide
   d. On the opposite end of the slides if there are several slides

9. Which is the method of starting patrons safely on a ride?
   a. Ride interval
   b. Stationing
   c. Ride monitor
   d. Dispatch

10. To ensure patrons learn the facility's rules and regulations—
    a. You could post lots of signs so that patrons will read at least some of them.
    b. You could use a taped message to state the rules.
    c. You should never use more than one language on a sign.
    d. You should not list more than five rules or a patron will get confused.

11. Which of the following is a recommendation for guarding winding rivers?
    a. Patrons should not stack up tubes.
    b. Patrons can ride on tubes or go down wearing a life jacket.
    c. At least two patrons should be in a tube at all times.
    d. Children are prohibited from winding rivers.

12. Which of the following is a guideline for speed slides?
    a. Use a signal if the lifeguard at the top cannot see the lifeguard at the bottom.
    b. Wear a life jacket to support you in the catch pool.
    c. Wear eyeglasses under goggles if needed to be able to see.
    d. Wear water shoes.

13. How deep is the water in a runout in a speed slide?
    a. 1 foot
    b. 6 inches
    c. 2 inches
    d. 2 feet

14. A head wall at a wave pool is primarily—
    a. An observation deck.
    b. A place where patrons can jump in.
    c. A place to store equipment.
    d. A house for the system that creates the waves.

15. Where would you **not** need a rescue tube to perform your job responsibilities?
    a. At a shallow-water attraction
    b. At a deep-water attraction
    c. In or beside a catch pool
    d. At the top of a slide

16. What should a lifeguard do if there is a spinal injury on a speed slide?
    a. Turn the water on higher so that it will support the victim.
    b. Apply in-line stabilization outside the slide.
    c. Do not use a backboard; space will be too tight.
    d. Have additional rescuers kneel along the outside of the slide.

17. A slide with a nearly vertical drop that gives riders the sensation of falling is a—
    a. Vertical slide.
    b. Drop slide.
    c. Free-fall slide.
    d. Speed slide.

18. What is another name for a waterpark facility?
    a. A waterfront facility
    b. An expanded pool facility
    c. A play structure facility
    d. A multi-attraction aquatic facility

19. Spinal injury—
    a. Can occur from rough horseplay in inner tubes.
    b. Is frequent in winding rivers.
    c. Is easier to manage in moving water.
    d. Cannot be managed with a backboard.

20. What should a lifeguard do when dispatching riders at a water slide?
    a. Dispatch riders more quickly if the line gets too long.
    b. Dispatch lighter riders more slowly than heavier riders.
    c. Allow patrons to bring equipment onto the water slide.
    d. Hose the slide regularly to keep it fast.

21. For a front-and-back carry, grasp the victim—
    a. By the wrists and under the knees.
    b. Under the elbows and by the ankles.
    c. By the wrists and the ankles.
    d. Under the elbows and under the knees.

22. The recommended riding position for a speed slide is—
    a. Lying headfirst on the back.
    b. Lying on the back with legs crossed.
    c. Lying on the stomach with feet first.
    d. Lying on the stomach with arms flat at the sides.

23. Nationwide, how many patrons visit waterparks annually?
    a. Hundreds
    b. Thousands
    c. Millions
    d. Hundreds of thousands

24. To perform a simple assist—
    a. Do not use a rescue tube.
    b. Grasp the victim with both hands under the armpits to help the victim to his or her knees.
    c. Grasp the victim with both hands under the armpits if the victim is under water and have the victim stand on his or her feet.
    d. Have the rescue tube at your side.

25. What is a common guideline for a water slide?
    a. Running, standing, kneeling, rotating, or tumbling are allowed on the slides.
    b. People may dive into catch pools.
    c. Patrons must be a certain height to ride water slides.
    d. Swimsuits or shorts with metal rivets, buttons, or fasteners are allowed on the water slides.

ANSWER SHEET: AMERICAN RED CROSS WATERPARK LIFEGUARDING MODULE EXAM A
AMERICAN RED CROSS WATERFRONT LIFEGUARDING MODULE EXAM B

Name _____ Date _____

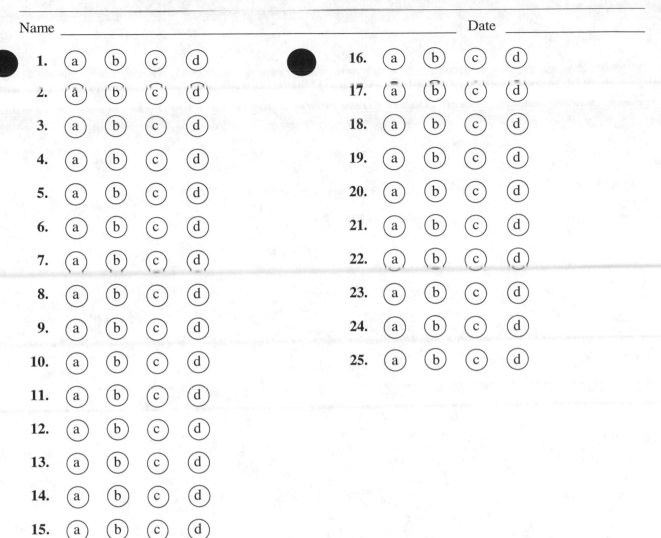

1. (a) (b) (c) (d)
2. (a) (b) (c) (d)
3. (a) (b) (c) (d)
4. (a) (b) (c) (d)
5. (a) (b) (c) (d)
6. (a) (b) (c) (d)
7. (a) (b) (c) (d)
8. (a) (b) (c) (d)
9. (a) (b) (c) (d)
10. (a) (b) (c) (d)
11. (a) (b) (c) (d)
12. (a) (b) (c) (d)
13. (a) (b) (c) (d)
14. (a) (b) (c) (d)
15. (a) (b) (c) (d)

16. (a) (b) (c) (d)
17. (a) (b) (c) (d)
18. (a) (b) (c) (d)
19. (a) (b) (c) (d)
20. (a) (b) (c) (d)
21. (a) (b) (c) (d)
22. (a) (b) (c) (d)
23. (a) (b) (c) (d)
24. (a) (b) (c) (d)
25. (a) (b) (c) (d)

You may wish to go back and check your answers to be sure that you matched the right answer with the right question.

ANSWER SHEET: AMERICAN RED CROSS WATERPARK LIFEGUARDING MODULE EXAM B
AMERICAN RED CROSS WATERFRONT LIFEGUARDING MODULE EXAM A

Name _____   Date _____

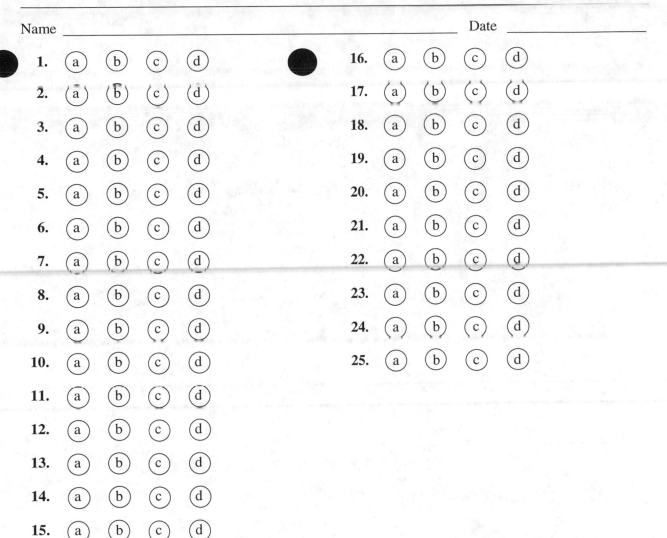

● 1. (a) (b) c   (d)   ● 16. (a) (b) (c) (d)
2. (a) (b) (c) (d)   17. (a) (b) (c) (d)
3. (a) (b) (c) (d)   18. (a) (b) (c) (d)
4. (a) (b) (c) (d)   19. (a) (b) (c) (d)
5. (a) (b) (c) (d)   20. (a) (b) (c) (d)
6. (a) (b) (c) (d)   21. (a) (b) (c) (d)
7. (a) (b) (c) (d)   22. (a) (b) (c) (d)
8. (a) (b) (c) (d)   23. (a) (b) (c) (d)
9. (a) (b) (c) (d)   24. (a) (b) (c) (d)
10. (a) (b) (c) (d)   25. (a) (b) (c) (d)
11. (a) (b) (c) (d)
12. (a) (b) (c) (d)
13. (a) (b) (c) (d)
14. (a) (b) (c) (d)
15. (a) (b) (c) (d)

You may wish to go back and check your answers to be sure that you matched the right answer with the right question.

American Red Cross Head Lifeguard Course

Exam A

IMPORTANT: Read all instructions before beginning this exam.

INSTRUCTIONS: Mark all answers in pencil on the separate answer sheet. **Do not write on this exam.** The questions on this exam are multiple choice. Read each question slowly and carefully. Then choose the best answer and fill in that circle on the answer sheet. If you wish to change an answer, erase your first answer completely. Return this exam with your answer sheet to your instructor when you are finished.

EXAMPLE

ANSWER SHEET

xx. (a) (b) (c) ●

xx. As an American Red Cross Head Lifeguard Instructor, your responsibilities include—

   a. Representing the American Red Cross in a positive manner.

   b. Creating a nonthreatening environment that encourages participants to meet course objectives.

   c. Remaining alert to your own cultural and ethnic stereotypes and being creative and flexible in presenting material in an effective and culturally sensitive manner.

   d. All of the above.

1. A head lifeguard needs which of the following characteristics?
   a. Technically correct swimming strokes
   b. The ability to predict weather changes
   c. Pool operator skills
   d. CPR and first aid skills

2. How far in advance should you ideally make up lifeguard schedules?
   a. One day in advance
   b. At least two weeks in advance
   c. One week in advance
   d. None of the above

3. Bulkheads present safety problems because—
   a. The patrons bump into them.
   b. Patrons swim beneath them.
   c. Patrons can not see around them.
   d. a and c.

4. Which safety precaution should you take for diving pools?
   a. Cover diving policies in your in-service training program.
   b. Post signs specifying rules and regulations next to the diving board.
   c. Have a lifeguard supervise diving activity only if is from a diving board or platform over 3 meters high.
   d. a and b.

5. If lifeguards need information about health, sanitation, and security measures at the facility, they should—
   a. Ask the maintenance staff.
   b. Check the local health department regulations.
   c. Look in the policies and procedures manual.
   d. Look in the emergency action plans.

6. A daily check should include —
   a. The facility office.
   b. All areas open to patrons.
   c. The first aid station.
   d. b and c.

7. To tell if pool water is sufficiently clear—
   a. Do a chemical test.
   b. See if you can clearly recognize drain covers and racing lines.
   c. Tell a lifeguard to lie down the pool bottom at the deep end and see if you can see him or her clearly from the shallow end.
   d. Get in the pool and look about underwater.

8. Maintenance and cleanliness duties are usually performed —
   a. Daily.
   b. Only before opening the pool.
   c. Only at closing time.
   d. Once a day.

9. To perform their job effectively, lifeguards need to be —
   a. Courteous and consistent.
   b. Thoughtful and introspective.
   c. Dynamic.
   d. All of the above.

10. Lifeguard applicants should be tested on —
    a. Fitness.
    b. Appearance
    c. CPR and first aid.
    d. b and d.

11. Before you hire a lifeguard, you should be sure he or she—
    a. Can demonstrate superior swimming stroke techniques.
    b. Has proof of age and current certifications.
    c. Can pass a timed swimming test.
    d. Has a valid driver's license.

12. Which of the following help provide facility security?
    a. Undamaged doors, gates, and fences
    b. Restricting patron access to certain times
    c. video surveillance
    d. All of the above

13. Ways of developing a staff schedule include—
    a. Assigning the best shifts to the best swimmers.
    b. Assigning shifts based on requests from lifeguards the day before.
    c. Assigning shifts based on set criteria, such as seniority.
    d. All of the above.

14. Communications as a form of injury prevention include—
    a. Explaining the facility's communication systems to patrons.
    b. Teaching lifeguards how to communicate with each other in ways patrons will not understand.
    c. Ensuring that warning signs and rules are posted at all facility entrances.
    d. Having sufficient lifeguards on duty so that one is always available to answer questions.

15. To reduce risks at spas, you should—
    a. Allow alcoholic beverages.
    b. Ensure the water temperature is not too high.
    c. Time every spa user.
    d. a and b.

16. Chemicals should be stored—
    a. Where lifeguards have easy access to them.
    b. In their original containers.
    c. Near the facility office.
    d. In clean, marked new containers.

17. Which is an intent of risk management?
    a. To prevent financial loss to the facility
    b. Improve working conditions at the facility
    c. To make the facility more profitable
    d. a and b

18. Which of the following characteristics would you look for
    when interviewing lifeguard applicants?
    a. Speed, strength, and endurance
    b. The ability to relate well to others
    c. The ability to focus single-mindedly on a situation
    d. A very relaxed, easy going attitude

19. In-service training should—
    a. Be held at least once a month.
    b. Be held once a season.
    c. Be held when all lifeguards can attend.
    d. a and c.

20. To provide backup coverage, the lifeguard(s) who remain out
    of the water need to—
    a. Quickly rotate positions.
    b. Call for help from off-duty lifeguards or other staff.
    c. Make sure someone covers the area of responsibility of the
       lifeguard who has gone into the water.
    d. Ask patrons to help scan the pool.

21. Which of the following is an advantage of overlapping zones?
    a. It allows double coverage
    b. It requires fewer lifeguards
    c. It eliminates any confusion lifeguards may have about their area of responsibility
    d. It sharpens lifeguards' scanning skills

22. During rotation—
    a. All lifeguards rotate simultaneously.
    b. A patron takes over surveillance duty for one guard.
    c. Incoming lifeguards get on the stands as the outgoing lifeguards are getting down.
    d. The outgoing lifeguard scans from the deck while the incoming lifeguard gets into the stand.

23. You can fail to live up to your established standard of care by—
    a. Being negligent.
    b. Ensuring that participants in aquatic activity classes receive adequate instructions.
    c. Providing lifeguard staff with adequate in-service training.
    d. All of the above.

24. As head lifeguard, you are legally responsible for—
    a. Your actions only.
    b. Your actions and those of the lifeguards.
    c. The actions of all staff.
    d. All events and activities that take place at the facility.

25. As head lifeguard, you have a duty to—
    a. Respond if an emergency occurs at the facility.
    b. Provide in-service training for the lifeguard staff.
    c. Learn EMT skills.
    d. a and b.

26. If a person is unconscious or otherwise unable to grant consent—
   a. If you provide care, you would be guilty of invasion of privacy.
   b. You would not be protected by "Good Samaritan" laws.
   c. You should wait for EMT's to arrive and provide care.
   d. The law assumes implied consent, therefore you can provide care.

27. Total coverage—
   a. Is effective only at waterfront facilities.
   b. Is only to be used if a small number of patrons are in the water.
   c. Is effective only at waterpark facilities.
   d. Requires at least three roving lifeguards.

28. An American Red Cross water safety specialist—
   a. Has learned how to monitor safe pool chemical levels.
   b. Comes to a facility after an emergency to help debrief staff.
   c. Has a graduate degree in physical education.
   d. Coordinates swimming, water safety, and other courses.

29. As head lifeguard, at most facilities you are typically concerned with—
   a. Supervising and training staff.
   b. Ensuring the patrons have fun.
   c. Identifying and correcting hazards.
   d. a and c.

30. Patron load means—
    a. The number of possessions a patron is allowed to bring into the facility.
    b. The number of patrons who use the facility in any given week.
    c. The maximum number of patrons allowed in the water or in the facility at any time.
    d. The minimum number of patrons in the water at any given time.

31. The post-traumatic stress disorder a lifeguard may suffer includes—
    a. A condition in which the lifeguard is not able to cope, respond, or recover from the stress of a traumatic event.
    b. Sleeplessness that occurs after the lifeguard is injured while rescuing someone.
    c. The lifeguard's use of drugs or alcohol to cope with the daily stresses of job responsibility.
    d. The period after a lifeguard's stress from an incident has passed.

32. Which rule would you NOT post at a water slide?
    a. No swimming in the catch pool.
    b. A maximum of 3 patrons allowed on the slide at one time.
    c. Slide feet first.
    d. Patrons must take a swimming test before using the slide.

33. For which type of special patron programming would you especially have lifeguards review first aid for sudden illness?
    a. A competitive program
    b. A recreational program
    c. A fitness program
    d. An instructional program

34. To effectively guard a play structure, you may need to—
    a. Restrict the number of patrons who can use it at one time.
    b. Add lifeguarding staff.
    c. Position lifeguards so they have a clear view.
    d. All of the above.

35. Which statement about rules and regulations is correct?
    a. Lifeguards should know when to physically remove a patron from the facility.
    b. Lifeguards should memorize the rules but need not discuss them with patrons.
    c. Lifeguards should know how to deal with patrons who break rules.
    d. In certain situations, lifeguards should change certain rules.

36. Techniques for reviewing emergency action plans include—
    a. Walking through the plan
    b. A Fitness program
    c. Reviewing rules & regulations
    d. Filling out an incident report form

37. The head lifeguard's responsibilities may include all the following except one Which of these is usually the facility manager's responsibility?
    a. Deciding who clears the swimming area in an emergency.
    b. Deciding what time to close the facility on week nights.
    c. Directing a lifeguard or other staff to meet arriving EMS personnel.
    d. Deciding where to begin a search for a reported missing person.

38. As head lifeguard, you should have the lifeguarding team practice your facility's emergency action plans —
    a. Daily.
    b. At the beginning of the season only.
    c. Regularly.
    d. At orientation.

39. When developing a lifeguard schedule, you should consider—
    a. The lifeguards' ages and personal interests.
    b. The lifeguards' work records.
    c. The types of activities planned.
    d. b and c.

40. Orienting new lifeguards to the facility—
    a. Is not necessary; lifeguards should learn about the facility gradually.
    b. Should include personnel policies and communication techniques.
    c. Should not be done for fewer than four lifeguards.
    d. Is not necessary for experienced lifeguards.

Name _____   Date _____

DIRECTIONS: FIll in the correct answer for each question.

1.	(a) (b) (c) (d)				**21.**	(a) (b) (c) (d)
2.	(a) (b) (c) (d)				**22.**	(a) (b) (c) (d)
3.	(a) (b) (c) (d)				**23.**	(a) (b) (c) (d)
4.	(a) (b) (c) (d)				**24.**	(a) (b) (c) (d)
5.	(a) (b) (c) (d)				**25.**	(a) (b) (c) (d)
6.	(a) (b) (c) (d)				**26.**	(a) (b) (c) (d)
7.	(a) (b) (c) (d)				**27.**	(a) (b) (c) (d)
8.	(a) (b) (c) (d)				**28.**	(a) (b) (c) (d)
9.	(a) (b) (c) (d)				**29.**	(a) (b) (c) (d)
10.	(a) (b) (c) (d)				**30.**	(a) (b) (c) (d)
11.	(a) (b) (c) (d)				**31.**	(a) (b) (c) (d)
12.	(a) (b) (c) (d)				**32.**	(a) (b) (c) (d)
13.	(a) (b) (c) (d)				**33.**	(a) (b) (c) (d)
14.	(a) (b) (c) (d)				**34.**	(a) (b) (c) (d)
15.	(a) (b) (c) (d)				**35.**	(a) (b) (c) (d)
16.	(a) (b) (c) (d)				**36.**	(a) (b) (c) (d)
17.	(a) (b) (c) (d)				**37.**	(a) (b) (c) (d)
18.	(a) (b) (c) (d)				**38.**	(a) (b) (c) (d)
19.	(a) (b) (c) (d)				**39.**	(a) (b) (c) (d)
20.	(a) (b) (c) (d)				**40.**	(a) (b) (c) (d)

You may wish to go back and check your answers to be sure that you matched the right answer with the right question.

American Red Cross Head Lifeguard Course

Exam B

IMPORTANT: Read all instructions before beginning this exam.

INSTRUCTIONS: Mark all answers in pencil on the separate answer sheet. **Do not write on this exam.** The questions on this exam are multiple choice. Read each question slowly and carefully. Then choose the best answer and fill in that circle on the answer sheet. If you wish to change an answer, erase your first answer completely. Return this exam with your answer sheet to your instructor when you are finished.

EXAMPLE

ANSWER SHEET

xx. ⓐ ⓑ ⓒ ⬤

xx. As an American Red Cross Head Lifeguard Instructor, your responsibilities include—

a. Representing the American Red Cross in a positive manner.

b. Creating a nonthreatening environment that encourages participants to meet course objectives.

c. Remaining alert to your cultural and ethnic stereotypes and being creative and flexible in presenting material in an effective and culturally sensitive manner.

d. All of the above.

1. Communications as a form of injury prevention include—
   a. Explaining the facility's communication systems to patrons.
   b. Teaching lifeguards how to communicate with each other in ways patrons will not understand.
   c. Ensuring that warning signs and rules are posted at all facility entrances.
   d. Having sufficient lifeguards on duty so that one is always available to answer questions.

2. Which is an intent of risk management?
   a. To prevent financial loss to the facility
   b. To improve working conditions at the facility
   c. To make the facility more profitable
   d. a and b

3. How far in advance should you ideally make up lifeguard schedules?
   a. One day in advance
   b. At least two weeks in advance
   c. One week in advance
   d. None of the above

4. Which of the following is an advantage of overlapping zones?
   a. It allows double coverage.
   b. It requires fewer lifeguards.
   c. It eliminates any confusion lifeguards may have about their area of responsibility.
   d. It sharpens lifeguards' scanning skills.

5. To provide backup coverage, the lifeguard(s) who remain out of the water need to—
   a. Quickly rotate positions.
   b. Call for help from off-duty lifeguards or other staff.
   c. Make sure someone covers the area of responsibility of the lifeguard who has gone into the water.
   d. Ask patrons to help scan the pool.

6. During rotation—
   a. All lifeguards rotate simultaneously.
   b. A patron takes over surveillance duty for one guard.
   c. Incoming lifeguards get on the stands as the outgoing lifeguards are getting down.
   d. The outgoing lifeguard scans from the deck while the incoming lifeguard gets into the stand.

7. Which safety precaution should you take for diving pools?
   a. Cover diving policies in your in-service training program.
   b. Post signs specifying rules and regulations next to the diving board.
   c. Have a lifeguard supervise diving activity only if is from a diving board or platform over 3 meters high.
   d. a and b.

8. Which rule would you not post at a water slide?
   a. A maximum of three patrons are allowed on the slide at one time.
   b. No swimming is allowed in the catch pool.
   c. Slide feet first.
   d. Patrons must take a swimming test before using the slide.

9. Total coverage—
   a. Is effective only at waterfront facilities.
   b. Is only to be used if a small number of patrons are in the water.
   c. Is effective only at waterpark facilities.
   d. Requires at least three roving lifeguards.

10. A head lifeguard needs which of the following characteristics?
    a. Technically correct swimming strokes
    b. The ability to predict weather changes
    c. Pool operator skills
    d. CPR and first aid skills

11. As head lifeguard, at most facilities you are typically concerned with—
    a. Supervising and training staff.
    b. Ensuring the patrons have fun.
    c. Identifying and correcting hazards.
    d. a and c.

12. Bulkheads present safety problems because—
    a. Patrons bump into them.
    b. Patrons swim beneath them.
    c. Patrons cannot see around them.
    d. a and c.

13. To reduce risks at spas, you should—
    a. Allow alcoholic beverages.
    b. Ensure the water temperature is not too high.
    c. Time every spa user.
    d. a and b.

14. A daily check should include—
    a. The facility office.
    b. All areas open to patrons.
    c. The first aid station.
    d. b and c.

15. If lifeguards need information about health, sanitation, and security measures at the facility, they should—
    a. Ask the maintenance staff.
    b. Check the local health department regulations.
    c. Look in the policies and procedures manual.
    d. Look in the emergency action plans.

16. Maintenance and cleanliness inspections —
    a. Cover the bottom of the swimming area only.
    b. Include the chemical storage area.
    c. Do not include windows, doors, and grates.
    d. Include the locker rooms.

17. To tell if pool water is sufficiently clear—
    a. Do a chemical test.
    b. See if you can clearly recognize drain covers and racing lines.
    c. Tell a lifeguard to lie down on the pool bottom at the deep end and see if you can see him or her clearly from the shallow end.
    d. Get in the pool and look around underwater.

18. Maintenance and cleanliness duties are usually performed—
    a. Daily.
    b. Only before opening the pool.
    c. Only at closing time.
    d. Once a week.

19. To perform their job effectively, lifeguards need to be—
    a. Courteous and consistent.
    b. Thoughtful and introspective.
    c. Dynamic.
    d. All of the above.

20. Which statement about rules and regulations is correct?
    a. Lifeguards should know when to physically remove a patron from the facility.
    b. Lifeguards should memorize the rules but need not discuss them with patrons.
    c. Lifeguards should know how to deal with patrons who break rules.
    d. In certain situations, lifeguards should change certain rules.

21. Chemicals should be stored—
    a. Where lifeguards have easy access to them.
    b. In their original containers.
    c. Near the facility office.
    d. In clean, marked new containers.

22. Which of the following help provide facility security?
    a. Undamaged doors, gates, and fences
    b. Restricting patron access to certain times
    c. Video surveillance
    d. All of the above

23. Lifeguard applicants should be tested on—
    a. Fitness.
    b. Appearance.
    c. CPR and First Aid.
    d. b and c.

24. As head lifeguard, you should have the lifeguarding team practice your facility's emergency action plans—
    a. Daily.
    b. At the beginning of the season only.
    c. Regularly.
    d. At orientation.

25. Orienting new lifeguards to the facility—
    a. Is not necessary; lifeguards should learn about the facility gradually.
    b. Should include personnel policies and communication techniques.
    c. Should not be done for fewer than four lifeguards.
    d. Is not necessary for experienced lifeguards.

26. The head lifeguard's responsibilities may include all of the following except one. Which of these is usually the facility manager's responsibility?
    a. Deciding who clears the swimming area in an emergency
    b. Deciding what time to close the facility on weeknights
    c. Directing a lifeguard or other staff to meet arriving EMS personnel
    d. Deciding where to begin a search for a reported missing person

27. You can fail to live up to your established standard of care by—
    a. Being negligent.
    b. Ensuring that participants in aquatic activity classes receive adequate instructions.
    c. Providing lifeguard staff with adequate in-service training.
    d. All of the above.

28. As head lifeguard, you are responsible for—
    a. Your actions only.
    b. Your actions and the actions of those you supervise.
    c. The actions of all staff.
    d. All events and activities that take place at the facility.

29. An American Red Cross water safety specialist—
    a. Has learned how to monitor safe pool chemical levels.
    b. Comes to a facility after an emergency to help debrief staff.
    c. Has a graduate degree in physical education.
    d. Coordinates swimming, water safety, and other courses.

30. Patron load means—
    a. The number of possessions a patron is allowed to bring into the facility.
    b. The number of patrons who use the facility in any given week.
    c. The maximum number of patrons allowed in the water or in the facility at any time.
    d. The minimum number of patrons in the water at any given time.

31. For which type of special patron programming would you especially have lifeguards review first aid for sudden illness?
    a. A fitness program
    b. A recreational program
    c. An instructional program
    d. A competitive program

32. When developing a lifeguard schedule, you should consider—
    a. The lifeguards' ages and personal interests.
    b. The lifeguards' work records.
    c. The types of activities planned.
    d. b and c.

33. Which rule might you post at a wading pool?
    a. All children must be accompanied by an adult.
    b. Children may not use the wading pool.
    c. No diving into the pool.
    d. a and b.

34. Before you hire a lifeguard, you should be sure he or she—
    a. Can demonstrate superior swimming stroke techniques.
    b. Has proof of age and current certifications.
    c. Can pass a timed swimming test.
    d. Has a valid driver's license.

35. As head lifeguard, you have a duty to—
    a. Respond if an emergency occurs at the facility.
    b. Provide in-service training for the lifeguard staff.
    c. Learn EMT skills.
    d. a and b.

36. If a person is unconscious or otherwise unable to grant consent—
    a. If you provide care, you will be guilty of invasion of privacy.
    b. If you provide care you will not be protected by "Good Samaritan" laws.
    c. You should wait for EMTs to arrive and provide care.
    d. The law assumes implied consent therefore, you can provide care.

37. Which of the following characteristics would you look for when interviewing lifeguard applicants?
    a. Speed, strength, and endurance
    b. The ability to relate well to others
    c. The ability to focus single-mindedly on a situation
    d. A very relaxed, easy going attitude

38. To effectively guard a play structure, you may need to—
    a. Restrict the number of patrons who can use it at one time.
    b. Add lifeguarding staff.
    c. Position lifeguards so they have a clear view.
    d. All of the above.

39. A lifeguard's post-traumatic stress disorder is best described as—
    a. The lifeguard's use of drugs or alcohol to cope with the daily stresses of job responsibility.
    b. Sleeplessness that occurs after the lifeguard is injured while rescuing someone.
    c. The period after a lifeguard's stress from an incident has passed.
    d. A condition in which the lifeguard is not able to cope with, respond to, or recover from the stress of a traumatic event.

40. Ways of developing a staff schedule include—
    a. Assigning the best shifts to the best swimmers.
    b. Assigning shifts based on requests from lifeguards the day before.
    c. Assigning shifts based on set criteria, such as seniority.
    d. All of the above.

Name _____ Date _____

DIRECTIONS: FIll in the correct answer for each question.

1.	(a)	(b)	c	(d)
2.	(a)	(b)	(c)	(d)
3.	(a)	(b)	(c)	(d)
4.	(a)	(b)	(c)	(d)
5.	(a)	(b)	(c)	(d)
6.	(a)	(b)	(c)	(d)
7.	(a)	(b)	(c)	(d)
8.	(a)	(b)	(c)	(d)
9.	(a)	(b)	(c)	(d)
10.	(a)	(b)	(c)	(d)
11.	(a)	(b)	(c)	(d)
12.	(a)	(b)	(c)	(d)
13.	(a)	(b)	(c)	(d)
14.	(a)	(b)	(c)	(d)
15.	(a)	(b)	(c)	(d)
16.	(a)	(b)	(c)	(d)
17.	(a)	(b)	(c)	(d)
18.	(a)	(b)	(c)	(d)
19.	(a)	(b)	(c)	(d)
20.	(a)	(b)	(c)	(d)

21.	(a)	(b)	(c)	(d)
22.	(a)	(b)	(c)	(d)
23.	(a)	(b)	(c)	(d)
24.	(a)	(b)	(c)	(d)
25.	(a)	(b)	(c)	(d)
26.	(a)	(b)	(c)	(d)
27.	(a)	(b)	(c)	(d)
28.	(a)	(b)	(c)	(d)
29.	(a)	(b)	(c)	(d)
30.	(a)	(b)	(c)	(d)
31.	(a)	(b)	(c)	(d)
32.	(a)	(b)	(c)	(d)
33.	(a)	(b)	(c)	(d)
34.	(a)	(b)	(c)	(d)
35.	(a)	(b)	(c)	(d)
36.	(a)	(b)	(c)	(d)
37.	(a)	(b)	(c)	(d)
38.	(a)	(b)	(c)	(d)
39.	(a)	(b)	(c)	(d)
40.	(a)	(b)	(c)	(d)

You may wish to go back and check your answers to be sure that you matched the right answer with the right question.

Index

KEY

#	a	b	c	d		#	a	b	c	d
1.	a	b	●	d		26.	a	b	c	●
2.	a	b	c	●		27.	a	●	c	d
3.	a	b	c	●		28.	●	b	c	d
4.	a	●	c	d		29.	a	●	c	d
5.	a	b	●	d		30.	a	b	c	●
6.	a	b	●	d		31.	a	b	c	●
7.	a	b	●	d		32.	a	b	c	●
8.	a	b	c	●		33.	a	b	c	●
9.	●	b	c	d		34.	a	●	c	d
10.	a	b	●	d		35.	●	b	c	d
11.	a	b	c	●		36.	a	b	c	●
12.	a	b	c	●		37.	a	b	●	d
13.	a	●	c	d		38.	a	b	●	d
14.	a	●	c	d		39.	a	b	c	●
15.	●	b	c	d		40.	a	b	●	d
16.	a	b	●	d		41.	a	●	c	d
17.	a	●	c	d		42.	a	b	●	d
18.	●	b	c	d		43.	a	●	c	d
19.	a	●	c	d		44.	a	b	●	d
20.	a	●	c	d		45.	a	b	c	●
21.	a	●	c	d		46.	a	●	c	d
22.	a	b	●	d		47.	●	b	c	d
23.	●	b	c	d		48.	a	b	●	d
24.	a	b	●	d		49.	a	b	●	d
25.	a	b	●	d		50.	a	b	●	d

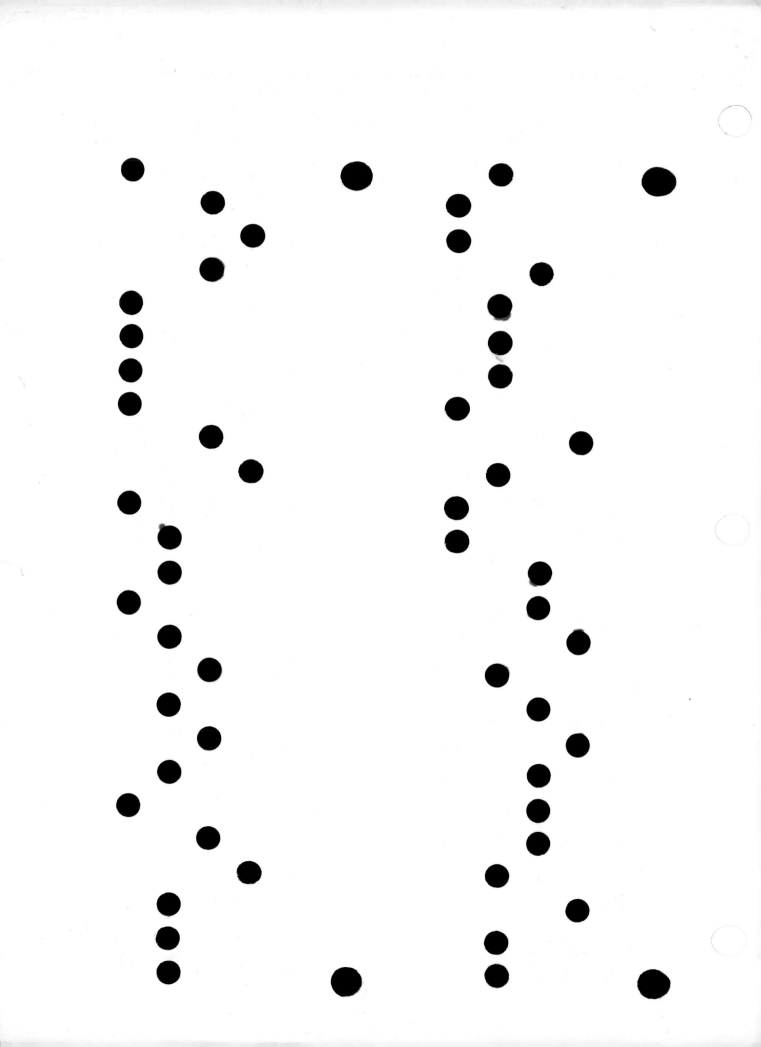

1. a b c **(d)**
2. a **(b)** c d
3. a **(b)** c d
4. a b c **(d)**
5. a b **(c)** d
6. a b c **(d)**
7. a **(b)** c d
8. **(a)** b c d
9. **(a)** b c d
10. a b **(c)** d
11. a **(b)** c d
12. a b c **(d)**
13. a b **(c)** d
14. a b **(c)** d
15. a **(b)** c d
16. a **(b)** c d
17. **(a)** b c d
18. a **(b)** c d
19. a b c **(d)**
20. a b **(c)** d
21. **(a)** b c d
22. a b c **(d)**
23. **(a)** b c d
24. a **(b)** c d
25. a b c **(d)**

26. a b c **(d)**
27. a **(b)** c d
28. a b c **(d)**
29. a b c **(d)**
30. a b **(c)** d
31. **(a)** b c d
32. a **(b)** c d
33. a b **(c)** d
34. a b c **(d)**
35. a b **(c)** d
36. **(a)** b c d
37. a **(b)** c d
38. a b **(c)** d
39. a b c **(d)**
40. a **(b)** c d
41. a b **(c)** d
42. **(a)** b c d
43. a **(b)** c d
44. **(a)** b c d
45. a b **(c)** d
46. a b c **(d)**
47. a b c **(d)**
48. **(a)** b c d
49. a **(b)** c d
50. a b c **(d)**

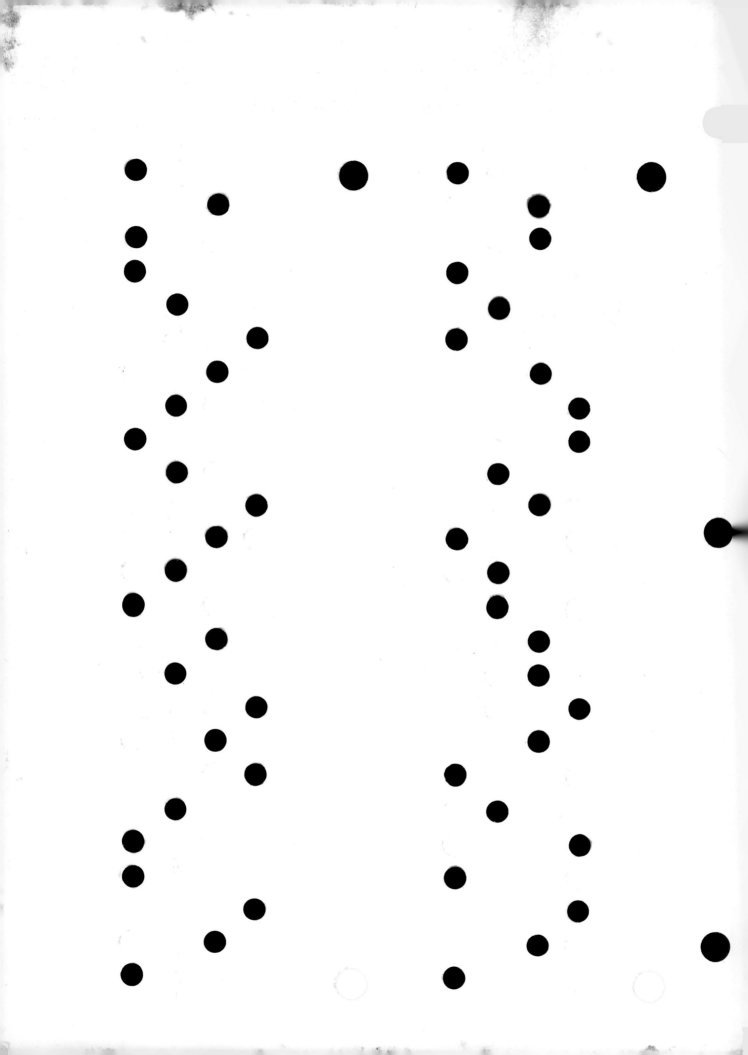

#	a	b	c	d		#	a	b	c	d
1.			●			26.				●
2.				●		27.		●		
3.			●			28.				●
4.				●		29.			●	
5.		●				30.			●	
6.		●				31.			●	
7.		●				32.				●
8.	●					33.		●		
9.			●			34.			●	
10.			●			35.		●		
11.	●					36.	●			
12.	●					37.	●			
13.				●		38.				●
14.	●					39.		●		
15.		●				40.		●		
16.			●			41.			●	
17.			●			42.		●		
18.		●				43.				●
19.	●					44.		●		
20.				●		45.			●	
21.				●		46.		●		
22.	●					47.				●
23.	●					48.	●			
24.	●					49.				●
25.				●		50.				●

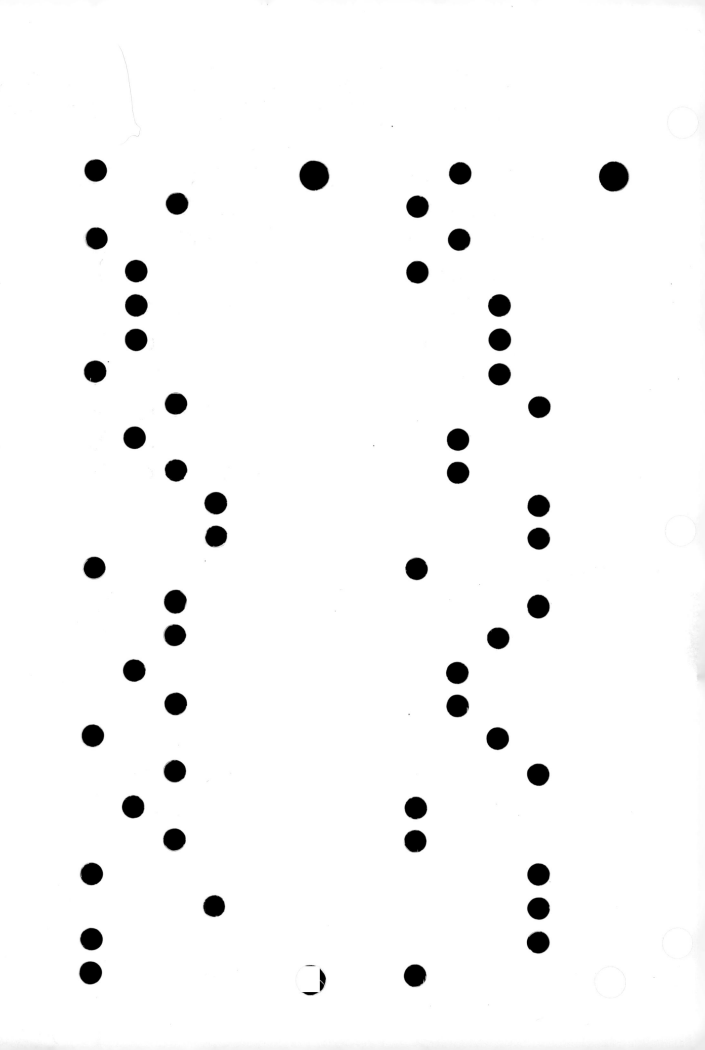

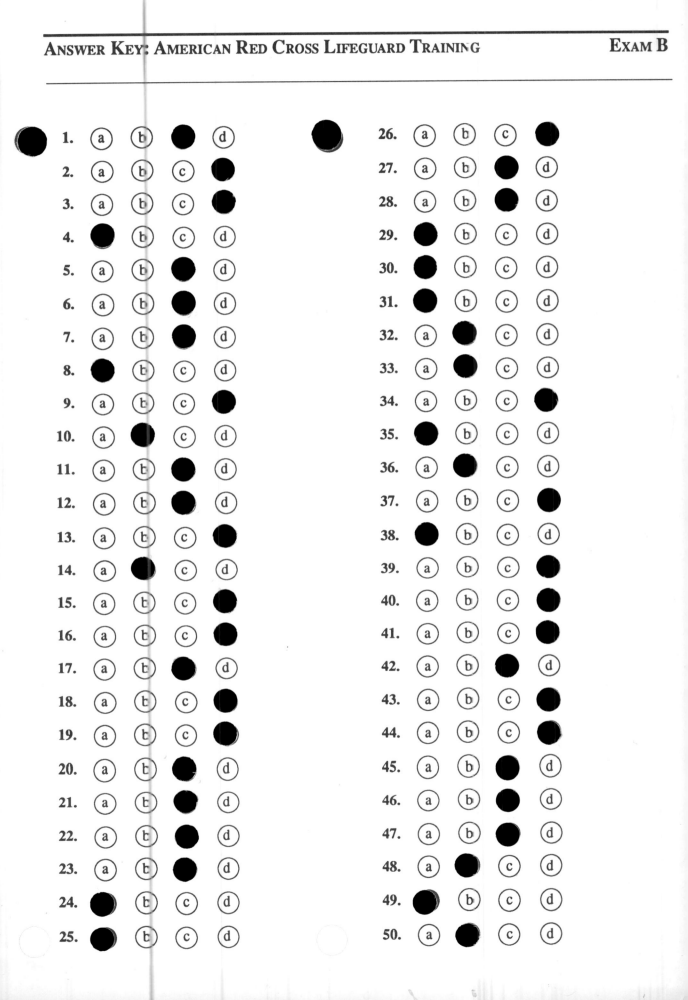

1. c
2. d
3. d
4. a
5. c
6. c
7. c
8. a
9. d
10. b
11. c
12. c
13. d
14. b
15. d
16. d
17. c
18. d
19. d
20. c
21. c
22. c
23. c
24. a
25. a

26. d
27. c
28. c
29. a
30. a
31. a
32. b
33. b
34. d
35. a
36. b
37. d
38. a
39. d
40. d
41. d
42. c
43. d
44. d
45. c
46. c
47. c
48. b
49. a
50. b

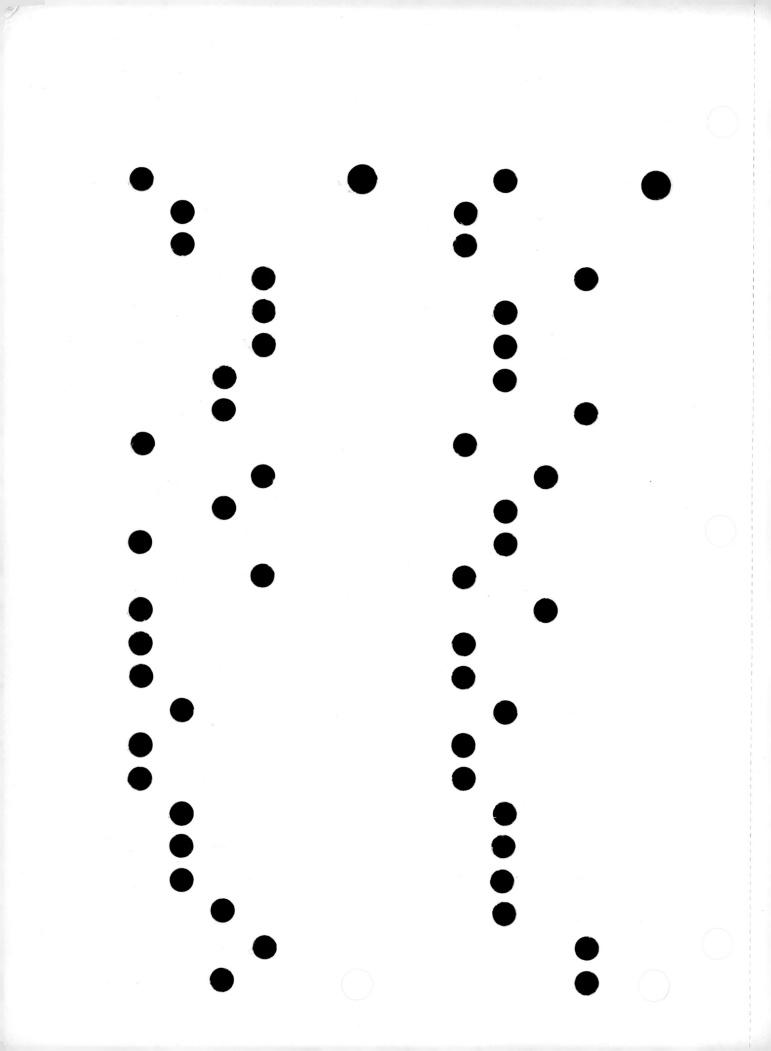

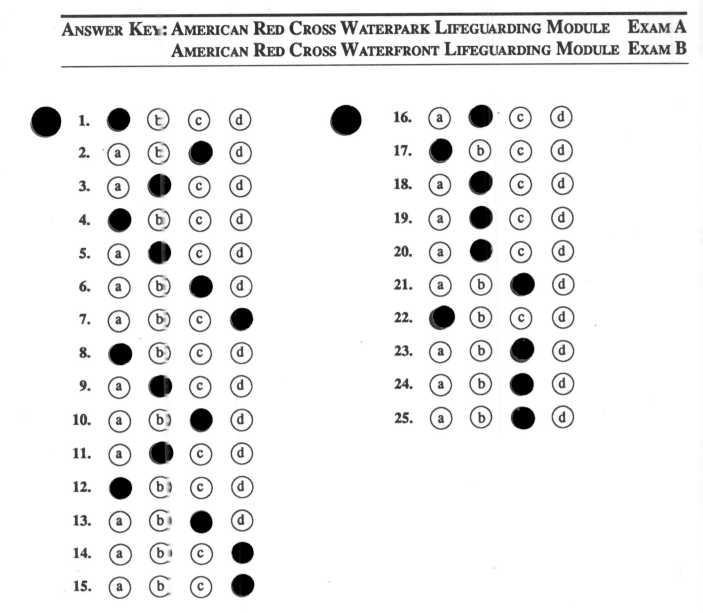

1. **a** b c d
2. a b **c** d
3. a **b** c d
4. **a** b c d
5. a **b** c d
6. a b **c** d
7. a b c **d**
8. **a** b c d
9. a **b** c d
10. a b **c** d
11. a **b** c d
12. **a** b c d
13. a b **c** d
14. a b c **d**
15. a b c **d**

16. a **b** c d
17. **a** b c d
18. a **b** c d
19. a **b** c d
20. a **b** c d
21. a b **c** d
22. **a** b c d
23. a b **c** d
24. a b **c** d
25. a b **c** d

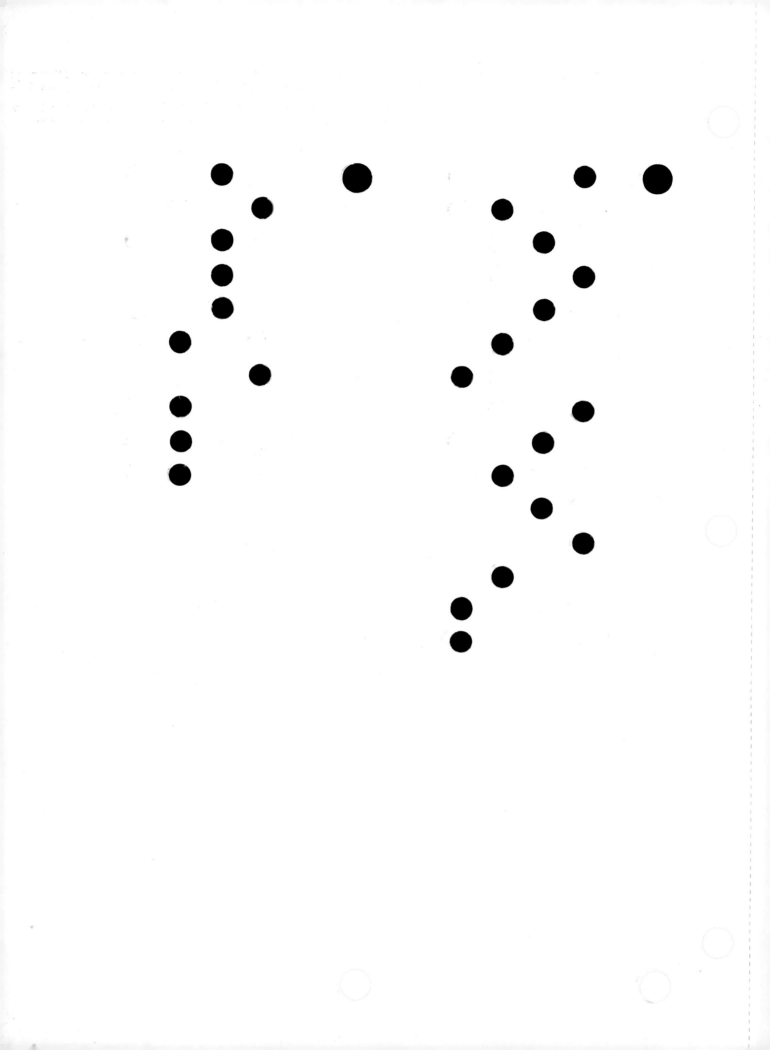

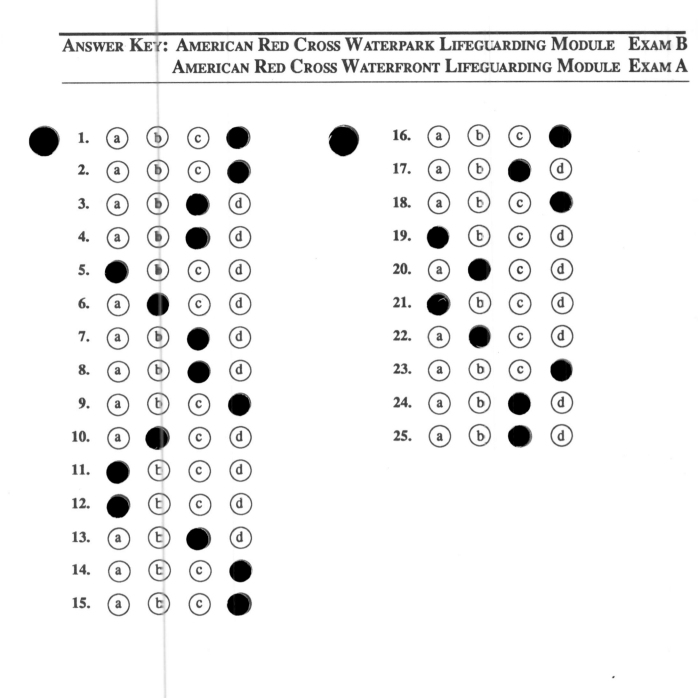

1. (a) (b) (c) ●
2. (a) (b) (c) ●
3. (a) (b) ● (d)
4. (a) (b) ● (d)
5. ● (b) (c) (d)
6. (a) ● (c) (d)
7. (a) (b) ● (d)
8. (a) (b) ● (d)
9. (a) (b) (c) ●
10. (a) ● (c) (d)
11. ● (b) (c) (d)
12. ● (b) (c) (d)
13. (a) (b) ● (d)
14. (a) (b) (c) ●
15. (a) (b) (c) ●

16. (a) (b) (c) ●
17. (a) (b) ● (d)
18. (a) (b) (c) ●
19. ● (b) (c) (d)
20. (a) ● (c) (d)
21. ● (b) (c) (d)
22. (a) ● (c) (d)
23. (a) (b) (c) ●
24. (a) (b) ● (d)
25. (a) (b) ● (d)

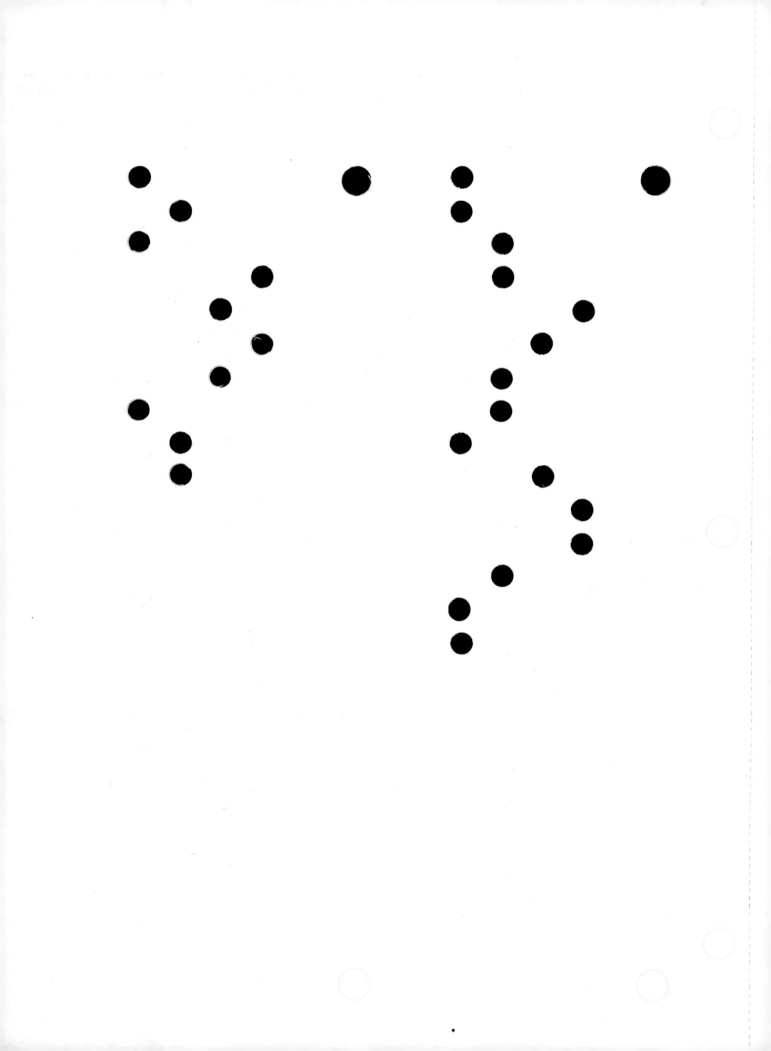

1. d
2. b
3. b
4. d
5. c
6. d
7. b
8. a
9. a
10. c
11. b
12. d
13. c
14. c
15. b
16. b
17. a
18. b
19. d
20. c

21. a
22. d
23. a
24. b
25. d
26. d
27. b
28. d
29. d
30. c
31. a
32. b
33. c
34. d
35. c
36. a
37. b
38. c
39. d
40. b

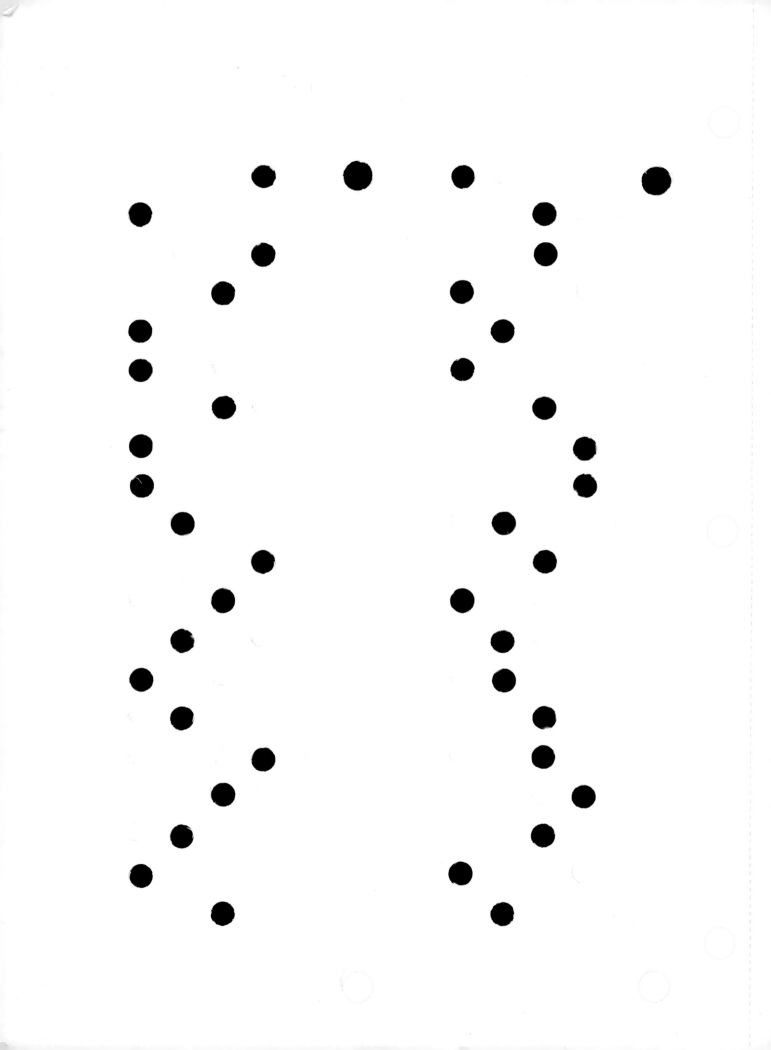

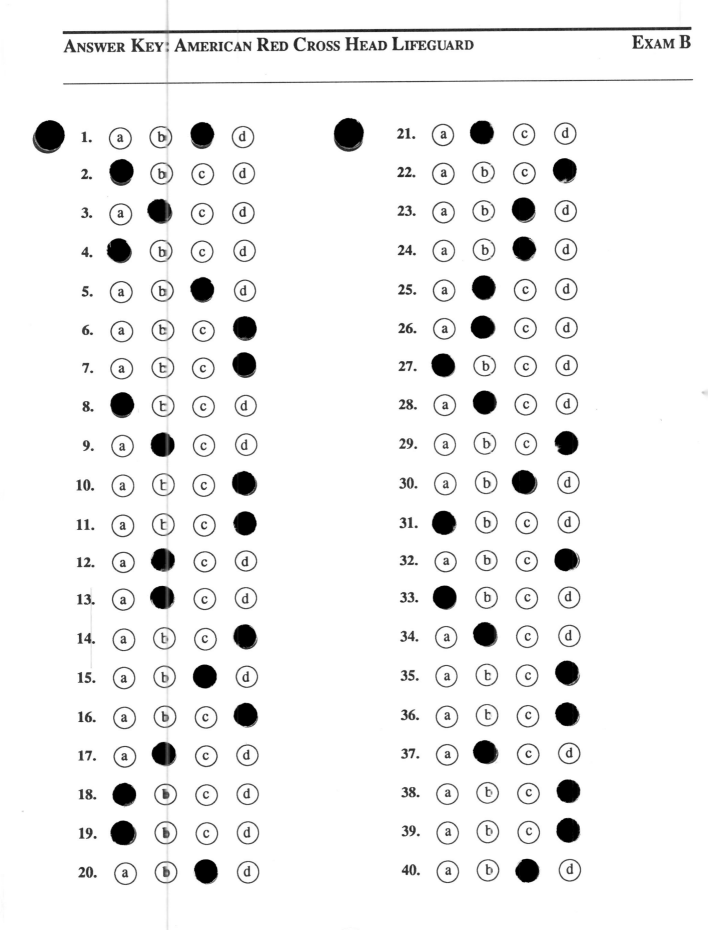

1. (a) (b) ● (d)   21. (a) ● (c) (d)
2. ● (b) (c) (d)   22. (a) (b) (c) ●
3. (a) ● (c) (d)   23. (a) (b) ● (d)
4. ● (b) (c) (d)   24. (a) (b) ● (d)
5. (a) (b) ● (d)   25. (a) ● (c) (d)
6. (a) (b) (c) ●   26. (a) ● (c) (d)
7. (a) (b) (c) ●   27. ● (b) (c) (d)
8. ● (b) (c) (d)   28. (a) ● (c) (d)
9. (a) ● (c) (d)   29. (a) (b) (c) ●
10. (a) (b) (c) ●   30. (a) (b) ● (d)
11. (a) (b) (c) ●   31. ● (b) (c) (d)
12. (a) ● (c) (d)   32. (a) (b) (c) ●
13. (a) ● (c) (d)   33. ● (b) (c) (d)
14. (a) (b) (c) ●   34. (a) ● (c) (d)
15. (a) (b) ● (d)   35. (a) (b) (c) ●
16. (a) (b) (c) ●   36. (a) (b) (c) ●
17. (a) ● (c) (d)   37. (a) ● (c) (d)
18. ● (b) (c) (d)   38. (a) (b) (c) ●
19. ● (b) (c) (d)   39. (a) (b) (c) ●
20. (a) (b) ● (d)   40. (a) (b) ● (d)

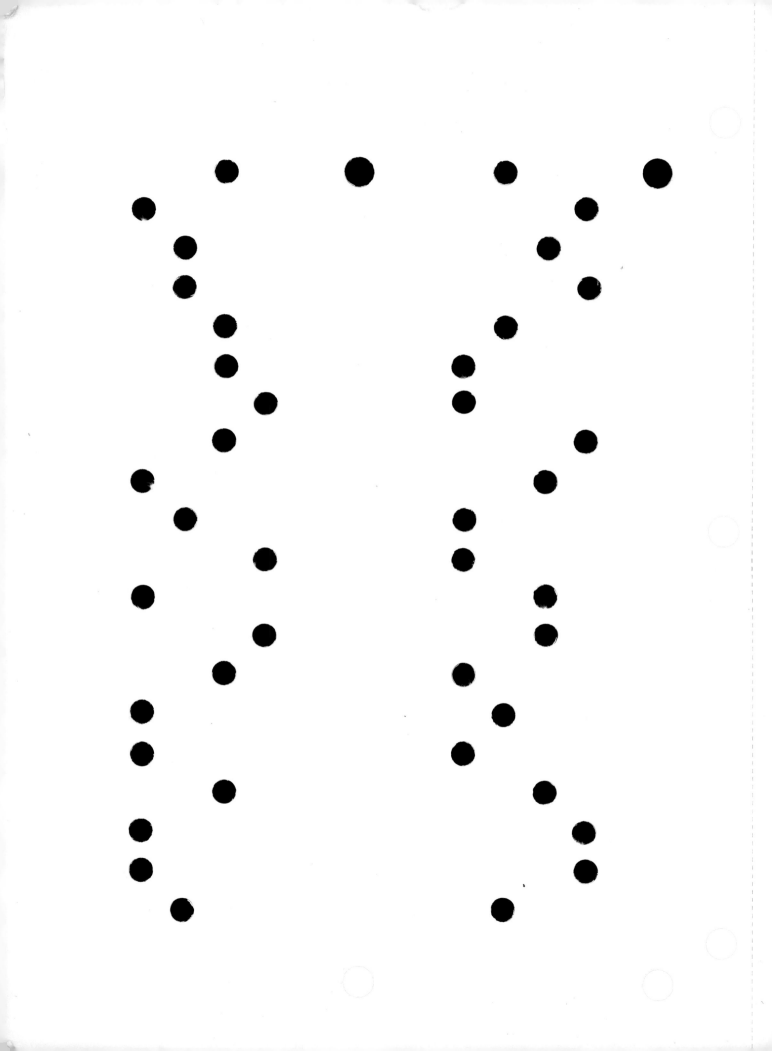

American Red Cross

Lifeguarding Program Instructor Evaluation

1 The course I am evaluating is:
- ○ Lifeguard Training
- ○ Waterfront Lifeguarding
- ○ Waterpark Lifeguarding
- ○ Head Lifeguard
- ○ Community Water Safety

2 Number of participants enrolled in this course:
- ○ 1–5
- ○ 6–10
- ○ 11–15
- ○ 16–20
- ○ More than 20

3 Were the participants able to complete the course within the number of hours indicated in the Instructor Manual?
- ○ Yes
- ○ No

4 If you answered "No" to question 3, approximately how much additional time was needed?
- ○ Less than 1 hour
- ○ 1–2 hours
- ○ 2–3 hours
- ○ More than 3 hours

  Why? _____

5 If you instructed a course that involved skill practice sessions, were the suggested times for skill practice:
- ○ Much too long
- ○ A little too long
- ○ About right
- ○ A little too short
- ○ Much too short

6 If your course involved skills, was the progression of skills appropriate?
- ○ Yes
- ○ No

If "No", please explain any problems.

_____
_____

7 If any of the participants failed the course, what was the most common reason for the failure?
- ○ Final written test
- ○ Unable to complete individual skill items
- ○ Final skills test
- ○ Inadequate attendance

8 In which setting did you primarily teach this course?
- ○ Pool
- ○ Waterfront (lake or ocean)
- ○ Waterpark

9 Was there a lifeguard on duty at the facility while you conducted water sessions?
- ○ Yes
- ○ No

10 How long have you been an American Red Cross Lifeguarding instructor?
- ○ Less than 6 months
- ○ 6 months to 1 year
- ○ 1 to 2 years
- ○ 3 to 5 years
- ○ More than 5 years

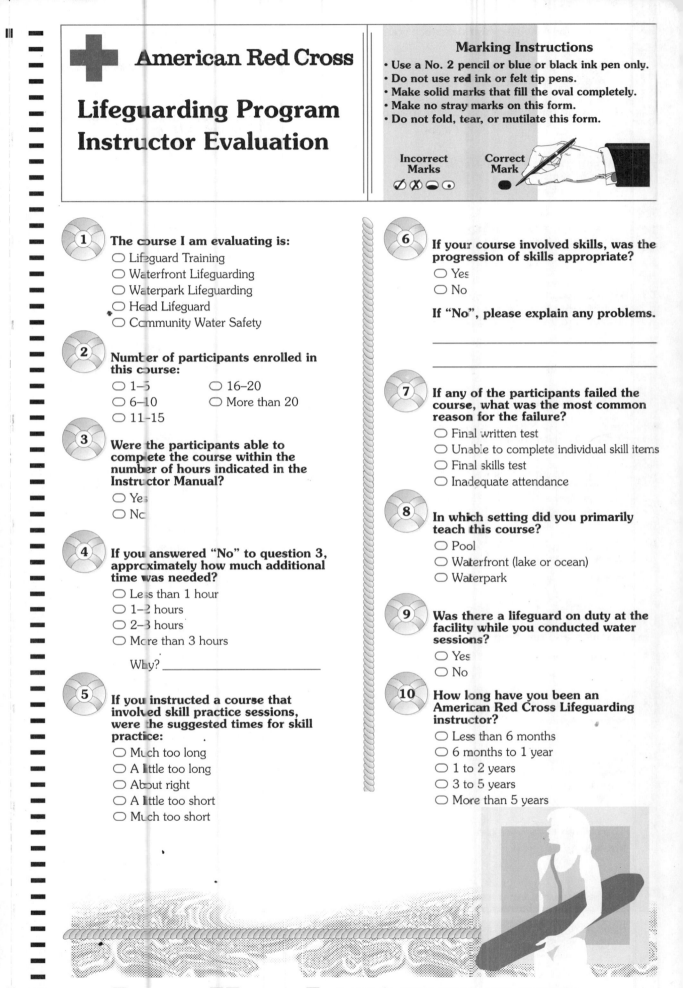

11 Which of the following best describes you?
- ○ Red Cross volunteer instructor
- ○ Red Cross paid instructor
- ○ Red Cross instructor paid by another agency

12 How many times have you taught this course?
- ○ 1
- ○ 2
- ○ 3 or more

13 Did you use a co-instructor to assist with this course?
- ○ Yes
- ○ No

14 Did you use a lifeguarding instructor aide to assist with this course?
- ○ Yes
- ○ No

15 How satisfied are you that your course participants learned enough to put their knowledge and skills into practice?
- ○ Very satisfied
- ○ Satisfied
- ○ Neither satisfied nor dissatisfied
- ○ Dissatisfied
- ○ Very dissatisfied

Mark one item on each line to show how much you agree or disagree with the following:

16 The participant manual was clear and understandable
Strongly Agree ▶▶▶ Strongly Disagree
① ② ③ ④ ⑤

17 The study questions/self-assessment exercise in the manual are helpful to the participants
Strongly Agree ▶▶▶ Strongly Disagree
① ② ③ ④ ⑤

18 The Instructor Manual was useful in planning and teaching this course
Strongly Agree ▶▶▶ Strongly Disagree
① ② ③ ④ ⑤

19 The lesson plans were clear and understandable
Strongly Agree ▶▶▶ Strongly Disagree
① ② ③ ④ ⑤

20 The Administrative section was clear and understandable
Strongly Agree ▶▶▶ Strongly Disagree
① ② ③ ④ ⑤

21 The written tests were clear and understandable
Strongly Agree ▶▶▶ Strongly Disagree
① ② ③ ④ ⑤

22 The Instructor Manual was useful in providing guidance for evaluating participants
Strongly Agree ▶▶▶ Strongly Disagree
① ② ③ ④ ⑤

23 If used, videos were clear and easy to follow
Strongly Agree ▶▶▶ Strongly Disagree
① ② ③ ④ ⑤

In an effort to better serve customers from all backgrounds, we ask that you answer a few questions about yourself:

24 Are you from Hispanic origin or background?
- ○ Yes
- ○ No

25 Do you consider yourself:
- ○ White
- ○ Black
- ○ Asian
- ○ Other ▶ What?

26 Do you regularly speak any language other than English with your family?
- ○ Yes
- ○ No

27 Age:

| ⓪①②③④⑤⑥⑦⑧⑨ |
| ⓪①②③④⑤⑥⑦⑧⑨ |

28 What is the highest grade that you have completed?
- ○ Eighth grade or less
- ○ Some high school
- ○ Completed high school
- ○ Some college courses
- ○ Completed college
- ○ Graduate school

Chapter Code				Instructor Code			
⓪	⓪	⓪	⓪	⓪	⓪	⓪	⓪
①	①	①	①	①	①	①	①
②	②	②	②	②	②	②	②
③	③	③	③	③	③	③	③
④	④	④	④	④	④	④	④
⑤	⑤	⑤	⑤	⑤	⑤	⑤	⑤
⑥	⑥	⑥	⑥	⑥	⑥	⑥	⑥
⑦	⑦	⑦	⑦	⑦	⑦	⑦	⑦
⑧	⑧	⑧	⑧	⑧	⑧	⑧	⑧
⑨	⑨	⑨	⑨	⑨	⑨	⑨	⑨

Thank you for taking the time to answer these questions. If you have any additional comments about the course, please write them on a separate sheet and include them with this evaluation.

American Red Cross

Lifeguarding Program Instructor Evaluation

1 The course I am evaluating is:
- ○ Lifeguard Training
- ○ Waterfront Lifeguarding
- ○ Waterpark Lifeguarding
- ○ Head Lifeguard
- ○ Community Water Safety

2 Number of participants enrolled in this course:
- ○ 1–5
- ○ 6–10
- ○ 11–15
- ○ 16–20
- ○ More than 20

3 Were the participants able to complete the course within the number of hours indicated in the Instructor Manual?
- ○ Yes
- ○ No

4 If you answered "No" to question 3, approximately how much additional time was needed?
- ○ Less than 1 hour
- ○ 1–2 hours
- ○ 2–3 hours
- ○ More than 3 hours

Why? _____

5 If you instructed a course that involved skill practice sessions, were the suggested times for skill practice:
- ○ Much too long
- ○ A little too long
- ○ About right
- ○ A little too short
- ○ Much too short

6 If your course involved skills, was the progression of skills appropriate?
- ○ Yes
- ○ No

If "No", please explain any problems.

_____

_____

7 If any of the participants failed the course, what was the most common reason for the failure?
- ○ Final written test
- ○ Unable to complete individual skill items
- ○ Final skills test
- ○ Inadequate attendance

8 In which setting did you primarily teach this course?
- ○ Pool
- ○ Waterfront (lake or ocean)
- ○ Waterpark

9 Was there a lifeguard on duty at the facility while you conducted water sessions?
- ○ Yes
- ○ No

10 How long have you been an American Red Cross Lifeguarding instructor?
- ○ Less than 6 months
- ○ 6 months to 1 year
- ○ 1 to 2 years
- ○ 3 to 5 years
- ○ More than 5 years

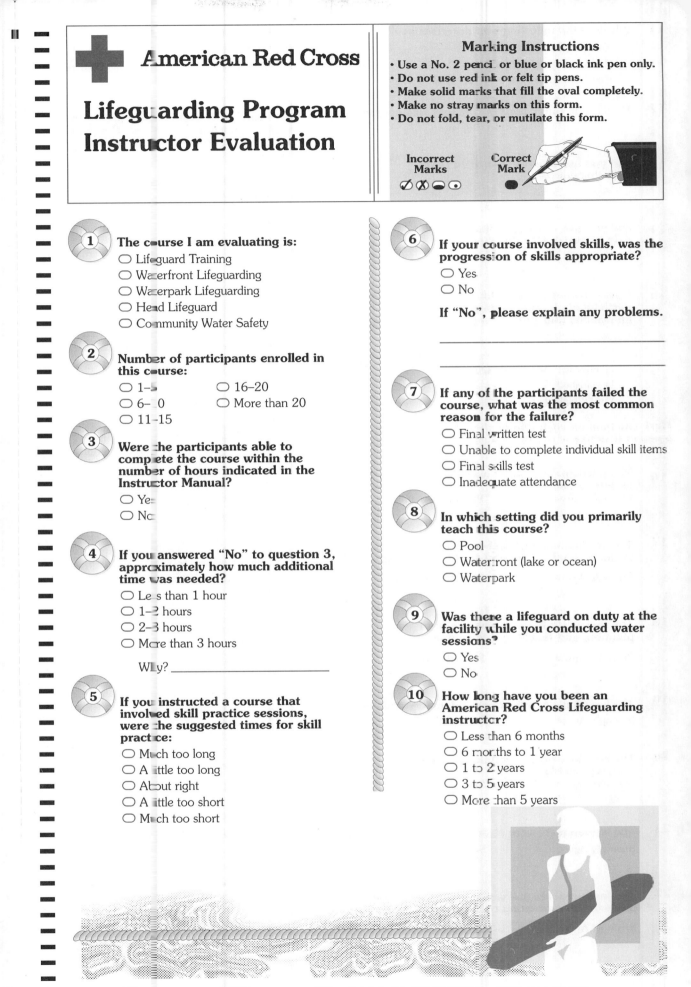

11 Which of the following best describes you?
- ○ Red Cross volunteer instructor
- ○ Red Cross paid instructor
- ○ Red Cross instructor paid by another agency

12 How many times have you taught this course?
- ○ 1   ○ 2   ○ 3 or more

13 Did you use a co-instructor to assist with this course?
- ○ Yes   ○ No

14 Did you use a lifeguarding instructor aide to assist with this course?
- ○ Yes   ○ No

15 How satisfied are you that your course participants learned enough to put their knowledge and skills into practice?
- ○ Very satisfied
- ○ Satisfied
- ○ Neither satisfied nor dissatisfied
- ○ Dissatisfied
- ○ Very dissatisfied

Mark one item on each line to show how much you agree or disagree with the following:

16 The participant manual was clear and understandable
Strongly Agree ▶ ▶ ▶ Strongly Disagree
① ② ③ ④ ⑤

17 The study questions/self-assessment exercise in the manual are helpful to the participants
Strongly Agree ▶ ▶ ▶ Strongly Disagree
① ② ③ ④ ⑤

18 The Instructor Manual was useful in planning and teaching this course
Strongly Agree ▶ ▶ ▶ Strongly Disagree
① ② ③ ④ ⑤

19 The lesson plans were clear and understandable
Strongly Agree ▶ ▶ ▶ Strongly Disagree
① ② ③ ④ ⑤

20 The Administrative section was clear and understandable
Strongly Agree ▶ ▶ ▶ Strongly Disagree
① ② ③ ④ ⑤

21 The written tests were clear and understandable
Strongly Agree ▶ ▶ ▶ Strongly Disagree
① ② ③ ④ ⑤

22 The Instructor Manual was useful in providing guidance for evaluating participants
Strongly Agree ▶ ▶ ▶ Strongly Disagree
① ② ③ ④ ⑤

23 If used, videos were clear and easy to follow
Strongly Agree ▶ ▶ ▶ Strongly Disagree
① ② ③ ④ ⑤

In an effort to better serve customers from all backgrounds, we ask that you answer a few questions about yourself:

24 Are you from Hispanic origin or background?
- ○ Yes   ○ No

25 Do you consider yourself:
- ○ White
- ○ Black
- ○ Asian
- ○ Other ▶ What? _____

26 Do you regularly speak any language other than English with your family?
- ○ Yes   ○ No

27 Age:

| ⓪①②③④⑤⑥⑦⑧⑨ |
| ⓪①②③④⑤⑥⑦⑧⑨ |

28 What is the highest grade that you have completed?
- ○ Eighth grade or less
- ○ Some high school
- ○ Completed high school
- ○ Some college courses
- ○ Completed college
- ○ Graduate school

Chapter Code	Instructor Code
⓪⓪⓪⓪	⓪⓪⓪⓪
①①①①	①①①①
②②②②	②②②②
③③③③	③③③③
④④④④	④④④④
⑤⑤⑤⑤	⑤⑤⑤⑤
⑥⑥⑥⑥	⑥⑥⑥⑥
⑦⑦⑦⑦	⑦⑦⑦⑦
⑧⑧⑧⑧	⑧⑧⑧⑧
⑨⑨⑨⑨	⑨⑨⑨⑨

Thank you for taking the time to answer these questions. If you have any additional comments about the course, please write them on a separate sheet and include them with this evaluation.

American Red Cross

Course Evaluation Form for Lifeguarding Instructor Candidates

Agree ▶ ▶ ▶ ▶ ▶ Disagree

1	The Instructor Trainer was well prepared.	①	②	③	④	⑤
2	The Instructor Trainer was clear and understandable.	①	②	③	④	⑤
3	The Administrative section of the Instructor Manual was clear and understandable.	①	②	③	④	⑤
4	The lesson plans in the Instructor Manual were clear and understandable.	①	②	③	④	⑤
5	The written tests in the Instructor Manual were clear and understandable.	①	②	③	④	⑤
6	Information in the Instructor Manual regarding skill evaluation was clear and understandable.	①	②	③	④	⑤
7	The classroom was clean and orderly.	①	②	③	④	⑤
8	Adequate time was provided for planning practice teaching sessions.	①	②	③	④	⑤
9	The Instructor Trainer provided helpful feedback during the practice teaching sessions.	①	②	③	④	⑤
10	The course was a good value for the price.	①	②	③	④	⑤
11	I would recommend this course to a friend.	①	②	③	④	⑤

12 How satisfied are you that you learned enough to put your knowledge and skills into practice?

- ○ Very satisfied
- ○ Satisfied
- ○ Neither satisfied nor dissatisfied
- ○ Dissatisfied
- ○ Very dissatisfied

13 Which of the following best describes how you plan to be involved as an instructor with the Red Cross?

○ Red Cross volunteer instructor
○ Red Cross paid instructor
○ Red Cross instructor paid by another agency

14 Were the suggested times for the practice teaching sessions:

○ Much too long
○ A little too long
○ About right
○ A little too short
○ Much too short

15 Overall, how satisfied are you with the training provided?

○ Very satisfied
○ Satisfied
○ Neither satisfied nor dissatisfied
○ Dissatisfied
○ Very dissatisfied

A Few Questions About You

In an effort to better serve customers from all backgrounds, we ask that you answer a few questions about yourself:

16 Are you from Hispanic origin?

○ Yes   ○ No

17 Do you consider yourself:
○ White   ○ Asian
○ Black   ○ Other ▶ What?
_____

18 Do you regularly speak any language other than English with your family?

○ Yes   ○ No

19

Age	
	⓪①②③④⑤⑥⑦⑧⑨
	⓪①②③④⑤⑥⑦⑧⑨

20 What is the highest grade that you have completed?

○ Eighth grade or less
○ Some high school
○ Completed high school
○ Some college courses
○ Completed college
○ Graduate school

Chapter Code	Instructor Code
⓪ ⓪ ⓪ ⓪	⓪ ⓪ ⓪ ⓪
① ① ① ①	① ① ① ①
② ② ② ②	② ② ② ②
③ ③ ③ ③	③ ③ ③ ③
④ ④ ④ ④	④ ④ ④ ④
⑤ ⑤ ⑤ ⑤	⑤ ⑤ ⑤ ⑤
⑥ ⑥ ⑥ ⑥	⑥ ⑥ ⑥ ⑥
⑦ ⑦ ⑦ ⑦	⑦ ⑦ ⑦ ⑦
⑧ ⑧ ⑧ ⑧	⑧ ⑧ ⑧ ⑧
⑨ ⑨ ⑨ ⑨	⑨ ⑨ ⑨ ⑨

Thank you for taking the time to answer these questions. If you have any additional comments about the course, please write them on a separate sheet and include them with this evaluation.